V

Basic Quantum Mechanics

ROBERT L. WHITE   *Stanford University*
Professor of Electrical Engineering and Materials Science

Basic Quantum Mechanics

New York   *San Francisco*   *St. Louis*   *Toronto*

London   *Sydney*   **McGRAW-HILL BOOK COMPANY**

Library of Congress catalog card number: 66-20009

   5 6 7 8 9 10 KPKP *7 9 8 7 6 5 4 3*

07 - 0 6 9 6 6 0 - 8

To Phyllis

Preface

THIS BOOK has been developed out of the material contained in a course bearing the same title offered in the Graduate School of Electrical Engineering at Stanford University. The enrollment in this two-quarter course is comprised predominantly (perhaps 75 percent) of first- and second-year graduate students in electrical engineering, with the remainder of the enrollment derived from the Applied Physics Division, Chemistry Department, and Materials Science Department. The background and professional objectives of such a group is substantially different from that of the enrollment typical of a graduate quantum-mechanics course in a physics department, and, in the opinion of the author, none of the several texts on introductory quantum mechanics currently available seemed optimum for this course or for these students. Consequently a set of mimeographed notes and subsequently this book evolved.

The organization and content of this book reflect the objectives and background of the audience to which it is directed. The objectives might be described as the acquisition of a rigorous conceptual and operational familiarity with quantum mechanics which will allow intelligent reading of technical articles at the level of the *Physical Review* or *Journal of Applied Physics* and the formulation and execution of original problems involving quantum-mechanical systems, especially such problems as might arise in solid-state or plasma physics or in quantum electronics. The subject of the book is not solid-state physics or quantum electronics, but the basic quantum mechanics needed to treat the phenomena arising in these areas, or needed to serve as a firm platform upon which more specialized or advanced quantum-mechanical treatments may be erected. The background of the audience might be summarized as being strong in the mathematics

vii

of differential equations and boundary-value problems and perhaps in linear algebra (matrix theory) but deficient in knowledge of the phenomena of atomic and molecular physics and weak in classical mechanics of a sophisticated or generalized nature (Lagrangian or Hamiltonian formulations).

The logical structure of the book is as follows: After two introductory chapters aimed at ameliorating background deficiencies, the reader is presented with the postulates and concepts upon which quantum mechanics is based. Following the discussion of the postulates of quantum mechanics, the three prototype problems of quantum mechanics, the harmonic oscillator, the particle in a box, and the hydrogen atom, are worked out, using matrix methods when appropriate. Finally, the techniques of perturbation theory are developed so that the properties of real systems may be calculated starting from the idealized prototype models as bases.

The author has chosen the postulatory approach to quantum mechanics for several reasons. The most compelling is that it probably leads to the clearest understanding of the logical structure of quantum mechanics in the minimum of time. The inductive approach, in which the assumptions are introduced gradually as plausible explanations for various observed phenomena, is probably less demanding of and more comfortable for the reader, but frequently leads to major confusion as to the real "rules" of quantum mechanics. The conceptual equivalence of the Schrödinger, the Born-Heisenberg, and the Dirac formulations of quantum mechanics is readily apparent to the student who understands the logical postulatory structure of quantum mechanics, and it is certainly true that one must be able to migrate freely between the various formalisms if one is to understand the technical literature of our times.

As remarked above, Chapters 1 and 2, devoted to a historical sketch of the origins of quantum mechanics and to a review of classical mechanics, respectively, are intended primarily as background material. In Chapter 3 the concepts and postulates of quantum mechanics are set forth, and the reader is introduced to the interpretation which quantum mechanics places upon operators, eigenvalues, eigenfunctions, etc. This chapter is the hard core of the book; much of what follows may be regarded as elaboration of the implications of the assumptions, postulates, and definitions of this chapter.

Following Chapter 3 we have six chapters devoted to the exposition of three prototype problems. A dual purpose is intended in these six chapters. On the one hand they contain an exposition of both the Schrödinger (or wave mechanics) formulation and the Born-Heisenberg (or matrix mechanics) formulation of quantum mechanics. On the other hand they contain solutions in some detail for the quantum-mechanical properties of three prototype systems: the harmonic oscillator, the particle in a box, and the hydrogen atom (or central force) problem. All theoretical physics proceeds by making models of actual systems and calculating the properties consequent upon the model assumed. Virtually all the problems solvable by nonrelativistic quantum mechanics reduce to one variation or another of the three prototypes discussed in these chapters. The reader is therefore being equipped by these chapters with a set of basic solutions and basic properties upon which to build his analyses of real systems.

The bridge by which the connection is made between the above highly simplified prototypes and the real systems resembling to some degree these prototypes is perturbation theory. Chapters 10 and 11 deal with perturbation theory, first time-independent (static) and then time-dependent perturbation theory. Since the interaction of quantum-mechanical systems with radiation is a primary concern of many in the audience to whom this book is directed, this subject is treated in considerable detail in the chapter on time-dependent perturbation theory.

In the final chapter the reader is introduced to some of the remarkable consequences of the simple fact that the fundamental particles such as the electron are identical particles, indistinguishable by any experiment. Quantum mechanics correctly predicts for multiparticle systems a number of properties which have no classical analog, and whose absence would cause our world to have a very different form indeed.

Though this book is directed primarily at the audience described earlier, it is hoped that it may prove useful to any student of quantum mechanics who desires an exposition of quantum mechanics from a postulatory point of view. As such it should prove suitable as an auxiliary text for introductory or advanced quantum-mechanics courses in physics departments, or for study by groups or individuals outside the university structure.

The author is indebted to a number of his colleagues for comments on and criticisms of this manuscript, and to the students who suffered through its evolution as class notes. He is indebted to his wife for her patience and encouragement during the many evenings and weekends which might have been more congenially spent. He is also indebted to Mrs. M. J. Sorensen for her expeditious and accurate typing of the manuscript in its several versions.

ROBERT L. WHITE

Contents

Basic Quantum Mechanics

CHAPTER 1   *Origins and Necessity for*

Quantum Mechanics

1.1 FIRST APPEARANCES OF THE QUANTUM At the end of the nine-teenth century the edifice of classical theoretical physics—newtonian me-chanics, maxwellian electromagnetic theory, statistical mechanics, and thermodynamics—seemed to be essentially complete and unshakable. A few puzzles remained, but it seemed eminently likely that they would be solved by the clever application of known principles.

One of the outstanding puzzles remaining concerned the spectral distri-bution of energy radiated from a "black body," a solid of ideal emissivity. This spectral distribution depends only on the temperature of the radiating body, and the experimentally observed distribution is shown for several temperatures in Fig. 1.1. Classical electromagnetic theory, when applied to this problem, yielded the famous Rayleigh-Jeans radiation formula—plotted as the dashed line in Fig. 1.1—which predicted a radiation intensity proportional to the inverse fourth power of the wavelength, i.e., increasing without limit as the wavelength is decreased. The Rayleigh-Jeans formula fitted the experimental data in the long wavelength limit but gave patently ridiculous predictions for the short wavelength region.

Max Planck found in 1900 that he could accurately predict the black-body radiation curve at all temperatures if he made the rather startling assumption that the black body could not radiate energy in a continuous fashion but only in discrete packages or quanti whose size was proportional to the frequency involved, being

$$\Delta E = h\nu \qquad (1.1)$$

Here ΔE is the size of the energy packet, ν is the frequency of the radiation, and h is a proportionality constant, now known as *Planck's constant*. If Planck let $h \to 0$, his expressions reduced to the Rayleigh-Jeans formula with its pernicious "ultraviolet catastrophe." If, however, Planck assigned

1

to h a value of 6.55×10^{-27} erg-sec, he could fit almost exactly the experimental data on black-body radiation.

Almost all Planck's contemporaries refused to take seriously this quantization of the radiation process. Although his final formulas were undoubtedly "correct" in the sense that they accurately predicted experimental results, it was widely believed that there would be forthcoming an alternate derivation which did not require the quantization assumption, which was entirely outside the spirit and formalism of maxwellian electrodynamics. One of the persons who did take Planck's quantization hypothesis seriously was a patent clerk named Albert Einstein.   Einstein utilized the quantum hypothesis to explain another puzzling phenomenon, the photoelectric effect.

The experimental facts concerning the photoelectric effect were these: If one shined light upon a metal, one found that electrons were emitted from the metal if the wavelength of the incident light was shorter than

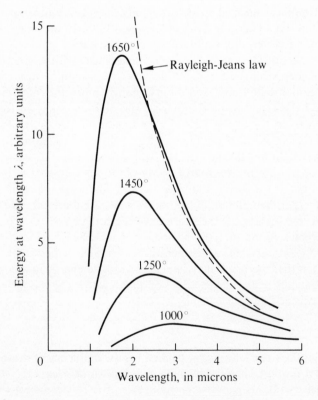

FIG. 1.1 *Black-body radiation $E(\lambda)$ vs. wavelength.*

some critical wavelength, which differed from metal to metal. If the wavelength of the incident radiation was longer than the critical wavelength, no electrons were emitted, no matter how intense the radiation. For incident light of wavelengths shorter than the critical wavelength, the number of electrons emitted was proportional to the intensity of the light, but the kinetic energy of the emergent electrons did not depend on the intensity of the incident light. For every wavelength there was a maximum

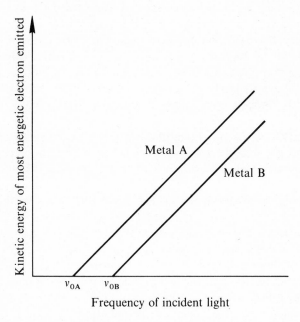

FIG. 1.2 E_{max} *for photoemitted electrons vs. frequency of incident light.*

kinetic energy E_{max} for the emergent electron, independent of the source intensity. The relation between E_{max} and wavelength of the incident light is shown in Fig. 1.2. In even the weakest light, some electrons would emerge with the maximum kinetic energy, as if the one electron had succeeded in capturing for itself all the energy arriving on several square centimeters of surface.

Einstein's explanation went as follows: Let us assume, as did Planck, that the radiation can only interact with the solid in such a fashion that it surrenders discrete quanta of energy to the solid. Suppose further that the size of these quanta is given by $h\nu$, as was also postulated by Planck. Then if these quanta of radiant energy are transferred entirely to an electron, this electron will emerge from the solid with a maximum energy given by

$$E_{max} = h\nu - e\varphi \tag{1.2}$$

where $e\varphi$ is the "work function" of the material involved and represents the minimum energy which must be given to an electron in this material to enable it to escape from the solid into the surrounding vacuum. The work function will, of course, vary from material to material. The value of the quantum constant h can be determined directly from the slope of the E_{max}-vs.-frequency curve of Fig. 1.2. The data available to Einstein was crude to such a degree that he could show only that the value of h required to fit the photoemission data was compatible with Planck's value; subsequent careful measurements by Millikan allowed a direct determination of h from the photoelectric effect, yielding 6.5×10^{-27} erg-sec, virtually identical with Planck's own values deduced from black-body radiation data.

Both Planck's black-body radiation theory and Einstein's theory of the photoelectric effect dealt with phenomena for which the experimental situation was fairly well defined prior to 1900. The first and second decades of the twentieth century—especially the second decade—saw the generation in abundance of new kinds of data with which classical theoretical physics had never before been confronted and with which it was unable to cope. The avalanche of new data resulted from simultaneous advances in several areas of experimental physics. In particular, scattering experiments began to yield important and surprising data on the structure of matter. The electron, the x-ray, and the α particles were all discovered and their properties identified in the late 1890's or early 1900's. Physicists thereupon directed beams of these particles (or this radiation) at targets of various materials, and from the scattered beam drew conclusions about the atomic structure of the target.

Perhaps the most significant scattering experiments were those of Geiger and Marsden, who measured the scattering of α particles by thin metal foils. Consideration of their data led Rutherford to postulate the "nuclear atom." Rutherford showed that the data on α-particle scattering could be beautifully explained if one assumed that the positive charge of the atom was concentrated in a very small region, some 10^{-12} cm in diameter at the center of the atom, and that the negative charge was diffusely spread throughout the whole atomic sphere some 10^{-8} cm in diameter. Prior to this time the Thomson model of the atom, which presumed the positive charge to be uniformly spread throughout the atomic sphere, had been generally accepted. It was already known from observations on the electromagnetic deflection of ions and electrons that most of the mass of the atom was associated with the positive charge. The success of the Rutherford model (which gave the atom a small, massive, positively charged nucleus) in explaining the scattering data was so striking that the Rutherford model was quickly and widely accepted. The stage was now set for the quantum theory of the atom.

1.2 THE BOHR ATOM AND EARLY QUANTUM THEORY The α-particle-scattering experiments established quite clearly the distribution of positive charge in the atom but only compounded the difficulties already present in explaining the location and behavior of the electrons in the atoms. Let us consider this problem for a moment.

What will be the distribution of electrons in the atom? Surely the electrons and the positive charge will assume some configuration of stable electrostatic equilibrium in the quiescent atom. If the electrons were in motion, the motion would have to involve acceleration (directed at least part of the time radially inward) in order to confine the electron to the rather restricted atomic volume. If the electrons were accelerating, they must, by classical electrodynamics, radiate electromagnetic energy. Since the undisturbed atom does not radiate, the electrons must, in equilibrium, be stationary. If the atom is perturbed, the electrons will be expected to oscillate about their equilibrium positions, emitting the characteristic radiation spectrum of the atoms involved.

Quite a bit was known from optical spectroscopy of the characteristic radiation of the various elements. In general, the arc or spark spectra of the various elements (even of the simplest atom, hydrogen) consist of a large number of "emission lines," characteristic radiation frequencies. The pattern of emission lines is different for each element and is characteristic of that element. The various frequencies emitted bear no simple harmonic relation to one another. Certain regular relations between the emitted frequencies (or wavelengths) had, however, been observed by the spectroscopists. Balmer, in 1885, observed that the emission lines of hydrogen could be grouped into series and that within each series the wavelengths of the lines were given by

$$\lambda = b\,\frac{n^2}{n^2 - a^2} \tag{1.3}$$

where a and b are constants and n takes on a succession of integral values (restricted to values greater than a). As n gets large, each spectral series converges on $\lambda = b$. Generalizing on this observation, Rydberg pointed out that the wave numbers $\tilde{\nu}_m$ (wave number is defined as ν/c, where ν is the frequency and c the velocity of light) associated with the various lines in a given series could be well represented by

$$\tilde{\nu}_m = \tilde{\nu}_\infty - \frac{R}{(m + \mu)^2} \tag{1.4}$$

where $\tilde{\nu}_\infty$ was the wave number upon which the series converged, μ was an integer which identified the spectral series within the total spectrum of an element, and m took on successive integral values for successive members of the series. Most importantly, R was a constant which was not only the same for various series within the spectrum of one element but very nearly the same for all elements!

Could such spectra be explained by either the Thomson or Rutherford models of the atom? Thomson had devoted considerable effort to this problem. Assuming the uniform spherical distribution of positive charges of the Thomson atom, the equilibrium position for the electron of a single-electron atom is at the center of the sphere. If displaced, the electron should oscillate about the equilibrium position in a simple harmonic fashion, giving rise to an emission spectrum consisting of a single frequency. This frequency, as calculated by Thomson, did indeed fall in the optical range, but the prediction of so simple a spectrum was incompatible with the observed rich hydrogen spectrum. For an n-electron atom, the electrons adopt some set of equilibrium positions, balancing out their mutual repulsion against the attractive positive charge distribution. If disturbed, the atom would have, for the n-electron case, n characteristic modes of oscillation and n characteristic radiated frequencies. Despite herculean labors, Thomson never succeeded in producing any substantial agreement between the theoretical and experimental spectra.

If the situation had been bad for the Thomson atom, it was worse for the Rutherford nuclear atom. Under the same requirements of electrostatic equilibrium, the one electron of hydrogen would reside right at the nucleus, and the entire atom would collapse to a radius of 10^{-12} cm—the dimensions of the nucleus! For the multielectron atom, mutual repulsion by the electrons would move them somewhat outside the nucleus, but atomic radii entirely out of agreement with experimental fact were regularly predicted. The dilemma of the electron's location and of the explanation of atomic spectra was therefore only compounded by the Rutherford nuclear model.

Niels Bohr, in 1912, produced a model of the atom which resolved these difficulties with spectacular success. To do so he not only utilized Planck's hypothesis that matter could produce radiation only in quanta equal to $h\nu$ but added a postulate even more outrageous from the point of view of classical electrodynamics. Bohr's postulate was that an electron in an atom could occupy certain special planetary orbits such that the electron would not radiate electromagnetic energy. (Classically the planetary electron would radiate energy at the orbital frequency, spiraling continuously inward as it lost energy through radiation.) Bohr proposed that these special nonradiating states, which he called *stationary states*, could be determined from the "quantum condition" that the angular momentum of the state be required to be $nh/2\pi$, where n was an integer and h was Planck's constant again. Radiation was accomplished on the Bohr model only when the atom hopped discontinuously from one stationary state to another, giving then a radiation whose frequency was

$$\nu = \frac{w_2 - w_1}{h} \tag{1.5}$$

where w_2 and w_1 are the energies of the initial state (w_2) and the terminal state (w_1).

The energy of an electron of mass m executing circular planetary motion about a nucleus of opposite charge (Ze where Z is the atomic number) is completely specified by the angular momentum of the state. If that angular momentum is required to be $nh/2\pi$, then the energy w_n of the state is

$$w_n = -\frac{2\pi^2 m e^4 Z^2}{h^2 n^2} \tag{1.6}$$

where m and e are the electronic mass and charge and Z is an integer giving the nuclear charge—the atomic number. The difference in energies between states n_1 and n_2 is then

$$w_{n_2} - w_{n_1} = C\left(\frac{1}{n_2^2} - \frac{1}{n_1^2}\right) \tag{1.7}$$

where

$$C = \frac{2\pi^2 m e^4 Z^2}{h^2} \tag{1.8}$$

The expressions (1.5) to (1.7) can readily be combined to give either Balmer's formula [Eq. (1.3)] or Rydberg's formula [Eq. (1.4)] for the wavelengths or the wave numbers of the atomic emission spectra. Furthermore, when Bohr substituted into Eq. (1.8) the best current values for the various physical constants involved, he obtained a theoretical prediction for the numeric value of Rydberg's constant R which was in almost exact agreement with Rydberg's empirically determined value! Bohr's theory therefore gave not only a qualitatively correct but a quantitatively accurate description of the sharp-line atomic spectra, solving a historic riddle. To be sure, there still remained numerous mysteries in atomic spectra, such as the multiplicity of some lines which the Bohr theory would predict single, but there could be no doubt that the main features of atomic spectra were correctly captured by Bohr's model.

We should note that Bohr's theory contained an uneasy alliance of classical mechanics and mechanics augmented or modified by certain quantum assumptions which were, in principle, in conflict with the classical portions of the theory. Classical mechanics was utilized in calculating the electron orbits, but classical electromagnetics was denied when the circulating electron was assumed not to radiate. There was available no clearly defined guiding principle which determined when one must invoke quantum conditions and when one might safely utilize classical theory. It is not surprising, therefore, that after Bohr's success with his model of the hydrogen atom there grew up a crazy quilt of atomic theory patched together of classical electromechanics and arbitrary quantum conditions on various constants of integration. This patchwork theory had a number of successes and a number of failures: There was clearly required some self-consistent framework into which the whole of quantum mechanics and of classical mechanics could be fitted. For over a decade after Bohr's atomic theory, the self-consistent theory eluded all attempts at formulation. Finally in 1925 two different schools of thought arrived almost simultaneously at what turned out to be conceptually identical theories resolving the conflict. Erwin Schrödinger, recognizing the similarity between the "stationary states" of quantum mechanics and the eigenvalues and eigenfunctions of differential equations, formulated his "wave mechanics" and the famous equation which bears his name. Max Born and Werner Heisenberg, recognizing a similarity between the behavior of dynamical variables and of certain linear operators (and between the matrices characterizing them), proposed their matrix mechanics. Although the two theories appeared superficially to be unrelated, they were quickly shown to be equivalent, and the physicist today moves back and forth between the two formulations as suits his convenience. We shall in this book develop both formulations. The Schrödinger formulation is perhaps simpler and produces predictions more easily visualized; the matrix method is more elegant and powerful.

1.3 THE DOMAIN OF QUANTUM MECHANICS Before we proceed with the principal business of this book—the development of the structure of quantum mechanics—let us pause to ask when and where quantum mechanics is required. Under what circumstances will classical mechanics suffice and under what circumstances must we use quantum mechanics?

Roughly speaking, quantum mechanics is required when the scale of the phenomena being discussed becomes very small, on the order of atomic dimensions (10^{-8} cm). We need quantum mechanics to describe the behavior of electrons in atoms or solids or the behavior of atoms in molecules. We may use classical mechanics to describe the motion of macroscopic objects, such as balls, wheels, pendulums, and projectiles.

The criterion of linear dimension is not entirely correct, however. For instance, the early experiments measuring the charge and mass of the electron, a very small particle indeed, were interpreted (correctly) through the use of classical mechanics. A more accurate criterion for establishing the appropriate domain for quantum mechanics is based directly on Planck's constant $h = 6.626 \times 10^{-27}$ erg-sec. Planck's constant has the dimensions of *energy* times *time*, a quantity known in classical mechanics as *action*. The dimensions of action can easily be shown to be also the same as *momentum* times *distance*, or angular momentum. Phrased in terms of Planck's constant, our criterion becomes:

> If the *action* or *angular momentum* involved in a given physical event is on the order of Planck's constant, then we must use quantum mechanics to describe the event accurately. If the *action* or *angular momentum* involved in a physical event is orders of magnitude larger than Planck's constant, classical mechanics will describe the event with satisfactory accuracy.

The angular momentum of the earth orbiting around the sun is $10^{102}h$, of the earth revolving about its axis is $10^{68}h$. The angular momentum of a bicycle wheel about its axle is some $10^{32}h$, of the balance wheel in a watch approximately $10^{24}h$. For any of these objects, the fact that its angular momentum is quantized and can change only by increments of $\hbar = h/2\pi$ is almost totally irrelevant, since no practical experiment could determine that its acceleration was not continuous but accomplished in finite increments, each of the order of 10^{-30} to 10^{-100} of the average angular momentum involved. Similarly, the action involved in braking a car to a stop is some $10^{38}h$, that of shooting a bullet from a gun is perhaps $10^{35}h$, and that of accelerating an electron to the screen of a television tube is $10^{10}h$. In all these events the quantization of the action is irrelevant because undetectably small compared with the total action involved.

Quite by contrast, the angular momentum of the electron about the nucleus of an atom is only a few times $\hbar$, as is also the angular momentum of rotation of a gaseous molecule. The action involved in the emission of radiation by an atom is generally equal to $\hbar$, or at most to a few times $\hbar$. For these physical systems and these events, the quantization of action and of angular momentum is eminently relevant, and we must use quantum mechanics to calculate the properties of such systems and their interaction with applied forces.

Quantum mechanics can be used to calculate the properties of the gross systems where classical mechanics is valid, though the effort involved would ordinarily be substantially greater than that required to calculate the same properties on a classical basis. The reverse is, of course, not true; classical mechanics cannot be generally extended down to the atomic realm.

An analogy with maps is perhaps useful. The type of map most useful to a landscape gardener is quite different from the type most useful to an aircraft pilot. To the landscape gardener the botanical species of each shrub is important, as is its exact location. To the aircraft pilot, desiring an optimum course to a distant city, all the bushes below will look pretty much alike and blurred together, and though he could in principle do his navigation from an aggregate of such detailed drawings, it is not practical to do so. A map of larger scale, with much detail suppressed, is much more useful to him. More generally, the existence of fine-scale detailed maps of an area always causes coarser-scale maps of the same area to be redundant and, to the extent detail is lost, incorrect. It is clearly ridiculous, however, to always require the use of maximum-detail maps for all applications, and though it is always possible to proceed from a detailed map to a coarser one, the reverse is not true.

The difference between quantum mechanics and classical mechanics is much more profound, however, than just that of scale.

Classical mechanics is a completely definite theory in the sense that the computational procedures do not introduce any statistical uncertainties into the system of themselves. Given a completely specified initial state, set of forces, and constraints, the values of the various system parameters can be calculated at any subsequent time with, in principle, arbitrary precision. An uncertainty or statistical spread in one of the initial conditions will be manifested as a corresponding uncertainty at all subsequent times, but the uncertainty is not introduced by the fundamental equations of motion or by a lack of definiteness in the calculational procedures.

Quantum mechanics, on the other hand, is fundamentally a probabilistic theory. Where classical mechanics will predict a specific result for the measurement of some dynamic quantity (momentum, velocity, etc.), quantum mechanics will predict that any of several values might be the result of an accurate measurement of the quantity involved and will assign a relative probability to the various results. In some instances, the "allowed" results may be grouped closely together, and the coarseness of the measuring apparatus or the grossness of the dynamic system may render impossible the distinction between the prediction of the "classical" theory and the "quantum" theory. In this limit—called the *correspondence limit*—the two theories merge, as they must.

The basis of the philosophic difference between the two theories, classical mechanics on one hand and quantum mechanics on the other, can be understood as follows: All physical theory is directed at explaining the results of experiments and at correlating these results in the simplest and most esthetically satisfying manner possible. Fundamentally the theory must explain the results of measurements. In the classical limit, the measurement on a system can in principle be made so as to produce a vanishingly small reaction upon the system. The interaction of a physical system with the measuring apparatus is a physical event which must involve *action* in the amount of at least Planck's constant h if any change of state of the measuring apparatus is to be effected, i.e., if a reading of any sort is to be obtained. For gross systems the resultant alteration of the total state of the system (involving, for instance, $10^{30}h$) is relatively so small as to be entirely negligible, so the measurement is presumed to have no effect upon the state whatsoever. For atomic systems, however, the action involved in the measurement is entirely commensurate with the action involved in the system's own characteristic evolution. By making a measurement on such a system, we inevitably interact with the system in such a way as to significantly alter the state of the system. The alteration of the system by the measurement can be treated only on a statistical or probabilistic basis; the theory which deals with the results of such a statistical measurement must also be statistical in character.

One final word on the topic of statistics: A statistical theory is not by any means intrinsically an inaccurate theory. Insurance companies plan the disposition of enormous sums of money on the basis of statistical but highly accurate predictions. Quantum mechanics cannot generally predict unambiguously the result of a single measurement on a single atom, just as the actuarial tables do not allow the insurance company to predict the exact date of death of a given individual. Quantum mechanics can, however, generally predict the distribution of results of a large number of measurements, just as the actuarial tables can predict quite accurately how many 36-year-olds will die in the United States in any one year.

Summary

The important points to remember from Chap. 1 are:

Quantum mechanics is necessary to describe the behavior of physical systems participating in events where the action involved is on the order of a few times h, Planck's constant. Classical mechanics applied to such systems and events predicts results contrary to experimental fact.

Classical mechanics is contained in quantum mechanics as a limiting case, but not vice versa. Classical mechanics may be used with negligible error to describe events where the action involved is orders of magnitude larger than h.

Since measurement always involves the interaction of a measuring system with the measured system and since the minimum interaction possible is determined by h, the measurement process has significant reaction upon the measured system if the event being observed also involves only a few h of action. The probabilistic nature of quantum mechanics reflects the unknown factors involved in the interaction of measuring system with measured system.

Problems

1.1 A point light-source radiating 1 watt of energy concentrated at a wavelength of 4000 Å is placed at a distance of 100 cm from a metal surface. The work function of the metal is 5 ev. Assume that an electron in an atom can collect all the electromagnetic energy (classically computed) that falls upon the atom (radius $\approx$ 1 Å). How long will it be after the light is turned on before any electron will have collected enough energy to escape from the metal?

1.2 According to classical electromagnetic theory, an accelerating charge must radiate electromagnetic energy. How long would it take the electron of a hydrogen atom, initially circulating the nucleus at a radius of 1 Å, to spiral inward to a radius of 0.5 Å if it were indeed radiating energy according to classical electromagnetic theory?

1.3 Quantum effects are not apparent in our everyday life, because Planck's constant h is so small. If it were a great deal larger we would be quite aware of such quantum effects. How large would h have to be before the "allowed" speeds of a bicycle would occur in increments of about 5 miles/hr? (Quantize the angular momentum of the wheels.) Would it be easier to learn to ride on a bicycle that has large wheels or one that has small wheels? One that has massive wheels or one that has light wheels?

Bibliography

The following books develop in more nearly complete fashion the general topics of this chapter:

Sproull, R. L.: "Modern Physics," 2nd ed., chaps. 1 to 5, John Wiley & Sons, Inc., New York, 1963.

Richtmeyer, F. K., E. H. Kennard, and T. Lauritsen: "Introduction to Modern Physics," 5th ed., chaps. 1 to 5, McGraw-Hill Book Company, New York, 1955.

Dicke, R. H., and J. P. Wittke: "Introduction to Quantum Mechanics," chap. 1, Addison-Wesley Publishing Company, Inc., Reading, Mass., 1960.

Messiah, A.: "Quantum Mechanics," vol. 1, Interscience Publishers, Inc., New York, 1961.

Eisberg, R. M.: "Fundamentals of Modern Physics," chaps. 1 to 6, John Wiley & Sons, Inc., New York, 1961.

A book written in a more informal vein is:

Einstein, A., and L. Infield: "The Evolution of Physics," Simon and Schuster, Inc., New York, 1961.

A book of definitely lighter (but accurate) nature is:

Gamov, G.: "Mr. Tompkins in Paperback," Cambridge University Press, New York, 1965. (This volume combines in one reprint two of Dr. Gamov's famous stories: "Mr. Tompkins in Wonderland" and "Mr. Tompkins Explores the Atom.")

CHAPTER 2

A Review of
Classical Mechanics

2.1 PERSPECTIVES For dynamical systems involving bodies of macroscopic dimensions moving at nonrelativistic velocities, classical mechanics produces impeccable agreement between theory and experiment. Quantum mechanics, if it is "correct," must produce the same answers when applied to the same systems. It is not surprising, therefore, that there is a strong formal parallelism between quantum and classical mechanics.

Schrödinger, Born, Heisenberg, Dirac, and the other scientists who first formulated quantum mechanics as we now know it leaned heavily upon classical mechanics for their guidance. They sought an expansion and generalization of mechanics beyond its classical outlines, but expected that the relations between dynamical variables codified by classical mechanics would be preserved, at least in outline, in the new mechanics. Such indeed proved to be the case, and many of the important equations of quantum mechanics can be obtained from classical equations by the literal substitutions of quantum-mechanical terms for their classical analogs in the classical equation.

We therefore develop and display now a number of the classical relations important to quantum mechanics. Unfortunately those equations of the classical mechanics most relevant to quantum mechanics are contained in the Hamilton-Jacobi formulation of classical mechanics. A good many of the readers of this book are probably not familiar with this formulation of classical mechanics, especially if their background is in engineering mechanics. For these readers, much of the present chapter represents new material, and that in condensed form. It is not the intent of this chapter to make the reader facile in the solution of problems in classical mechanics by this somewhat esoteric method; it is rather to develop and display certain equations of classical mechanics so that the rationale of their quantum-mechanical analogs will be clearer when they are presented.

At the end of this chapter are listed several books on classical mechanics, with comments as to degree of difficulty and sophistication. Although the reader need not master the Lagrangian and Hamiltonian solution techniques, he should educate himself to the point that he is able to write down easily the Lagrangian and Hamiltonian functions for simple mechanical systems such as planetary electrons and rotating rigid bodies.

2.2 THE CONCEPTS OF CLASSICAL MECHANICS; NEWTON'S LAW

The basic concepts of classical mechanics are *particle, mass, time, position, velocity, momentum, acceleration, energy,* and *force.* From the particles we also may construct *rigid bodies,* and if we assign to rigid bodies the property of elasticity we obtain also the concept of *waves,* a variation in some physical property periodic in time and space. All the properties required to define the system, e.g., mass, time, position, and velocity, are regarded as simultaneously knowable with a precision limited only by experimental accuracy, and are knowable exactly in *Gedanken* experiments. Not all the concepts are independent, of course, for velocity is the time rate of change of position, etc.

Classical mechanics seeks to formulate in a quantitative fashion the relation between these various quantities. The simplest formulation of such a relation is Newton's law

$$\mathbf{F} = m\ddot{\mathbf{r}} \qquad (2.1)$$

relating the force acting on a body to its mass and its accelerations. (We denote the differentiation with respect to time by a dot above the appropriate symbol and the second derivative with respect to time by a double dot over the symbol).

Newton's law is, of course, a postulate, and is justified solely in that it leads to predictions consistent with observation. It may seem to us that this postulate is simply the statement of an obvious relation, but such was not the opinion in Newton's time. The prevailing mechanics was Aristotelian, as it had been for milleniums, and Aristotle had stated that all motion except vertical motion was "unnatural" and would cease unless forced to continue. Newton's postulate flew directly in the face of conventional opinion on the matter and caused substantial controversy.

Newton's law led to a great variety of dynamical predictions which were susceptible to direct experimental check, and was, of course, found to be fully valid. We may reckon the development of classical mechanics as starting with Newton's law, and the beginning student in mechanics still tackles each problem by writing out Newton's law for the particular set of masses and forces involved in the system of interest. Frequently all the forces involved are what is called *conservative,* that is, derivable from a single-valued potential V by

$$\mathbf{F} = -\nabla V \tag{2.2}$$

In the simplest terms, the requirement for the existence of such a conservative force field is that the potential of a particle at point $\mathbf{r}$ be independent of the course by which the particle reached that point, which further implies an independence of the potential of the particle from its velocity at that point.

For many simple systems, particularly those amenable to treatment in cartesian coordinates, the newtonian approach is certainly the simplest and most straightforward. As the dynamical system involved becomes more complex, however, the method becomes more cumbersome. For systems where spherical, cylindrical, etc., coordinates are simplest and most natural, the newtonian approach becomes especially awkward because of the metrics involved relating the coordinates to the element of length. A correct newtonian formulation also requires accurate bookkeeping so that no components of force or acceleration are overlooked, a task that becomes difficult for complicated systems with arbitrary constraints.

It is therefore desirable to have a more general and powerful formulation, one that is useful in an arbitrary coordinate scheme. Such a formulation was provided by Lagrange.

cf Triffet, p136 f

2.3 LAGRANGE'S EQUATIONS   Lagrange's equations may be derived in any of several fashions, but the derivations all have in common a recourse to a variational principle. Consider a system of N particles, each of mass m_i initially (at time t_1) at positions x_i, y_i, and z_i and acted upon by some set of forces $\mathbf{F}_i$. The motion of these particles will evolve with time in accord with Newton's law, and after some period (for instance, at time t_2) the particles will all occupy new positions. We now ask ourselves "What was special about the trajectories these particles took in space and time as compared with adjacent alternative trajectories they might have taken?" Some function of the system parameters must certainly be minimized, or at least extremalized, by the actual motion as compared with conceivable displaced motions. Such considerations have led to the principle of least action in its various forms. Such a principle was first advanced on theological grounds by Maupertius and later proved by Euler and Lagrange. We will use a simple form of this variational principle called *D'Alembert's principle*.

Let us start out by writing down Newton's law for our N-particle system in cartesian coordinates. For each particle,

$$\mathbf{F}_i = m_i \ddot{\mathbf{r}}_i \tag{2.3}$$

We can rewrite this statement as

$$m_i \ddot{\mathbf{r}}_i - \mathbf{F}_i = 0 \qquad (2.4)$$

and think of the particle as being in equilibrium between the applied force $\mathbf{F}_i$ and a fictitious force equal to $m_i \ddot{\mathbf{r}}_i$. This hypothetical equilibrium will hold for each point along the actual trajectory of the particle. If we imagine a small <u>displacement</u> from any point on the actual trajectory, the <u>virtual</u> work done will be zero to first order in the displacement, because of the nature of an equilibrium point. We have, therefore,

$$\sum_i (m_i \ddot{\mathbf{r}}_i - \mathbf{F}_i) \cdot \delta \mathbf{r}_i = 0 \qquad \text{\textit{if Goldstein p 14f}} \qquad (2.5)$$

where $\delta \mathbf{r}_i$ is the virtual (small) displacement and the summation is over the i particles of the system. Equation 2.5 is a statement of D'Alembert's principle.

Thus far we have remained in cartesian coordinates. For many problems it is useful and convenient to use other coordinate schemes. These other coordinate schemes would include the various curvilinear coordinate schemes, (spherical, cylindrical, parabolic, etc.) or perhaps even special mixed schemes suggested by the specific problem at hand. For instance, consider the motion of two particles which interact with each other. In cartesian coordinates we would describe the position of the particles by position vectors $\mathbf{r}_1$ and $\mathbf{r}_2$ and express the interaction between them also as a function of $\mathbf{r}_1$ and $\mathbf{r}_2$. A far more practical coordinate scheme for solving the problem is one in which we specify the center of mass of the system with one vector $\mathbf{R}$ and the *relative* position of the two particles $(\mathbf{r}_1 - \mathbf{r}_2)$ by a second vector $\mathbf{r}$. We still require six numbers, the components of the two vectors, to describe the particles' positions at any instant, but we have chosen a different set of numbers in the two cases. It may be convenient to write the equations of motion of the center of mass in cartesian coordinates X, Y, and Z and the equations of motion of the relative positions in spherical coordinates r, θ, φ. We wish, therefore, a formulation of mechanics readily adaptable to any coordinate scheme convenient for the problem to be solved.

We will now engage in a series of algebraic manipulations which have as their objective (1) expressing D'Alembert's principle in generalized coordinates and (2) extracting from the resultant expression a simple and direct scheme for obtaining the equations of motion, in generalized co-ordinates, for the relevant dynamical system. First we introduce the generalized coordinates $q_1, q_2, q_3, \ldots, q_{3N}$ for the N-particle system and write down the equations which relate the cartesian $\mathbf{r}_i$ to these coordinates (and the time).

$$\mathbf{r}_1 = \mathbf{r}_1(q_1,q_2,q_3,\ldots,q_{3N},t)$$

$$\mathbf{r}_2 = \mathbf{r}_2(q_1,q_2,q_3,\ldots,q_{3N},t) \qquad (2.6)$$

$$\cdots\cdots\cdots\cdots\cdots\cdots\cdots\cdots\cdots\cdots\cdots\cdots\cdots\cdots$$

$$\mathbf{r}_N = \mathbf{r}_N(q_1,q_2,q_3,\ldots,q_{3N},t)$$

The number of generalized coordinates required to specify completely the N-particle system may be reduced by the constraints of the system to less than $3N$ (in our earlier two-particle example, we might have had that the particles were rigidly attached together, and $|\mathbf{r}| = r = \text{const.}$), but the logic of our development is not altered by this circumstance, so we will not discuss the point further. Since we have the N $\mathbf{r}_i$ in the generalized coordinates, velocities and accelerations can also be expressed in the generalized coordinates, for example,

$$\mathbf{v}_i = \dot{\mathbf{r}}_i = \sum_j \left(\frac{\partial \mathbf{r}_i}{\partial q_j} \dot{q}_j + \frac{\partial \mathbf{r}_i}{\partial t} \right) \qquad (2.7)$$

The summation in j is now over the $3N$ generalized coordinates, which may or may not (and usually may not) be associated with specific particles. In what follows within this chapter we shall stick to the convention that a summation in *i* is a summation over particles and that a summation in *j* is a summation over generalized coordinates.

We now convert Eq. (2.5) into generalized coordinates

$$\sum_i (m_i\ddot{\mathbf{r}}_i - \mathbf{F}_i) \cdot \delta\mathbf{r}_i = \sum_i \sum_j (m_i\ddot{\mathbf{r}}_i - \mathbf{F}_i) \cdot \frac{\partial \mathbf{r}_i}{\partial q_j} \delta q_j$$

$$= \sum_i \sum_j \left[(m_i\ddot{\mathbf{r}}_i - \mathbf{F}_i) \cdot \frac{\partial \mathbf{r}_i}{\partial q_j} \right] \delta q_j \qquad (2.8)$$

Examining now, term by term, the expression in brackets, we have

$$\sum_i \sum_j m_i\ddot{\mathbf{r}}_i \cdot \frac{\partial \mathbf{r}_i}{\partial q_j} = \sum_i \sum_j \left[\frac{d}{dt}\left(m_i\dot{\mathbf{r}}_i \cdot \frac{\partial \mathbf{r}_i}{\partial q_j} \right) - m_i\dot{\mathbf{r}}_i \frac{d}{dt}\frac{\partial \mathbf{r}_i}{\partial q_j} \right] \qquad (2.9)$$

From inspection of Eq. (2.7) we see that

$$\frac{\partial \mathbf{r}_i}{\partial q_j} = \frac{\partial \dot{\mathbf{r}}_i}{\partial \dot{q}_j} \qquad (2.10)$$

and we can also show the identity

$$\frac{d}{dt}\frac{\partial \mathbf{r}_i}{\partial q_j} = \sum_k \frac{\partial}{\partial q_k}\left(\frac{\partial \mathbf{r}_i}{\partial q_j} \right)\dot{q}_k + \frac{\partial}{\partial t}\frac{\partial \mathbf{r}_i}{\partial q_j} = \frac{\partial}{\partial q_j}\left(\sum_k \frac{\partial \mathbf{r}_i}{\partial q_k}\dot{q}_k + \frac{\partial \mathbf{r}_i}{\partial t} \right) = \frac{\partial}{\partial q_j}\dot{\mathbf{r}}_i \quad (2.11)$$

The summation in k is over the $3N$ generalized coordinates; the second step follows because of the interchangeability of the order of the partial derivatives, and the third step follows from the second by comparison with Eq. (2.7).

Inserting the identities (2.10) and (2.11) into Eq. (2.9), we obtain

$$\sum_i \sum_j m_i \ddot{\mathbf{r}}_i \cdot \frac{\partial \mathbf{r}_i}{\partial q_j} = \sum_i \sum_j \left[\frac{d}{dt} \left((m_i \dot{\mathbf{r}}_i \cdot \frac{\partial \dot{\mathbf{r}}_i}{\partial \dot{q}_j}) \right) - m \dot{\mathbf{r}}_i \cdot \frac{\partial}{\partial q_j} \dot{\mathbf{r}}_i \right]$$

$$= \sum_j \left[\frac{d}{dt} \frac{\partial}{\partial \dot{q}_j} \left(\sum_i \tfrac{1}{2} m_i v_i^2 \right) - \frac{\partial}{\partial q_j} \left(\sum_i \tfrac{1}{2} m_i v_i^2 \right) \right] \quad (2.12)$$

We may readily identify $\sum_i \tfrac{1}{2} m_i v_i^2$ as the kinetic energy T of the system, so the first term of Eq. (2.8) becomes

$$\sum_i m_i \ddot{\mathbf{r}}_i \cdot \delta \mathbf{r}_i = \sum_j \left[\frac{d}{dt} \left(\frac{\partial T}{\partial \dot{q}_j} \right) - \frac{\partial T}{\partial q_j} \right] \delta q_j \quad (2.13)$$

If we define a generalized force Q_j by

$$Q_j = \sum_i \mathbf{F}_i \cdot \frac{\partial \mathbf{r}_i}{\partial q_j} \quad (2.14)$$

the second term of Eq. (2.8) may be reduced to

$$\sum_i \mathbf{F}_i \cdot \delta \mathbf{r}_i = \sum_j Q_j \, \delta q_j \quad (2.15)$$

The generalized coordinates may not have the dimension of length (i.e., may be an angle), so the generalized forces need not have the dimensions of a force, but the product $Q_j \, \delta q_j$ must have the dimensions of work. We note further that Q_j and δq_j are both scalars rather than vectors, so a simple product rather than a vector product is appropriate.

We are now in a position to write D'Alembert's principle in generalized coordinate form as

$$\sum_j \left\{ \left[\frac{d}{dt} \left(\frac{\partial T}{\partial \dot{q}_j} \right) - \frac{\partial T}{\partial q_j} \right] - Q_j \right\} \delta q_j = 0 \quad (2.16)$$

Since Eq. (2.16) is true for arbitrary δq_j, the bracketed quantity itself must be zero, and we have

$$\frac{d}{dt} \left(\frac{\partial T}{\partial \dot{q}_j} \right) - \frac{\partial T}{\partial q_j} = Q_j \quad (2.17)$$

as a prototype form of Lagrange's equation.

If the Q_j are derivable from a potential U by the prescription

$$Q_j = \frac{d}{dt} \left(\frac{dU}{\partial \dot{q}_j} \right) - \frac{\partial U}{\partial q_j} \quad (2.18)$$

we can define a function

$$L = T - U \tag{2.19}$$

such that, by Eqs. (2.17) and (2.18)

$$\frac{d}{dt}\left(\frac{\partial L}{\partial \dot{q}_j}\right) - \frac{\partial L}{\partial q_j} = 0 \tag{2.20}$$

For conservative systems,

$$\frac{\partial U}{\partial \dot{q}_j} = 0 \qquad Q_j = -\frac{\partial U}{\partial q_j} \tag{2.21}$$

and Lagrange's equation [Eq. (2.20)] is certainly valid. Indeed, it is for this special case that the designation *Lagrange's equation* is usually reserved. In this case, the potential is conventionally notated as V and the Lagrangian L function given by

$$L \equiv T - V \tag{2.22}$$

the difference between the kinetic and potential energies of the systems.

Many of the systems of physical interest are indeed conservative systems, such as the particle in a central-force field. The most important case of a nonconservative system is that of the charged particle moving in a magnetic field **B**. Here the Lorentz force on the particle is given by

$$\mathbf{F} = \frac{q}{c}(\mathbf{v} \times \mathbf{B}) \tag{2.23}$$

where q is the charge on the particle in gaussian units. Here the force is obviously velocity dependent and cannot be obtained from the gradient of a scalar field.

Fortunately, it is possible to define a potential U which does lead, through the operations of Eq. (2.18), to the Lorentz force. In terms of the conventional scalar potential φ and vector potential **A**, which are related to the electric field **E** and magnetic field **B** by

$$\mathbf{E} = -\boldsymbol{\nabla}\varphi - \frac{1}{c}\frac{\partial \mathbf{A}}{\partial t} \qquad B = \boldsymbol{\nabla} \times \mathbf{A} \tag{2.24}$$

the appropriate potential is given by

$$U = q\varphi - \frac{q}{c}\mathbf{A}\cdot\mathbf{v} \tag{2.25}$$

Proof that this potential leads to the Lorentz force is left to the student (Prob. 2.4).

2.4 HAMILTON'S EQUATION A major objective of this chapter is to derive and display certain equations of classical mechanics which have important analogs in quantum mechanics. Perhaps no function is more important to quantum mechanics than the Hamiltonian function, commonly referred to simply as *the Hamiltonian of the system*. We now proceed to obtain this function and examine its characteristics and properties.

Lagrange's equation (2.20) leads to $3N$ equations of the second order in the time derivative, one equation for each of the $3N$ q_j. The Lagrangian function, given by Eq. (2.22), contains overtly the $3N$ q_j, the $3N$ $\dot{q}_j$, and perhaps explicitly the time. The q_j are regarded as the independent variables; the $\dot{q}_j$ are dependent variables, obtainable from the independent variables, the q_j, by time derivation.

It is possible, however, to treat the $\dot{q}_j$ as independent variables, and develop a formalism which leads to $6N$ equations of motion which are first order in the time derivative. The $6N$ equations collapse, upon insertion of the information that the $\dot{q}_j$ are the time derivatives of the q_j, into the $3N$ equations of Lagrange.

The Hamilton-Jacobi formulation of classical mechanics follows a course which is roughly equivalent to regarding the $\dot{q}_j$ as independent variables; however, a new independent variable, the momentum conjugate to q_j, is established for each of the q_j. The momentum p_j conjugate to q_j is defined as

$$p_j = \frac{\partial L}{\partial \dot{q}_j} \quad - \text{ cf } (2.20) \tag{2.26}$$

For the conservative system consisting of particles moving in a potential which depends on coordinates only, we have, in cartesian coordinates,

$$L = \sum_{i=1}^{N} \tfrac{1}{2} m_i \dot{\mathbf{r}}_i^2 - V(\mathbf{r}_i, t) \tag{2.27}$$

and

$$p_i = \frac{\partial L}{\partial \dot{x}_i} = m_i \dot{x}_i \tag{2.28}$$

corresponding to the usual definition of linear momentum. For generalized coordinates, the conjugate momenta p_j may, of course, have dimensions other than linear momentum. For nonconservative systems, the generalized momenta may not correspond simply to a mechanical momentum. Consider, for instance, the charged particle moving in a magnetic and electric field, with the Lagrangian, again in cartesian coordinates,

$$L = \tfrac{1}{2} m \dot{\mathbf{r}}^2 - q\varphi + \frac{q}{c} \mathbf{A} \cdot \dot{\mathbf{r}} \tag{2.29}$$

Now
$$p_x = m\dot{x} + \frac{q}{c}A_x \tag{2.30}$$

and we see that the generalized momentum contains a component arising from the vector potential **A**.

The *Hamiltonian* function is a function of the q_j and p_j and their time derivatives given by

$$H \equiv \sum_j p_j \dot{q}_j - L(q_j, \dot{q}_j, t) \tag{2.31}$$

This is the function which we will find to be of such great utility in quantum mechanics, and we now show how the Hamiltonian function leads to the $6N$ first-order equations of motion previously mentioned.

Regarding H as a function of q_j, p_j, and t, we have that its differential is

$$dH = \sum_j \left(\frac{\partial H}{\partial q_j} dq_j + \frac{\partial H}{\partial p_j} dp_j \right) + \frac{\partial H}{\partial t} dt \tag{2.32}$$

Summation over coords

However, if we momentarily regard Eq. (2.31) as a function of q_j, $\dot{q}_j$, p_j, and t, we have an alternate form of the differential of H, namely,

$$dH = \sum_j \left(\underbrace{p_j\, d\dot{q}_j + \dot{q}_j\, dp_j}_{d(p_j \dot{q}_j)} - \frac{\partial L}{\partial q_j} dq_j - \frac{\partial L}{\partial \dot{q}_j} d\dot{q}_j \right) - \frac{\partial L}{\partial t} dt \tag{2.33}$$

In view of our definition of the generalized momenta [Eq. (2.26)], the first and last terms in the parentheses cancel, leaving us with $\quad p_j = \dfrac{\partial L}{\partial \dot{q}_j}$

$$dH = \sum_j \left(\dot{q}_j\, dp_j - \frac{\partial L}{\partial q_j} dq_j \right) - \frac{\partial L}{\partial t} dt \tag{2.34}$$

From Lagrange's equation [Eq. (2.20)]

$$\frac{\partial L}{\partial q_j} = \frac{d}{dt} \frac{\partial L}{\partial \dot{q}_j} = \frac{d}{dt} p_j = \dot{p}_j \tag{2.35}$$

and Eq. (2.34) reduces further to

$$dH = \sum_j (\dot{q}_j\, dp_j - \dot{p}_j\, dq_j) - \frac{\partial L}{dt} dt \tag{2.36}$$

Comparing Eq. (2.36) with Eq. (2.32), we arrive at the identifications

$$\dot{q}_j = \frac{\partial H}{\partial p_j} \qquad -\dot{p}_j = \frac{\partial H}{\partial q_j} \qquad -\frac{\partial L}{\partial t} = \frac{\partial H}{\partial t} \tag{2.37}$$

These are the canonical equations of Hamilton, the $6N$ first-order equations replacing the $3N$ second-order equations of the Lagrangian. The pairs of variables q_j and p_j appearing in these equations are known as *canonically conjugate variables*.

2.5 PHYSICAL SIGNIFICANCE OF THE HAMILTONIAN FUNCTION   We examine now the physical significance of the Hamiltonian function. First let us look at the total time derivative of the Hamiltonian:

From (2.31),
$$\frac{dH}{dt} = \sum_j \left(\frac{\partial H}{\partial q_j} \dot{q}_j + \frac{\partial H}{\partial p_j} \dot{p}_j \right) + \frac{\partial H}{\partial t} \tag{2.38}$$

Substituting in for $\partial H/\partial q_j$ and $\partial H/\partial p_j$ from the canonical equations [Eq. (2.37)] above, we see that the terms in parentheses cancel, and the <u>total derivative of H</u> is equal to its <u>partial derivative</u> with respect to time:

$$\frac{dH}{dt} = \frac{\partial H}{\partial t} \tag{2.39}$$

If, then, the Hamiltonian does <u>not</u> contain the time explicitly (and this is frequently the case in systems of physical interest), the Hamiltonian is a constant of the motion. —$i.e.,$ $\frac{dH}{dt} = 0$

If the generalized coordinates are not time dependent, i.e., if the transformations Eq. (2.6) do not explicitly contain the time, the kinetic energy of the system can always be expressed as a homogeneous quadratic function of the $\dot{q}_j$:

$$T = \sum_j \sum_k \alpha_{jk} \dot{q}_j \dot{q}_k \tag{2.40}$$

(2.26) $L = T - V$

For a conservative system,

$$p_j = \frac{\partial L}{\partial \dot{q}_j} = \frac{\partial T}{\partial \dot{q}_j} \tag{2.41}$$

since the potential V does not contain the $\dot{q}_j$. Then

$$\sum_j p_j \dot{q}_j = \sum \frac{\partial T}{\partial \dot{q}_j} \dot{q}_j = 2 \sum_j \sum_k \alpha_{jk} \dot{q}_k \dot{q}_j = 2T \tag{2.42}$$

and we see that $cf (2.40)$

$$H = \sum_j p_j \dot{q}_j - L = 2T - (T - V) = T + V \tag{2.43}$$

We have shown, then, for a system which

   a. Is conservative
   b. Does not contain t explicitly in its Hamiltonian
   c. Does not contain t explicitly in its generalized coordinates

that the Hamiltonian H is

   1. A constant of the motion
   2. Equal to the total energy of the system, kinetic plus potential

For a dynamic system which meets criteria a and b above, but not c, H is still a constant of the motion but is not equal to the total energy.

Finally, we examine again that nonconservative system of great atomic interest, the charged particle in a magnetic field. From Eqs. (2.19) and (2.25),

$$L = T - U = \tfrac{1}{2}m\dot{\mathbf{r}}^2 + \frac{q}{c}\mathbf{A} \cdot \dot{\mathbf{r}} - q\varphi \qquad (2.44)$$

with the canonical momentum

$$\mathbf{p} = m\dot{\mathbf{r}} + \frac{q}{c}\mathbf{A} \qquad (2.45)$$

Examining the Hamiltonian function, we find that

$$H = \mathbf{p} \cdot \dot{\mathbf{r}} - L = (m\dot{\mathbf{r}}^2 + \frac{q}{c}\mathbf{A} \cdot \dot{\mathbf{r}}) - (\tfrac{1}{2}m\dot{\mathbf{r}}^2 + \frac{q}{c}\mathbf{A} \cdot \dot{\mathbf{r}} - q\varphi)$$

$$= \tfrac{1}{2}m\dot{\mathbf{r}}^2 + q\varphi = T + V \qquad (2.46)$$

Here again the Hamiltonian is equal (for the time-independent coordinate frame) to the total energy of the system, kinetic plus potential, and if t does not enter the Hamiltonian explicitly (through $\mathbf{A}$ or φ), the total energy of the system is conserved, and H is a constant of the motion.

It is customary to write the Hamiltonian for a particle in a conservative force as

$$H = \frac{p^2}{2m} + V \qquad (2.47)$$

H can be cast in similar form for the particle in the nonconservative vector potential as well by using Eq. (2.45), obtaining

$$H = \frac{\left(\mathbf{p} - \frac{q}{c}\mathbf{A}\right)^2}{2m} + V \qquad (2.48)$$

It must be borne in mind that $\mathbf{p}$ in Eq. (2.48) is a generalized momentum and is not simply the linear momentum of the particle.

2.6 POISSON BRACKETS   We draw one more weapon from the arsenal of classical mechanics before passing on to quantum mechanics. This is the expression known as the *Poisson bracket*.

Consider two functions F and G of the canonically conjugate variables $q_j p_j$. The Poisson bracket of F and G, $\{F,G\}$, is defined by

$$\{F,G\} = \sum_j \left(\frac{\partial F}{\partial q_j}\frac{\partial G}{\partial p_j} - \frac{\partial F}{\partial p_j}\frac{\partial G}{\partial q_j} \right) \qquad (2.49)$$

The Poisson bracket turns out to be a useful expression when used with Hamilton's conjugate equations for determining the time dependence of various functions. Taking the time derivative of $F(q_j, p_j)$, we have

$$\frac{dF}{dt} = \frac{\partial F}{\partial t} + \sum_j \left(\frac{\partial F}{\partial q_j} \dot{q}_j + \frac{\partial F}{\partial p_j} \dot{p}_j \right) \qquad \text{ie, } F \sim \text{fn of conjugate vbls} \qquad (2.50)$$

From Hamilton's conjugate equations [Eq. (2.37)], we can write this expression:

$$\frac{dF}{dt} = \frac{\partial F}{\partial t} + \sum_j \left(\frac{\partial F}{\partial q_j} \frac{\partial H}{\partial p_j} - \frac{\partial F}{\partial p_j} \frac{\partial H}{\partial q_j} \right) = \frac{\partial F}{\partial t} + \{F, H\} \qquad (2.51)$$

We can therefore examine for its time dependence an arbitrary function of the conjugate variables, perhaps not containing the time explicitly, by forming the Poisson bracket with the Hamiltonian. If $\partial F/\partial t = 0$ and $\{F, H\}$ vanishes, or if neither one is zero but their sum vanishes, the function F is a constant of the motion.

The Poisson brackets have some interesting properties which will subsequently prove to be very useful. Some of these relations among Poisson brackets, which follow from the definition of the Poisson bracket and which we may regard as defining the algebra of Poisson brackets, are

$$\{F, G\} = -\{G, F\}$$

$$\{F, F\} = 0$$

$$\{F, K\} = 0 \qquad [K = \text{const., or } F(t) \text{ only}] \qquad (2.52)$$

$$\{E + F, G\} = \{E, G\} + \{F, G\}$$

$$\{E, FG\} = \{E, F\}G + F\{E, G\}$$

If F and G are q_j and p_k, respectively, we find a special set of relations of great significance to quantum mechanics:

$$\{q_j, q_k\} = 0$$

$$\{p_j, p_k\} = 0 \qquad (2.53)$$

$$\{q_j, p_k\} = \delta_{jk}$$

p32

By δ_{jk} we mean *Kronecker's delta*, which is 1 if $j = k$, and zero otherwise. We see that the Poisson bracket of two conjugate variables is unity but that the Poisson bracket of nonconjugate variables always vanishes.

Summary

The important things to retain from this chapter are:

The definition of the Lagrangian function
The definition and physical interpretation of the Hamiltonian function
The concept and definition of the momentum conjugate to a generalized coordinate
Hamilton's conjugate equations relating $\dot{q}_j$ and $\dot{p}_j$ to $\partial H/\partial p_j$ and $\partial H/\partial q_j$
The connection between the time dependence of an arbitrary function and its Poisson bracket with the Hamiltonian function
The algebra of Poisson brackets
The Poisson brackets of the various q_j and p_j with one another

Problems

2.1 A wagon of mass M carries a simple pendulum of mass m and length L which can swing in the direction of motion of the wagon. Let $\dot{x}$ denote the velocity of the wagon and θ the inclination of the pendulum to the vertical. Show that the kinetic energy T of the system is given by the expression

$$2T = (M + m)\dot{x}^2 + 2mL \cos \theta \dot{x}\dot{\theta} + mL^2\dot{\theta}^2$$

2.2 A thin rod of length $2a$ and mass m is hinged at one end by a horizontal hinge pin to a thin vertical shaft which can rotate freely. Initially the rod is held horizontal, and an angular velocity ω about the vertical axis is imparted to the system. Show that thereafter

$$\frac{4}{3} \sin^3\theta \; \ddot{\theta} - \frac{4}{3} \omega^2 \cos \theta + \frac{g}{a} \sin^4 \theta = 0$$

where θ is the angle made by the rod with the vertical.

2.3 A cube of mass M containing a smooth spherical cavity of radius a rests on a smooth horizontal table, and a particle of mass m rests on the bottom of the cavity. The cube is given a horizontal velocity v_0. Show that the Lagrangian function of the system is

$$L = \tfrac{1}{2}[(M + m)\dot{x}^2 + 2ma \cos \theta \dot{x}\dot{\theta} + ma^2\dot{\theta}^2] - mga(1 - \cos \theta)$$

and that the equations of motion are

$$(M + m)\dot{x} + ma \cos \theta \dot{\theta} = \text{const.}$$

and
$$a\ddot{\theta} + \cos \theta \ddot{x} + g \sin \theta = 0$$

where x is the coordinate of M and θ is the angle between the downward drawn vertical and the radius of the cavity drawn to the particle.

2.4 Show that the Lorentz force

$$\mathbf{F} = \frac{q}{c}(\mathbf{v} \times \mathbf{B}) + q\mathbf{E}$$

is derivable from the potential

$$U = q\varphi - \frac{q}{c}\mathbf{A} \cdot \mathbf{v}$$

by the operation

$$Q_j = \frac{d}{dt}\left(\frac{\partial U}{\partial \dot{q}_j}\right) - \frac{\partial U}{\partial q_j}$$

2.5 A pendulum consists of two equal bars AB and BC, which are smoothly joined at B and suspended from A. The mass of each bar is m and each length is $2a$. Find the normal periods for small oscillations in a vertical plane under gravity.

2.6 A carriage has four wheels, each of which is a uniform disk of mass m. The mass of the carriage without wheels is M. Without slipping, the carriage rolls down a plane slope inclined to the horizontal at an angle α, the floor of the carriage remaining parallel to the slope. A perfectly rough spherical ball of mass m' rolls on the floor of the carriage along a line parallel to a line of greatest slope. Show that the acceleration of the carriage down the plane is

$$\frac{7M + 28m + 2m'}{7M + 42m + 2m'}g\sin\alpha$$

Will the acceleration of the ball ever be directed uphill?

2.7 A yo-yo consists of two disks of mass M and radius R connected by a pin of radius r and negligible mass. Find the linear velocity of the center of the yo-yo as it descends its string under gravity.

Bibliography

The following three books treat classical mechanics on an intermediate level and include more detailed developments of all the material reviewed in this chapter:

Wangsness, R. K.: "Introduction to Theoretical Physics," John Wiley & Sons, Inc., New York, 1963.

Corben, H. C., and P. Stehle: "Classical Mechanics," 2nd ed., John Wiley & Sons, Inc., New York, 1960.

Synge, J. L., and B. A. Griffith: "Principles of Mechanics," 3rd ed., McGraw-Hill Book Company, New York, 1959.

The following book, which treats classical mechanics on an advanced level, is a particularly thorough and complete treatise on the subject:

Goldstein, H.: "Classical Mechanics," Addison-Wesley Publishing Company, Inc., Reading, Mass., 1950.

CHAPTER 3

The Concepts and Formulation of Quantum Mechanics

3.1 THE CONCEPTS OF QUANTUM MECHANICS All theoretical science proceeds by making an idealized model of the system of interest, because only for such idealized models is it possible to set down tractable equations leading to verifiable conclusions. The closer the idealized model approximates the real system the better the agreement between calculated and observed properties will be. When we say an idealized model of a physical system is reasonable, or logical, or readily comprehensible, we mean that the model has proposed no idealization which violates our experience or prejudices about the way the "real" system is constructed.

The model which classical mechanics makes of our universe is quite simply related to the world as we usually experience it. The principal concepts (particle, mass, time, position, etc.) are derived directly from our sensual contact with the physical world. The idealizations are quite straightforward and introduce no fundamentally new assumptions about the quantities involved. For instance, we know that the point particle of zero spatial extent does not "really" exist, but we can readily conceive of particles that are so small that their actual extent is negligible compared with all other dimensions entering the problem. Even the more complex quantities, such as the Lagrangian function, while not as simply comprehended, are at least built out of the familiar bricks of particles with masses, velocities, etc.

The model which quantum mechanics makes of the physical world is one degree more abstract than the model which classical mechanics proposes. Quantum mechanics associates with each physical observable (e.g., position, momentum, and energy) a mathematical operator and proposes that we can infer the behavior of a physical system from the behavior of appropriate mathematical operators and the equations built out of them. The relation of quantum mechanics to classical mechanics is in some ways like the relation of analytic geometry to engineering drawing. The connection between a wheel and its representation as a circle in an engineering drawing is fairly straightforward. The connection between a circle and the equation $(x - a)^2 + (y - b)^2 = C^2$ is less obvious. It takes somewhat more practice to think in terms of second derivatives than it does to think in terms of curvatures, precisely because the analytic concepts are further abstracted from our daily experience than are their graphical representations. Similarly, it takes some practice and familiarization before it becomes as "natural" to think in the mathematical terms of quantum mechanics as it is to think in the more familiar terms of classical mechanics.

The concepts with which we shall deal in quantum mechanics are *operators, state functions, expectation values, wave functions, eigenfunctions, probability amplitudes, eigenvalues,* and *stationary states.* Most of these concepts have been encountered by the reader before, but in some other context. The concepts of eigenfunctions and eigenvalues are borrowed directly from the mathematics of differential equations, where they occur regularly whenever boundary conditions are introduced into wavelike equations. The concept of an expectation value is borrowed directly from statistics and probability theory. Operators and operator theory occur in many branches of engineering and mathematical physics; the theory of linear operators (and their representation as matrices) is a major branch of modern mathematics. To a large extent, then, these concepts are not truly unfamiliar; what is unfamiliar is the manner in which quantum mechanics assembles these concepts into a theory of the static and dynamic behavior of matter and radiation.

3.2 THE POSTULATES OF QUANTUM MECHANICS The logical structure of quantum mechanics may be regarded as consisting of several sweeping postulates, plus a number of corollaries and auxiliary definitions. These postulates will now be presented, first in slightly diffuse wording (forced by the circumstance that we have not yet defined some of the terms required for a more incisive statement) and then again at the end of this chapter in a more rigorous form.

POSTULATE 1   *With every physical observable a, we may associate a mathematical operator A from whose properties we may deduce the possible results of measurements of the physical observable a.*

The character of the operators we encounter in quantum mechanics will be discussed in some length in the next section. For the present, we observe that each operator defines implicitly an eigenvalue equation of the form

$$Au_n = a_n u_n \tag{3.1}$$

where A is the operator under discussion, u_n is one of the functions out of the complete set of functions upon which the operation A is meaningfully defined, and a_n is a number (perhaps complex). The solutions u_n of Eq. (3.1) are the eigenfunctions of A and the numbers a_n are the eigenvalues of A. It often happens that physically acceptable solutions of Eq. (3.1), i.e., solutions meeting certain boundary conditions, exist only for specific discrete values of a_n. Then the eigenvalues are said to be *discrete*. It also often happens that physically acceptable solutions exist for a continuous range of values a_n, in which case the eigenvalue spectrum is said to be *continuous*.

POSTULATE 2   *The only possible result of a measurement of the physical observable a is one of the eigenvalues of the operator A.*

We begin to see already the connection between the mathematical operator A and the world of experimental observations. The results of physical measurements are related to the scheme of mathematical operators, as we shall see in some detail subsequently, through the identification of eigenvalues with actual numeric values of observables.

POSTULATE 3   *For every dynamical system there exists a state function Ψ which contains all the information that is known about the system.*

The state function Ψ therefore tells us, for a particular system at a particular time, which of the eigenvalues a_n we will obtain by making a measurement of the observable a on our system and with what relative probability we might obtain the various allowed a_n. It contains also the information on all other relevant observables, specifying the relative probability of obtaining their various eigenvalues if we make the appropriate measurements.

POSTULATE 4   *If we know Ψ for any system at some particular time, then the evolution of Ψ at all subsequent times is determined by*

$$-\frac{\hbar}{i}\frac{\partial \Psi}{\partial t} = H_{\text{op}}\Psi$$

where H_{op} is the operator associated with the Hamiltonian of the system.

Postulate 4, as we shall see, leads us directly to Schrödinger's equation, perhaps the most important single equation in quantum mechanics.

These are the four fundamental postulates of quantum mechanics. The rest of this book will be devoted to the development of the consequences of these postulates.

These postulates have been presented compactly and in rapid sequence in this section so that the reader may see the bare logical bones of quantum mechanics. Before these naked postulates have any real meaning for the reader, we will have to spend considerable time expanding and discussing the concepts and consequences involved.

3.3 THE OPERATORS OF QUANTUM MECHANICS

An operator may be regarded simply as an instruction to do something to an object or set of objects. An operator must always have a "domain of operands," a set of objects upon which it may meaningfully operate.

We are familiar with mathematical operators in many forms. The expression $3x$ may be regarded as divisible into the operation "multiply by 3" and the operand x. The expression $du(x)/dx$ may be regarded as being composed of the operator d/dx and the operand $u(x)$. The domain of d/dx is that of all functions of x.

The operators with which we will deal in quantum mechanics are all linear operators. By *linear operator* we mean one such that

$$O(au + bv) = O(au) + O(bv) = a(Ou) + b(Ov) \qquad (3.2)$$

where O is the operator, u and v are operands in its domain, and a and b are numeric coefficients.

The algebra of linear operators is very similar to ordinary algebra, with some important exceptions. Linear operators are additive:

$$(A + B + C) = (C + B + A) = (A + C + B) = \text{etc.} \qquad (3.3)$$

distributive:

$$A(B + C) = AB + AC \qquad (3.4)$$

and associative:

$$ABC = \{AB)C = A(BC) \qquad (3.5)$$

but not commutative:

$$AB \neq BA \qquad \text{(in general)} \qquad (3.6)$$

The lack of commutation of operators is of central importance to quantum mechanics, as we shall shortly see. This lack of commutativity can be illustrated by the two operators x (multiply by x) and d/dx (take the derivative with respect to x):

$$\left(x\frac{d}{dx} - \frac{d}{dx}x\right)u(x) = \left(x\frac{d}{dx} - x\frac{d}{dx} - 1\right)u(x) = -u(x) \quad (3.7)$$

The commutator of two operators is usually indicated by the "commutator bracket":

$$[A,B] = (AB - BA) \quad (3.8)$$

We might, then, write the result above as

$$\left[x, \frac{d}{dx}\right] = -1 \quad (3.9)$$

The commutator bracket obeys a very interesting algebra of its own. Some of these relations are

$$[A,B] = -[B,A]$$
$$[A,A] = 0$$
$$[A,K] = 0 \quad (K \text{ a const.}) \quad (3.10)$$
$$[A + B, C] = [A,C] + [B,C]$$
$$[A,(BC)] = [A,B]C + B[A,C]$$

Upon comparing Eq. (3.10) with the algebra of Poisson brackets, Eq. (2.52), we find that the algebras are identical, and there is a perfect analogy between the Poisson bracket of classical mechanics and the commutator of operators in the quantum mechanics.

In examining the properties of Poisson brackets, we observed that the Poisson bracket of a generalized coordinate with its own conjugate momentum did not vanish, whereas the Poisson bracket of a generalized coordinate with any other generalized coordinate or any other generalized momentum did indeed vanish.

$$\{q_j,q_k\} = 0$$
$$\{p_j,p_k\} = 0 \quad (2.53)$$
$$\{q_j,p_k\} = \delta_{jk}$$

We are led by this observation, and by the correspondence of the commutator brackets of operator algebra to the Poisson brackets of classical mechanics, to an important property of the operators of quantum mechanics. In analogy with Eq. (2.53), we now make an assertion concerning the commutativity of the operators of quantum mechanics:

$$[Q_j, Q_k] = 0$$

$$[P_j, P_k] = 0 \qquad\qquad (3.11)$$

$$[Q_j, P_k] = i\hbar\, \delta_{jk}$$

The operator associated with any generalized coordinate (a physical observable) commutes with the operator associated with any other generalized coordinate. Likewise, the operators associated with two generalized momenta always commute. But the operator associated with a given generalized coordinate and the operator associated with its own conjugate momentum do not commute. Not only do they fail to commute, but their commutator bracket is equal to a very specific quantity, $i\hbar$, involving Planck's constant. It is at precisely this point that Planck's constant enters quantum mechanics, in a condition placed upon the operators which we may associate with observables. If we were to make a numerically different assumption concerning the commutator of Q_j and P_j, we would obtain numerically different predictions from the quantum mechanical treatment of physical systems. We would predict, for instance, a quantitatively incorrect optical emission spectrum for the hydrogen atom, or a blackbody radiation law at variance with experimental fact, or the wrong infrared spectrum for solids. The commutation condition on the operators associated with conjugate variables is one more assumption basic to quantum mechanics, justified subsequently by the correct predictions which follow the assumption.

We have discussed so far the general nature of quantum mechanical operators and the quantum condition upon them without producing any specific examples. We now produce that set of operators proposed by Schrödinger in his classic formulation of quantum mechanics. We therefore embark on one particular formulation of quantum mechanics, the Schrödinger, or wave-mechanical, formulation of quantum mechanics. Schrödinger proposed a set of differential operators to be associated with generalized coordinates and their conjugate momenta, which may be stated as follows: With each generalized coordinate q_j we associate the operator "multiply by q_j"; with the generalized momentum p_j conjugate to q_j, we associate the operator "$\dfrac{\hbar}{i}\dfrac{\partial}{\partial q_j}$." For other more complicated observables which are arbitrary functions of q_j and p_j, we form the associated operator simply by interpreting q_j to mean "multiply by q_j" whenever it appears and by making the literal substitution of $\dfrac{\hbar}{i}\dfrac{\partial}{\partial q_j}$ for p_j whenever p_j appears.

In cartesian coordinates, this set of operators may be written

Dynamical Variable		Associated Operator
x	$\rightarrow$	x (multiply by x)
p_x	$\rightarrow$	$\dfrac{\hbar}{i}\dfrac{\partial}{\partial x}$
y	$\rightarrow$	y (multiply by y)
p_y	$\rightarrow$	$\dfrac{\hbar}{i}\dfrac{\partial}{\partial y}$
z	$\rightarrow$	z (multiply by z) (3.12)
p_z	$\rightarrow$	$\dfrac{\hbar}{i}\dfrac{\partial}{\partial z}$
$F(x)$	$\rightarrow$	$F(x)$ [multiply by $F(x)$]
$F(p_x)$	$\rightarrow$	$F\left(\dfrac{\hbar}{i}\dfrac{\partial}{\partial x}\right)$
$\mathbf{p}$	$\rightarrow$	$\dfrac{\hbar}{i}\nabla$
$\mathbf{p}^2$	$\rightarrow$	$-\hbar^2\nabla^2 = -\hbar^2\Delta$

Using these operator associations, we may build up the operator to be associated with any physical observable we may choose. Perhaps the most important operator in quantum mechanics is the Hamiltonian operator— the quantum-mechanical operator to be associated with the classical Hamiltonian of a system. We have seen in Chap. 2 that for conservative systems in general and for certain special nonconservative systems the Hamiltonian corresponds to the total energy of the system, kinetic plus potential.

$$H = T + V \qquad (2.43)$$

The kinetic energy of a particle in translational motion is equal to $p^2/2m$, where p^2 is its linear momentum, so for such a particle,

$$H = \frac{p^2}{2m} + V(\mathbf{r}) = \frac{1}{2m}(p_x^2 + p_y^2 + p_z^2) + V(\mathbf{r}) \qquad (3.13)$$

where $V(\mathbf{r})$ specifies the potential energy of the particle at any point in space. According to the prescription of Eq. (3.12), the appropriate operator for this Hamiltonian is

$$H_{\text{op}} = \frac{1}{2m}\left[\left(\frac{\hbar}{i}\frac{\partial}{\partial x}\right)^2 + \left(\frac{\hbar}{i}\frac{\partial}{\partial y}\right)^2 + \left(\frac{\hbar}{i}\frac{\partial}{\partial z}\right)^2\right] + V(\mathbf{r})$$

$$= -\frac{\hbar^2}{2m}\left(\frac{\partial^2}{\partial x^2} + \frac{\partial^2}{\partial y^2} + \frac{\partial^2}{\partial z^2}\right) + V(\mathbf{r}) = -\frac{\hbar^2}{2m}\nabla^2 + V(\mathbf{r}) \quad (3.14)$$

The correct procedure for forming the Hamiltonian operator of more complicated systems or in different coordinate schemes will be discussed later in this chapter and in the Appendix.

Now that we have discussed at some length the operators of quantum mechanics, we may well inquire as to the appropriate operands for these operators. The operands are the set of all possible state functions of the system. In the Schrödinger formulation of quantum mechanics, the state functions are single-valued functions of the coordinates, are continuous, are continuous in their first derivatives with respect to the coordinates, and are subject to the constraint that they must be "square integrable," a constraint we will discuss further in the next section.

3.4 THE STATE FUNCTION AND STATE-FUNCTION SPACE Quantum mechanics is a probabilistic theory. It generally predicts not one unambiguous result for the measurement of a physical observable but rather several different results, with some distribution of relative probability for finding these several results. The state function of a system Ψ therefore contains its information about that system in probabilistic form. Ψ is itself a probability function.

In the Schrödinger formulation of quantum mechanics, Ψ is a "probability amplitude." $\Psi(\mathbf{r},t)$ is a continuous function of the coordinates (generalized coordinates, if convenient), single valued and continuous in its first derivatives, but in general complex. We obtain a probability (necessarily positive and real) from a probability amplitude by multiplying the amplitude by its own complex conjugate, just as we obtain the intensity of a wave, electromagnetic or acoustic, from the corresponding field or displacement vector.

Suppose that $\Psi(\mathbf{r},t)$ is the state function for a single particle. We then place upon the product

$$P(\mathbf{r},t) = \Psi^*(\mathbf{r},t)\Psi(\mathbf{r},t) \quad (3.15)$$

the interpretation that $P(\mathbf{r},t)\mathbf{dr}$ is the probability that the particle will at time t be found in the volume element between $\mathbf{r}$ and $\mathbf{r} + \mathbf{dr}$. $P(\mathbf{r},t)$ is a probability density. Ψ itself may be complex, and takes on both positive and negative values, but $\Psi^*\Psi$ is, of course, real and positive. $\Psi(\mathbf{r},t)$ will generally be large where the particle is likely to be found and will generally be small where the particle is not likely to be found.

Since the probability of finding the particle *somewhere* at time t is unity, we place the normalization requirement upon Ψ that

$$\int \Psi^*(\mathbf{r},t)\Psi(\mathbf{r},t)\,d\tau = 1 \tag{3.16}$$

where $d\tau$ is the differential element of volume, and the integral is extended over the entire region containing the particle. In order that the normalization indicated in Eq. (3.16) be possible, it is necessary that the state function $\Psi(\mathbf{r},t)$ be "square integrable"; the integral of $\Psi^*\Psi$ over the appropriate coordinate space must converge as the integral is extended throughout the relevant volume, perhaps to $\pm\infty$ in the linear coordinates. The requirement of square integrability placed upon Ψ by its physical interpretation is one of the important boundary conditions upon Ψ and will appear in a number of the eigenvalue problems we shall subsequently solve.

There are many possible state functions for any system, corresponding to the different combinations of position and velocity that the particle or particles can assume. The state functions of quantum mechanics have the important property of being linearly additive. If $\Psi_1(\mathbf{r},t)$ is a possible state function for a system and $\Psi_2(\mathbf{r},t)$ is another possible state function, then so also is their linear sum.

$$\Psi(\mathbf{r},t) = \lambda_1\Psi_1(\mathbf{r},t) + \lambda_2\Psi_2(\mathbf{r},t) \tag{3.17}$$

where λ_1 and λ_2 will have to be chosen so as to preserve the normalization requirement of Eq. (3.16). We note that the probability amplitude associated with this new $\Psi(\mathbf{r},t)$ is given by

$$\Psi^*(\mathbf{r},t)\Psi(\mathbf{r},t) = |\lambda_1|^2\,\Psi_1^*(\mathbf{r},t)\Psi_1(\mathbf{r},t) + |\lambda_2|^2\Psi_2^*(\mathbf{r},t)\Psi_2(\mathbf{r},t)$$
$$+ \lambda_1^*\lambda_2\Psi_1^*(\mathbf{r},t)\Psi_2(\mathbf{r},t) + \lambda_2^*\lambda_1\Psi_2^*(\mathbf{r},t)\Psi_1(\mathbf{r},t) \tag{3.18}$$

The first two terms on the right-hand side of Eq. (3.18) are what we would obtain by adding the probability densities associated with Ψ_1 and Ψ_2 separately; the other two terms represent interference effects and may make the probability density at any point $\mathbf{r}$ greater than or less than $|\lambda_1|^2\,\Psi_1^*\Psi_1 + |\lambda_2|^2\,\Psi_2^*\Psi_2$, depending on the relative sign and magnitude of the cross terms. State functions, then, behave very much like the solutions to the (linear) wave equations of electromagnetism or acoustics in that they allow superposition (the linear sum of two solutions also a solution) and in that they show interference effects.

Note that the state function Ψ of Eq. (3.17) might well be that for a single particle, so the interference given by the cross terms of Eq. (3.18) does not represent the interference of one particle with another but a self-interference which has no analog in classical mechanics. The wavelike characteristics of particles arise from just this interference effect, and all experiments which demonstrate the wavelike nature of particles are based upon examining the probability density of particles in a superposition state and finding interference effects. The particle, when it is observed by the flash it produces on a luminescent screen or by the click it makes in a counter, always behaves like a particle in the familiar sense of the word—a localized lump of mass and perhaps charge. It is the distribution of probability for finding this discrete particle which obeys wavelike equations and shows the interference and reinforcement effects typical of wave phenomena.

Consider now the set of all possible state functions of a system. This is the set of single-valued square-integrable continuous functions $\Psi(\mathbf{r},t)$. We will for convenience lift for the present the normalization requirement of Eq. (3.16), but bear in mind that any square-integrable function can be "reduced to unity norm" by multiplication with a suitably chosen constant, called the *normalization constant*. We now assert that the set of all possible state functions of a system comprise a general vector space called a *Hilbert space*. What are the characteristics of such a space?

First, a Hilbert space is a linear space. By *linear space* we mean one such that

1. The sum of any two members of the space is also a member of the space.
2. The product of any member of the space by a number (perhaps complex) is also a member of the space.
3. Any linear combination of two members of the space (that is, $\lambda_1 \Psi_1 + \lambda_2 \Psi_2$, where λ_1 and λ_2 may be complex) is also a member of the space.

We can see that these properties are generalized versions of the properties of the familiar three-dimensional vectors in real space. For the three-dimensional vectors of real space, the multiplicative constants are constrained to be real, but except for that, conditions 1 through 3 above are clearly satisfied. The sum of any two vectors in three-dimensional space is also a vector in three-dimensional space. The vector obtained by multiplying a given vector by some scalar constant is also a member of the set of three-dimensional vectors, and the general linear combination of vectors is still a vector in the same space.

One more property is required of a set of functions before they may be considered to comprise a vector space, and that is the existence of a scalar or "inner" product of any two members of the space. For three-dimensional vectors in real space, this is the "dot product" $\mathbf{r}_1 \cdot \mathbf{r}_2$. For our state functions, we define the scalar product as

$$\langle \Psi_1, \Psi_2 \rangle = \int \Psi_1^*(\mathbf{r},t)\Psi_2(\mathbf{r},t)\, d\tau \tag{3.19}$$

where $d\tau$ is again the volume element and the integral is over all the relevant volume. We see that the scalar product of a state function with itself is the integral of the probability density:

$$\langle \Psi_1, \Psi_1 \rangle = \int \Psi_1^*(\mathbf{r},t)\Psi_1(\mathbf{r},t)\, d\tau = \int P(\mathbf{r},t)\, d\tau \tag{3.20}$$

In extracting from a state function the information it contains about the system, we always use scalar products of one kind or another. The state function of a system—including the wave functions of the Schrödinger formulation—is never directly observable. We cannot do experiments which map out $\Psi(\mathbf{r},t)$ directly. We can only measure the values of relevant physical observables, such as position, momentum, and energy, and compare these quantities with what the state function predicts, via the appropriate scalar product, for the same quantity. Just how to form the relevant scalar products and how to interpret them will be explained shortly.

In order to manipulate the various general vectors of our state-function space and to make the various calculations involving these state functions, it is necessary to have some set of basis functions or basis vectors. A general state function can then be specified by giving its "components" along the various basis vectors. In three-dimensional space, we usually choose some set of orthogonal unit vectors as a basis, and write all general vectors in terms of the projection of the general vector upon the basis vectors. For instance, we write

$$\mathbf{r} = x\mathbf{i} + y\mathbf{j} + z\mathbf{k} \tag{3.21}$$

to describe and specify completely the vector $\mathbf{r}$. Note that the description consists of two ingredients: a set of basis vectors $\mathbf{i}$, $\mathbf{j}$, and $\mathbf{k}$ and a set of "measure numbers" x, y, and z given by forming the scalar product of $\mathbf{r}$ with the basis vectors.

$$x = \langle \mathbf{i}, \mathbf{r} \rangle = \mathbf{i} \cdot \mathbf{r}$$
$$y = \langle \mathbf{j}, \mathbf{r} \rangle = \mathbf{j} \cdot \mathbf{r} \tag{3.22}$$
$$z = \langle \mathbf{k}, \mathbf{r} \rangle = \mathbf{k} \cdot \mathbf{r}$$

It is enormously convenient to have the basis vectors orthonormal, that is, such that their scalar products with themselves are unity and with one another are zero:

$$\mathbf{i} \cdot \mathbf{i} = \mathbf{j} \cdot \mathbf{j} = \mathbf{k} \cdot \mathbf{k} = 1$$
$$\mathbf{i} \cdot \mathbf{j} = \mathbf{i} \cdot \mathbf{k} = \mathbf{j} \cdot \mathbf{k} = 0$$

(3.23)

Choosing such an orthonormal basis is so convenient because the computation of the scalar products of general vectors will never require keeping track of such cross-product terms as $\mathbf{i} \cdot \mathbf{j}$, etc., since these terms will automatically be zero. It is also important to note that the three basis vectors $\mathbf{i}$, $\mathbf{j}$, and $\mathbf{k}$ "span the space" of all three-dimensional vectors. Any general three-dimensional vector can be completely expressed in terms of these three basis vectors, and there are no remaining components pointing in some fourth or fifth orthogonal direction.

It is clear that the manipulation of general vectors is greatly facilitated by having a set of orthonormal basis vectors. Where do we obtain a suitable set of basis vectors (functions) for our Hilbert space of state functions? From the eigenvalue equations to which the linear operators of Sec. 3.3 give rise! Each operator eigenvalue equation generates a set of eigenfunctions, and each of these sets of eigenfunctions comprises a possible set of basis functions spanning state-function space.

p 61, 41

3.5 EIGENVALUE EQUATIONS, EIGENFUNCTIONS, AND BASIS VECTORS

The very starting point of quantum mechanics is the association of mathematical operators with dynamical observables. In Sec. 3.3 we discussed the linear nature of these operators, considered their algebra (especially their commutation properties), and produced one satisfactory set of quantum mechanical operators—the differential operators of Schrödinger. We will discuss in this section the eigenvalue equations to which these operators give rise, the eigenfunctions satisfying the eigenvalue equations, and the physical interpretation of the eigenvalues of the equations.

Let us, as before, associate a linear operator A with some dynamical observable a. This operator defines implicitly an eigenvalue equation

$$Au_n = a_n u_n$$

(3.24)

Consider, for instance, the operator $\dfrac{\hbar}{i} \dfrac{\partial}{\partial x}$ which we will regularly associate with the dynamical observable p_x, the x component of linear momentum. We obtain from it an equation

$$\frac{\hbar}{i} \frac{\partial}{\partial x} u(x) = p_x u(x)$$

(3.25)

which has the eigenfunctions

$$u(x) = e^{(i/\hbar)p_x x} \qquad (3.26)$$

as may be verified by direct substitution. Note that solutions of the form of Eq. (3.26) are eigenfunctions no matter what the numeric value of p_x, so Eq. (3.25) is an example of an eigenvalue equation with *continuous* eigenvalues. Other operators we will encounter will have solutions only for certain discrete values of the eigenvalue a_n.

By the second postulate of quantum mechanics, we now place a physical interpretation upon the eigenvalues a_n produced by an eigenvalue equation such as Eq. (3.24), namely, that the only possible results of a physical measurement of the dynamical variable a be one of the eigenvalues a_n. The first consequence of this interpretation is that the eigenvalues a_n are all required to be *real*. We never obtain an imaginary number for the result of a laboratory measurement of a dynamical variable such as position, momentum, or energy. The eigenfunctions may be complex, as is $e^{(i/\hbar)p_x x}$, but the eigenvalue must be *real*. The operator A must, then, not only be linear but also be such that it has exclusively real eigenvalues, even though its eigenfunctions may be complex. Such an operator is called a *Hermitian* operator. The Hermitian character of the operator has a number of formal consequences which make its manipulation simpler than is the case for a general linear operator. (We will encounter these later.)

The second consequence of associating the eigenvalues of the operator with the results of a physical measurement is, in general, to restrict the possible results of a measurement to a certain set of "allowed" values. For the one operator whose eigenvalue equation we have written, p_x, it developed that the eigenvalues were continuous, and any numeric value is an "allowed" value for linear momentum. Linear momentum is then not "quantized" in quantum mechanics, and may take on a continuous range of values. On the other hand, many operators, such as energy or angular momentum, will turn out to have a discrete eigenvalue spectrum; only certain "allowed" values of energy or angular momentum will be observed, and the variable is said to be *quantized*.

If we know, then, the eigenvalues of the operator to be associated with a given observable, we know the full list of possible results of a measurement of that observable. Which of these possible results will we obtain if we make an actual measurement on an actual system? That depends, of course, on the system being observed and on the previous dynamical history of the system: its "initial conditions" or state of preparation. How is the system and its dynamical state specified? By its state function. How do we extract this information from the state function? To answer this question we must first understand the connection between the state function of a system and the eigenfunctions of the operator associated with a physical observable. The connection is as follows.

Each of the linear Hermitian operators of quantum mechanics generates a set of eigenfunctions which is complete, orthogonal and spans completely state-function space. The eigenfunctions of a Hermitian operator provide, therefore, a set of functions ideally suited to serve as the basis functions into which we can resolve any general state function.

p 39, 61

Let us examine the three important properties which an ideal set of basis functions must possess: completeness, orthogonality, and unit "length." First, what do we mean in this case by completeness? We mean that the set of basis functions is such that any state function may be expressed as a sum of the basis wave functions, with each wave function included in proper amount as specified by its "expansion coefficient." If, for instance, we were considering some one-dimensional case where ψ, the state function, was a function of x alone, we could write

$$\psi(x) = \sum_n c_n u_n(x) \tag{3.27}$$

where the $u_n(x)$ are the eigenfunctions of the Hermitian operator A and the c_n are the appropriate expansion coefficients. The situation is analogous to that of expressing a three-dimensional vector in terms of its components (the c_n) along some basis vectors [the $u_n(x)$], or to the Fourier expansion of some general function of x in terms of the basis functions $\sin nx$ and $\cos nx$. Just as it was true in the three-dimensional vector case, the expansion coefficient c_n is the projection upon the basis vector (or function) of the general vector, and may be computed by forming the scalar product of the basis function with the general function [see Eq. (3.22)]:

$$c_n = \langle u_n(x), \psi(x) \rangle \tag{3.28}$$

p 43

In the Schrödinger wave-mechanical formulation of quantum mechanics, the scalar product is defined for the one-dimensional case as

$$\langle u_n(x), \psi(x) \rangle = \int_{-\infty}^{+\infty} u_n^*(x)\psi(x)\,dx \tag{3.29}$$

The procedure is entirely analogous to other expansions with which the reader is undoubtedly familiar, for example, the expansion of some general electrical potential in the complete set of spherical harmonics, or the expansion of some time-dependent quantity as a harmonic series in $e^{in\omega t}$ or in $\sin n\omega t$ and $\cos n\omega t$. Again, completeness must be defined with respect to some particular domain, and it is only with respect to the domain of single-valued, square-integrable, continuous, etc., functions that the eigenfunctions of our Hermitian operators form complete basis sets. They will not suffice for the expansion of an arbitrary function containing an arbitrary number of infinities and discontinuities, but fortunately such ill-behaved functions will never correspond to real state functions and will not be of concern to us in quantum mechanics. The completeness, with respect to realizable state functions, of the eigenfunctions of Hermitian operators is very difficult to prove in general. It has been proved specifically for a number of operators, for instance, those associated with position, linear momentum, and angular momentum, and we shall accept as an article of faith the completeness of these eigenfunction sets for the general Hermitian operator of quantum mechanics.

Secondly, we wish the eigenfunctions to be orthogonal. Stated formally, we wish

$$\langle u_k, u_l \rangle = 0 \qquad \text{if } k \neq l \tag{3.30}$$

The orthogonality of the eigenfunctions is quite easy to prove, but the proof requires the knowledge of a formal property of the Hermitian operators which we have not yet derived. Since we will derive this property during the discussion of expectation values to follow shortly, the orthogonality proof will be deferred until later in this chapter.

Finally, we wish the basis functions to be of unity norm, that is, we wish

$$\langle u_k, u_k \rangle = 1 \tag{3.31}$$

The eigenfunctions belonging to discrete eigenvalues will always turn out to be quite simply square integrable, and the reduction of the eigenfunctions to unit "length" simply requires multiplication by the appropriate constant, called a *normalizing constant*. The eigenfunctions corresponding to continuous eigenvalues often give more trouble, but the trouble can invariably be cured by various mathematical artifices usually involving the Dirac delta function. The Dirac delta function is a singular function which has the properties

$$\delta(k) = \begin{cases} 0 & \text{if } k \neq 0 \\ \infty & \text{if } k = 0 \end{cases}$$

$$\int_{-\infty}^{+\infty} \delta(k)\, dk = 1 \tag{3.32}$$

and may be thought of as an impulse function of infinite height and zero width, having unit area nonetheless. It obviously must be defined as the limiting case of more tractable functions, and has several formal definitions which will be introduced as needed. The Dirac delta function is meaningful only under an integral sign, where it has the effect of evaluating the integral at the singularity of the delta function, for example,

$$\int_{-\infty}^{+\infty} F(x)\,\delta(x-a)\,dx = F(a) \tag{3.33}$$

We will encounter such integrals in defining our scalar products, in particular that of Eq. (3.31). As stated above, it will always prove possible to reduce our eigenfunctions to unity norm, fulfilling the last of the requirements for an ideal basis function set.

3.6 MEASUREMENT IN QUANTUM MECHANICS: EXPECTATION VALUES

Let us now consider how we extract from our state function the information it contains about the various dynamical observables. Suppose that our system is in some state which we will specify as $\Psi(\mathbf{r},t)$ and that we make a measurement at time t_0 of the dynamical observable a (for example, position, energy, or angular momentum). What will our measurement yield? Let us assume the observable a has a set of discrete eigenvalues a_n with which are associated orthonormal eigenfunctions $u_n(\mathbf{r})$. Since the $u_n(\mathbf{r})$ are a complete set, we can rewrite our state function in the form of an expansion in the $u_n(\mathbf{r})$.

$$\Psi(\mathbf{r},t_0) = \sum_n c_n(t_0)u_n(\mathbf{r}) \tag{3.34}$$

where the $c_n(t_0)$ are obtained from   ~ cf (3.28)

$$c_n(t_0) = \langle u_n(\mathbf{r}), \Psi(\mathbf{r},t_0)\rangle = \int u_n^*(r)\Psi(\mathbf{r},t_0)\,d\mathbf{r} \tag{3.35}$$

p 41

and the integral is over all the relevant volume.

Suppose first that our $\Psi(\mathbf{r},t)$ was such that we have fortuitously only one term in our expansion in the $c_n(t_0)$, that is, that

$$\Psi(\mathbf{r},t_0) = c_k(t_0)u_k(\mathbf{r}) \tag{3.36}$$

From the requirement that $\langle \Psi(\mathbf{r},t), \Psi(\mathbf{r},t)\rangle = 1$ and the orthonormality of the $u_n(\mathbf{r})$, we see immediately that

$$|c_k(t_0)|^2 = 1 \tag{3.37}$$

Therefore $c_k(t_0) = 1$, or at most differs from unity by a phase factor. Observe now the effect of the operator A upon this state function:

$$A\Psi(\mathbf{r},t_0) = Ac_k(t_0)u_k(\mathbf{r}) = a_k c_k(t_0)u_k(\mathbf{r}) \tag{3.38}$$

Operating upon this state with A has produced the same state again, multiplied by the real scalar a_k. Consider now the scalar product

$$\langle \Psi(\mathbf{r},t_0), A\Psi(\mathbf{r},t_0)\rangle = \langle c_k(t_0)u_k(\mathbf{r}), a_k c_k(t_0)u_k(\mathbf{r})\rangle$$
$$= a_k\langle c_k(t_0)u_k(\mathbf{r}), c_k(t_0)u_k(\mathbf{r})\rangle = a_k \tag{3.39}$$

The scalar product of the state function with the operator times the state function gave the eigenvalue of the operator. We assert that this eigenvalue a_k is what would be measured for the value of the observable a if the system were in the special state given by Eq. (3.36), that is, in the eigenstate $u_k(\mathbf{r})$ at $t = t_0$.

Suppose now that our system is not in such a special state, and that the expansion of the state function at $t = t_0$ contains a number of terms.

$$\Psi(\mathbf{r},t_0) = \sum_n c_n(t_0)u_n(\mathbf{r}) \tag{3.34}$$

The individual $c_n(t_0)$ must be calculated from Eq. (3.35), but we already know from the normalization of $\Psi(\mathbf{r},t)$ something about their amplitudes.

$$\begin{aligned}
\langle\Psi(\mathbf{r},t_0), \Psi(\mathbf{r},t_0)\rangle &= \langle\sum_{n'} c_{n'}(t_0)u_{n'}(\mathbf{r}), \sum_n c_n(t_0)u_n(\mathbf{r})\rangle \\
&= \sum_{n'}\sum_n \int c_{n'}(t_0)^* c_{n'}(t_0)u_{n'}(\mathbf{r})^* u_n(\mathbf{r})\, d\mathbf{r} \\
&= \sum_{n'}\sum_n c_{n'}(t_0)^* c_n(t_0)\delta_{n'n} \\
&= \sum_n |c_n(t_0)|^2 = 1 \tag{3.40}
\end{aligned}$$

The sum of the squares of the coefficients must add up to unity. This is known as the *closure relation*.

Consider the effect of the operator A acting upon this more complicated state function:

$$A\Psi(\mathbf{r},t_0) = A \sum_n c_n(t_0)u_n(\mathbf{r}) = \sum_n a_n c_n(t_0)u_n(\mathbf{r}) \tag{3.41}$$

If we think of the state function as a general vector in state-function space, we can see that operating on this vector with our operator A has both rotated this vector into some new direction and changed its "length." (For the previous case, $\Psi(\mathbf{r},t)$ an eigenstate of A, we changed only the vector's "length," not its "direction.") Now, finally, consider the scalar product

$$\begin{aligned}
\langle a \rangle &= \langle\Psi(\mathbf{r},t_0), A\Psi(\mathbf{r},t_0)\rangle = \int \Psi(\mathbf{r},t_0)^* A\Psi(\mathbf{r},t_0)\, d\mathbf{r} \\
&= \int \sum_{n'} c_{n'}^*(t_0)u_{n'}^*(\mathbf{r}) A \sum_n c_n(t_0)u_n(\mathbf{r})\, d\mathbf{r} \\
&= \sum_{n'}\sum_n \int c_{n'}^*(t_0)c_n(t_0)a_n u_{n'}^*(\mathbf{r})u_n(\mathbf{r})\, d\mathbf{r} \\
&= \sum_{n'}\sum_n c_{n'}^*(t_0)c_n(t_0)a_n\delta_{n'n} = \sum_n |c_n(t_0)|^2\, a_n \tag{3.42}
\end{aligned}$$

The scalar $\langle a \rangle$ is called the *expectation value* of the observable a which would be measured at time t_0 for the system whose state function was

$\Psi(\mathbf{r},t_0)$. The expectation value is a weighted sum of the various possible expectation values a_n, and the weighting factor is the magnitude of the square of the expansion coefficient $c_n(t_0)$ of the state function in the eigen-functions of A. The expectation value $\langle a \rangle$ is a statistical quantity which is an ensemble average. It is the average value of results of a large number of measurements on a large number of identically prepared systems, all measurements being made simultaneously at $t = t_0$. The results of a single measurement on a single system will be one of the a_n, and the relative probability of obtaining a given a_n is given by $|c_n(t_0)|^2$. The expectation value of a, $\langle a \rangle$, is then seen to be a weighted sum of the possible results of a single measurement multiplied by the relative probability of obtaining that result.

Suppose, for instance, that the state function of our system at $t = t_0$ had just three "components" when expanded in the $u_n(\mathbf{r})$. Suppose that our state function was

$$\Psi(\mathbf{r},t_0) = \frac{1}{2} u_1(\mathbf{r}) + \frac{1}{2} u_2(\mathbf{r}) + \frac{1}{\sqrt{2}} u_3(\mathbf{r}) \qquad (3.43)$$

If a single measurement of a is made on a system with this state function, one of three possible values will result: a_1, a_2, or a_3. These are all "correct" results of a single measurement. If a large number of measurements are made on an ensemble of systems, each with this state function, the value a_1 will be obtained $(\frac{1}{2})^2 = \frac{1}{4}$ of the time, the value a_2 will be obtained $(\frac{1}{2})^2 = \frac{1}{4}$ of the time, and the value a_3 will be obtained $(1/\sqrt{2})^2 = \frac{1}{2}$ of the time. The average, or expectation, value of a will be

$$\langle a \rangle = \tfrac{1}{4}a_1 + \tfrac{1}{4}a_2 + \tfrac{1}{2}a_3 \qquad (3.44)$$

A theory is useful insofar as it makes predictions about things which can be measured. We may well inquire if the expectation value of an operator is in fact what is measured in a typical experiment.

For systems small enough to require quantum mechanics for their accurate description, it is seldom feasible to make a single measurement on a single system. Usually the average value of the observable is indeed measured simultaneously on a large number of systems. For instance, the measurement of conductivity in a solid gives a measure of the average translation of a large number of electrons, or the measurement of the magnetic susceptibility of a solid measures the average polarization of a large number of microscopic magnets, or the measurement of the emission spectrum of a gas gives the simultaneous observation of the radiation from a large number of identical atoms or molecules. It is indeed the expectation value of an observable which is usually measured in a real experiment.

Let us return to the definition of the expectation value of an observable.

$$\langle a(t) \rangle = \langle \Psi(\mathbf{r},t), A\Psi(\mathbf{r},t) \rangle = \int \Psi^*(\mathbf{r},t) A\Psi(\mathbf{r},t) \, d\mathbf{r} \qquad (3.45)$$

Note that if we know how to perform the operation of A on the state function $\Psi(\mathbf{r},t)$, it is not necessary to go through the intermediate steps of expanding $\Psi(\mathbf{r},t)$ in the eigenfunctions of A to be able to compute $\langle a \rangle$. Suppose, for instance, that we know the Schrödinger wave function for an electron in an atom and that we want to know the expectation value of x, the average value of the x coordinate of the electron. Then by our definition of expectation values

$$\langle x(t) \rangle = \int \Psi^*(\mathbf{r},t) X\Psi(\mathbf{r},t) \, d\mathbf{r} = \int \Psi^*(\mathbf{r},t) x\Psi(\mathbf{r},t) \, d\mathbf{r}$$

$$= \int x P(\mathbf{r},t) \, d\mathbf{r} \qquad (3.46)$$

Here we have used X to designate the operator associated with x, and then substituted the explicit form of that operator, namely, multiply by x. The expectation value of x turns out to be, not surprisingly, the weighted average of x times the probability that the electron is at position $\mathbf{r}$ with coordinate x.

If we had desired instead the expectation value of the x component of linear momentum, we would compute it from

$$\langle p_x(t) \rangle = \int \Psi^*(\mathbf{r},t) P_x \Psi(\mathbf{r},t) \, d\mathbf{r} = \int \Psi^*(\mathbf{r},t) \frac{\hbar}{i} \frac{\partial}{\partial x} \Psi(\mathbf{r},t) \, d\mathbf{r} \quad (3.47)$$

Since the operator P_x has a more complicated effect upon $\Psi(\mathbf{r},t)$ than simple multiplication by a coordinate, we cannot simplify our integral in this case as we did for x, but evaluation of the integral of Eq. (3.47) will indeed give us the expectation value for p_x. It is only necessary to go through the eigenfunction expansion of $\Psi(\mathbf{r},t)$ when we wish to know, in addition to the expectation value of the observable, the allowed results of single measurements and the relative probability of obtaining them.

The expectation value of an observable must be a real quantity, since it too is an observable quantity. Formally we may require that

$$\langle a \rangle = \langle a \rangle^* \qquad (3.48)$$

to ensure the realness of $\langle a \rangle$. From this requirement we can deduce an important formal property of the Hermitian operators. From the definition of $\langle a \rangle$ and Eq. (3.48), we may deduce the following:

$$\langle a \rangle = \langle a \rangle^*$$

$$\int \Psi^* A \Psi \, d\mathbf{r} = \left[\int \Psi^* A \Psi \, d\mathbf{r} \right]^*$$

$$= \int \Psi^{**} A^* \Psi^* \, d\mathbf{r}$$

$$= \int \Psi A^* \Psi^* \, d\mathbf{r}$$

$$= \int [A^* \Psi^*] \Psi \, d\mathbf{r} \tag{3.49}$$

We have here suppressed the argument $(\mathbf{r},t)$ of Ψ to reduce the clutter of the equations and have bracketed $A^*\Psi^*$ in the last line to make clear that A^* operates upon Ψ^* rather than on the product function $\Psi^*\Psi$. The important point of Eq. (3.49) is that the value of the expectation value is the same if A^* operates on Ψ^* as it is if A operates on Ψ. In these Schrödinger scalar-product integrals, we may then shift the operator in the integrand from operating on Ψ to operating on Ψ^* if we also convert the operator A into its complex conjugate A^*. We will find this theorem useful in proving several properties of eigenfunctions and expectation values.

3.7 EIGENFUNCTION ORTHOGONALITY AND THE SHARING OF EIGEN-FUNCTION SETS We stated in an earlier section that the eigenfunctions of a Hermitian operator formed a complete orthonormal set and that the proof of orthogonality in particular would be deferred till later. We are now in a position to prove the orthogonality of these eigenfunctions.

Suppose first we have a nondegenerate set of eigenfunctions, that is, that there is one and only one eigenfunction uniquely associated with each eigenvalue. Consider then two eigenvalues a_n and a_m, where $a_n \neq a_m$.

$$\left. \begin{array}{l} Au_n = a_n u_n \\ Au_m = a_m u_m \end{array} \right\} \qquad a_n \neq a_m \tag{3.50}$$

Multiplying the first left-hand member of Eq. (3.50) by u_m^* and integrating over the appropriate region, we have

$$\int u_m^* A u_n \, d\tau = a_n \int u_m^* u_n \, d\tau \tag{3.51}$$

We write now the complex conjugate of the second left-hand member of Eq. (3.50).

$$A^*u_m^* = a_m^*u_m^* = a_m u_m^* \tag{3.52}$$

The asterisk can be removed from a_m^* since an eigenvalue is required to be real. Multiplying Eq. (3.52) from the right by u_n and integrating gives

$$\int A^*u_m^* u_n \, d\tau = a_m \int u_m^* u_n \, d\tau \tag{3.53}$$

Because of the Hermitian nature of the operator A, we may bring it through u_m^* in the left-hand side of Eq. (3.53), remove the conjugation, and allow it to operate on u_n.

$$\int A^*u_m^* \, u_n \, d\tau = \int u_m^* A u_n \, d\tau \tag{3.54}$$

Combining Eqs. (3.53), (3.54), and (3.55), we have

$$a_m \int u_m^* u_n \, d\tau = \int u_m^* A u_n \, d\tau = a_n \int u_m^* u_n \, d\tau \tag{3.55}$$

which may be rewritten

$$(a_n - a_m) \int u_m^* u_n \, d\tau = 0 \tag{3.56}$$

Since by hypothesis $a_n \neq a_m$, we must have

$$\int u_m^* u_n \, d\tau = 0 \qquad \langle u_m, u_n \rangle = 0 \tag{3.57}$$

and the orthogonality is proved for the nondegenerate case.

For the degenerate case, where more than one eigenfunction is associated with the same eigenvalue, the orthogonality proof is somewhat more complicated. For states corresponding to different eigenvalues, the orthogonality may be proved as for the nondegenerate case. For eigenfunctions belonging to the same eigenvalue, $a_m = a_n$, and the above proof fails. We shall now show that it is always possible to construct from the several degenerate eigenfunctions belonging to the same eigenvalue a set which is orthogonal. We shall, in fact, produce a procedure for constructing the orthogonal set, a scheme known as the *Schmidt orthogonalization procedure*.

Suppose we have associated with the eigenvalue a_n of operator A a set of m eigenfunctions which we will label

$$\mu_{1n}, \mu_{2n}, \mu_{3n}, \ldots, \mu_{mn} \tag{3.58}$$

such that the condition

$$k_{1n}\mu_{1n} + k_{2n}\mu_{2n} + k_{3n}\mu_{3n} + \cdots + k_{mn}\mu_{mn} = 0 \qquad (3.59)$$

implies that all the k_{jn} are identically zero. This is a formal definition of *linear independence*, and simply states that none of the members of the set can be fully reproduced as a linear sum of the rest. From this set of functions we arbitrarily pick one member as the starting point of our new set. Call this first member of our orthogonal set u_{1n}, and let us pick μ_{1n} for the starting function.

$$u_{1n} = \mu_{1n} \qquad (3.60)$$

We now calculate a scalar product which is also the normalizing factor for the first function.

$$c_{11} = \langle u_{1n}, u_{1n} \rangle = \int u_{1n}^* u_{1n}\, d\tau = \int \mu_{1n}^* \mu_{1n}\, d\tau \qquad (3.61)$$

If the μ_{jn} were already normalized to unity, c_{11} will be equal to unity.

Next we calculate the scalar product of u_{1n} with the second wave function of our original set. We are calculating in effect the projection of u_{1n} upon μ_{2n}. We call this scalar product (perhaps complex) c_{12}.

$$c_{12} = \langle u_{1n}, \mu_{2n} \rangle = \int u_{1n}^* \mu_{2n}\, d\tau \qquad (3.62)$$

We can now form the second orthogonalized basis function:

$$u_{2n} = \mu_{2n} - \frac{c_{12}}{c_{11}} u_{1n} \qquad (3.63)$$

That u_{2n} is orthogonal to u_{1n} we can readily verify by direct calculation:

$$\langle u_{1n}, u_{2n} \rangle = \int u_{1n}^* u_{2n}\, d\tau$$

$$= \int u_{1n}^* \mu_{2n}\, d\tau - \frac{c_{12}}{c_{11}} \int u_{1n}^* u_{1n}\, d\tau$$

$$= c_{12} - \frac{c_{12}}{c_{11}} c_{11}$$

$$= 0 \qquad (3.64)$$

If we define further normalization constants and scalar products

$$\langle u_{2n}, u_{2n} \rangle = c_{22}$$

$$\langle u_{1n}, \mu_{3n} \rangle = c_{13} \qquad (3.65)$$

$$\langle u_{2n}, \mu_{3n} \rangle = c_{23}$$

we can immediately write a third basis function, orthogonal to u_{1n} and u_{2n}:

$$u_{3n} = \mu_{3n} - \frac{c_{13}}{c_{11}} u_{1n} - \frac{c_{23}}{c_{22}} u_{2n} \tag{3.66}$$

This third function can readily be shown to be orthogonal to u_{1n} and u_{2n}. The same procedure may be followed repeatedly until m orthogonal functions have been constructed. The set of m orthogonal wave functions thus constructed is not unique, as any one of the μ_{kn} could have been used as a starting function, or, indeed, any linear combination of the μ_{kn}.

The Schmidt procedure has a simple analogy in ordinary vector space. Suppose we have a set of three independent (noncolinear) but nonorthogonal vectors. We may construct a set of orthogonal vectors as follows: Choose one vector as a starting point. Select a second vector, and subtract from it its projection onto the first vector. The remainder will be orthogonal to the first vector. Take the third vector and subtract from it its projections upon the two orthogonal vectors. It will now be orthogonal to both the others. Such a procedure can be extended into an n-dimensional vector space—for instance, the vector space of functions which are solutions of the same differential equations. The Schmidt orthogonalization procedure does just that.

From the fact that every Hermitian operator generates a complete set of orthogonal eigenfunctions, we are led to suspect that we will be confronted by a great proliferation of possible basis systems for state-function space when we actually get down to specific calculations. This proliferation would be greatly reduced if the various eigenfunction sets were not all distinct, that is, if more than one operator generated the same set of eigenfunctions. We will now demonstrate that this is indeed the case, and that many operators may in fact share the same set of eigenfunctions.

Let us ask under what circumstances two operators will share the same eigenfunction. Suppose, for instance, that the eigenfunction u_n is an eigenfunction of operator A, belonging to the eigenvalue a_n, and is simultaneously also an eigenfunction of the operator B, belonging to the eigenvalue b_n:

$$Au_n = a_n u_n \qquad Bu_n = b_n u_n \tag{3.67}$$

What does this sharing imply about operators A and B? Let us operate on the first of Eq. (3.67) with B and on the second with A:

$$BAu_n = Ba_n u_n = a_n Bu_n = a_n b_n u_n$$
$$ABu_n = Ab_n u_n = b_n Au_n = b_n a_n u_n \tag{3.68}$$

Subtracting the first of Eq. (3.68) from the second, we obtain

$$ABu_n - BAu_n = a_n b_n u_n - b_n a_n u_n$$
$$(AB - BA)u_n = (a_n b_n - b_n a_n)u_n$$
$$= 0 \tag{3.69}$$

We see then that if u_n is a common eigenfunction of operator A and B then A and B must commute:

$$[A,B] = 0 \tag{3.70}$$

There are many commuting operators in quantum mechanics; for instance, the operators associated with generalized coordinates and momenta commute with one another, excepting only the conjugate pairs [see Eq. (3.11)]. There are therefore many instances of shared eigenfunctions.

We have shown that if an eigenfunction is shared by two operators then these operators must commute. It is also possible to prove the converse: that if two operators commute they then share a set of eigenfunctions. The proof for the nondegenerate case is quite simple. Suppose A and B commute and that u_n is an eigenfunction of A:

$$Au_n = a_n u_n \tag{3.71}$$

Then
$$BAu_n = a_n Bu_n$$
$$A[Bu_n] = a_n[Bu_n] \tag{3.72}$$

where the second line follows from the first because of the commutativity of A and B, and the brackets have been introduced to emphasize that the second equation states that the function Bu_n is an eigenfunction of A belonging to the eigenvalue a_n. Since A was assumed to be nondegenerate, the eigenfunction of A belonging to the eigenvalue a_n is unique, so Bu_n can differ from u_n by at most a multiplicative constant, which we shall call b_n.

$$Bu_n = b_n u_n \tag{3.73}$$

It therefore follows that u_n, assumed to be an eigenfunction of A, is also an eigenfunction of B.

The proof for the degenerate case is similar in principle but more tedious in execution, so it will be omitted here. The Schmidt orthogonalization procedure, the reader will recall, produces a set of orthogonal basis wave functions within the degenerate manifold, but this set of orthogonal eigenvectors is not unique. The proof concerning the sharing of eigenfunctions for the degenerate case consists of generating that particular set which is simultaneously satisfactory for both operators A and B. If A and B commute, it is always possible to produce such a set.

The most important operator in quantum mechanics is undoubtedly the Hamiltonian operator, as will be discussed in the next chapter. We will often in the course of future calculations examine an operator to see if it commutes with the Hamiltonian operator, for we usually will have determined the eigenfunctions of the Hamiltonian operator and will wish to know if they are simultaneously eigenfunctions of the operator in hand.

Summary

Chapter 3 has contained a number of the important postulates and definitions of quantum mechanics. We collect the important points here:

POSTULATE 1   *With every physical observable a, we may associate a linear Hermitian operator A, from whose properties we may deduce the possible results of measurements of the physical observable a.*

Each linear Hermitian operator defines implicitly an eigenvalue equation of the form

$$Au_n = a_n u_n$$

where the eigenvalues are all real and the eigenfunctions (generally complex) form a complete orthogonal set spanning state-function space.

POSTULATE 2   *The only possible result of a single measurement on a single system of the physical observable a is one of the eigenvalues of the operator A.*

POSTULATE 3   *For every dynamical system there exists a state function Ψ which contains all the information which is known about the system.*

If the state function Ψ of a system is also an eigenfunction u_n of some operator A, then the result of a measurement of observable a on the system will yield invariably the value a_n.

If the state function Ψ of the system is some more general function, then the expectation value of a, the average of a large number of simultaneous measurements on an ensemble of identically prepared systems, is given by

$$\langle a \rangle = \langle \Psi, A\Psi \rangle$$

Two operators A and B will share eigenfunctions if $[A,B] = 0$.

The operators assignable to generalized coordinates and their conjugate momenta will bear the commutation relations

$$[Q_j, Q_k] = 0$$

$$[P_j, P_k] = 0$$

$$[Q_j, P_k] = i\hbar \delta_{jk}$$

One set of satisfactory operators to be associated with physical variables, that used by Schrödinger, is

Observable	Operator
q_j	q_j (multiply by q_j)
p_j	$\dfrac{\hbar}{i} \dfrac{\partial}{\partial q_j}$
$F(q_j)$	$F(q_j)$
$F(p_j)$	$F\left(\dfrac{\hbar}{i} \dfrac{\partial}{\partial q_j}\right)$

POSTULATE 4   *If we know* Ψ *for any system at some particular time, then the evolution of* Ψ *at all subsequent times is determined by*

$$-\frac{\hbar}{i} \frac{\partial \Psi}{\partial t} = H_{op}\Psi$$

where H_{op} *is the operator associated with the Hamiltonian of the system.*

Problems

3.1 All dice games are based on the discrete, stable, positional equilibria of a cube on a plane surface. We may think of the numbers showing on top of the dice as a quantized observable A.

a What are the eigenvalues a_n of the observable for a single die?
b What is $\langle a \rangle$ for an "honest" die thrown upon a flat table?
c One die is dropped on a table and is observed to be in the state $a_n = 3$. The table is then shaken in such a fashion that there is a probability of one-third that the die will roll off the original face onto one of the adjacent faces. Write the state function of the die after the table is shaken.
d Suppose the table is shaken a second time in precisely the same manner as was prescribed in c above. What will the state function of the system be after the second shake?

3.2 Suppose we chose the operation x^2, multiply by x^2, to associate with the observable x. Can you produce a derivative operator P_x which we may associate with p_x and which will satisfy the commutation relations, Eq. (3.11)?

3.3 Prove that if A and B commute and are both degenerate that they share a common set of eigenfunctions.

3.4 Prove the following commutation relations:

a
$$[P_x, X^n] = \frac{\hbar}{i} n x^{n-1}$$

b
$$[X, P_x^2 F(x)] = -\frac{2\hbar}{i} P_x F(x)$$

c
$$[X, P_x F(x) P_x] = \frac{\hbar}{i} [F(x) P_x + P_x F(x)]$$

d
$$[X, F(x) P_x^2] = -\frac{2\hbar}{i} F(x) P_x$$

e
$$[P_x, P_x^2 F(x)] = \frac{\hbar}{i} P_x^2 F'(x)$$

f
$$[P_x, P_x F(x) P_x] = \frac{\hbar}{i} P_x F'(x) P_x$$

g
$$[P_x, F(x) P_x^2] = \frac{\hbar}{i} F'(x) P_x^2$$

where $F(x)$ is an analytic expression in x, and $F'(x)$ means the first derivative of $F(x)$ with respect to x.

3.5 The cartesian components of angular momentum I are given by

$$l_x = y p_z - z p_y$$
$$l_y = z p_x - x p_z$$
$$l_z = x p_y - y p_x$$

Write the associated Schrödinger operators L_x, L_y, and L_z.
Using these operators, prove the commutation relations for angular momentum.

$$[L_x, L_y] = i\hbar L_z$$
$$[L_y, L_z] = i\hbar L_x$$
$$[L_z, L_x] = i\hbar L_y$$

Write the operators for $L^2 = L_x^2 + L_y^2 + L_z^2$ and show that

$$[L^2, L_x] = [L^2, L_y] = [L^2, L_z] = 0$$

Bibliography

Every introductory text on quantum mechanics contains implicitly at least the postulates, definitions, and concepts presented in this chapter. These concepts and postulates are treated explicitly and compactly in the following texts:

Messiah, A.: "Quantum Mechanics," vol. 1, chap. 5, Interscience Publishers, Inc., New York, 1961.

Dicke, R. H., and J. P. Wittke: "Introduction to Quantum Mechanics," chap. 6, Addison-Wesley Publishing Company, Inc., Reading, Mass., 1960.

Rojansky, V. B.: "Introductory Quantum Mechanics," chap. 3, Prentice-Hall, Inc., Englewood Cliffs, N.J., 1938.

Leighton, R. B.: "Principles of Modern Physics," chap. 2, McGraw-Hill Book Company, New York, 1959.

CHAPTER 4

The Hamiltonian Operator and Schrödinger's Equation

4.1 SCHRÖDINGER'S EQUATION The concept of energy enters most sophisticated theories of dynamics in a very important way. Both the Lagrangian and Hamiltonian formulations of classical dynamics are based essentially on energy expressions. It is not therefore surprising that the Hamiltonian operator, associated with the total energy of the system, should enter quantum mechanics in a dominant role. The Hamiltonian operator enters quantum mechanics through what we have labeled as Postulate 4 (Sec. 3.2) and what is generally called *Schrödinger's equation*:

$$H_{op}\Psi = -\frac{\hbar}{i}\frac{\partial \Psi}{\partial t} \qquad (4.1)$$

Let us first form the Hamiltonian operator for a typical simple system and then examine the resulting Schrödinger equation.

We will form the Hamiltonian operator by writing the classical Hamiltonian for the system, then making the literal operator substitutions of Eq. (3.12). Consider first the classical Hamiltonian of a particle moving in a conservative force field (we will confine our attention for some time to conservative potentials).

$$H = \frac{p^2}{2m} + V(\mathbf{r},t) \qquad (4.2)$$

Substituting the appropriate operators from Eq. (3.12), we have the associated operator

$$H_{op} = -\frac{\hbar^2}{2m}\nabla^2 + V(\mathbf{r},t) \qquad (4.3)$$

Equation (4.1) then becomes, for this system,

$$\left[-\frac{\hbar^2}{2m}\nabla^2 + V(\mathbf{r},t)\right]\Psi(\mathbf{r},t) = -\frac{\hbar}{i}\frac{\partial\Psi(\mathbf{r},t)}{\partial t} \qquad (4.4)$$

which we immediately recognize as "Schrödinger's equation including the time," or simply as "Schrödinger's equation." We frequently see this equation in cartesian coordinates and with the minus signs cleared in the form

$$\frac{\hbar^2}{2m}\left(\frac{\partial^2}{\partial x^2} + \frac{\partial^2}{\partial y^2} + \frac{\partial^2}{\partial z^2}\right)\Psi(\mathbf{r},t) - V(\mathbf{r},t)\Psi(\mathbf{r},t) = \frac{\hbar}{i}\frac{\partial}{\partial t}\Psi(\mathbf{r},t) \qquad (4.5)$$

Schrödinger's equation is a very unusual equation in mathematical physics because of the appearance of the imaginary quantity i. The typical wave equations of classical physics equate second derivatives with respect to coordinates to second derivatives with respect to time. Classical diffusion equations equate second derivatives with respect to coordinates to the first derivative with respect to time, but contain explicitly no imaginary quantities. The appearance of the first time derivative in Schrödinger's equation has the agreeable consequence that specifying $\Psi(\mathbf{r},t)$ at one particular time specifies $\Psi(\mathbf{r},t)$ at all subsequent times without the specification of any further boundary conditions. Were the equation second order in all derivatives, we would also have to specify both $\Psi(\mathbf{r},t)$ and either its first time derivatives or first space derivatives. On the other hand, the appearance of i in Schrödinger's equation guarantees that our solutions will be generally complex—a less agreeable consequence.

In many instances of physical interest, $V(\mathbf{r},t)$ describes a static potential and is not a function of time but of spatial coordinates only. If V is a function of $\mathbf{r}$ only, Schrödinger's equation can always be separated into two equations, one involving only spatial coordinates and the other only the time. We may then write our general solution as a product of two functions, one of time and the other of spatial coordinates only:

$$\Psi(\mathbf{r},t) = \psi(\mathbf{r})\phi(t) \qquad (4.6)$$

Substituting Eq. (4.6) into Eq. (4.4) and dividing through by $\Psi(\mathbf{r},t)$, we obtain

$$\frac{1}{\psi(\mathbf{r})}\left[-\frac{\hbar^2}{2m}\nabla^2 + V(\mathbf{r})\right]\psi(\mathbf{r}) = -\frac{1}{\phi(t)}\frac{\hbar}{i}\frac{\partial\phi(t)}{\partial t} \qquad (4.7)$$

Since the left-hand side of Eq. (4.7) is a function of spatial coordinates only and the right-hand side is a function of time only, the two sides must be separately equal to a constant, which we will denote by E. Then

$$\left[-\frac{\hbar^2}{2m}\nabla^2 + V(\mathbf{r})\right]\psi(\mathbf{r}) = E\psi(\mathbf{r}) \qquad (4.8)$$

and
$$-\frac{\hbar}{i}\frac{\partial}{\partial t}\phi(t) = E\phi(t) \tag{4.9}$$

Equation (4.8) is Schrödinger's time-independent wave equation. The constant E has the dimensions of energy, and from the classical meaning of the Hamiltonian in a conservative system, we know it to be the total energy of the particle, kinetic plus potential. Equation (4.8) usually appears in a slightly rewritten form as

$$\left[\frac{\hbar^2}{2m}\nabla^2 + \left(E - V(\mathbf{r})\right)\right]\psi(\mathbf{r}) = 0 \tag{4.10}$$

Equation (4.9) is readily integrated to give

$$\phi(t) = Ne^{-(i/\hbar)Et} \tag{4.11}$$

where N is a normalization constant. It is convenient when normalizing $\Psi(\mathbf{r},t)$ to normalize the spatial and temporal functions $\psi(\mathbf{r})$ and $\phi(t)$ separately to unity:

$$\langle\psi(\mathbf{r}), \psi(\mathbf{r})\rangle = 1 \qquad \overset{*}{\phi}(t)\,\phi(t) = 1 \tag{4.12}$$

Normalizing $\phi(t)$ yields immediately that N must itself be of unit "length," and can only be a phase factor:

$$N = e^{i\delta} \tag{4.13}$$

where δ is arbitrary. Since $\phi(t)$ will always appear as a product with $\psi(\mathbf{r})$ in any state function, it is customary to set $\delta = 0$ and absorb any phase factor for the total wave function in the spatial part $\psi(\mathbf{r})$. There is no need to keep track of arbitrary phase factors in both functions. With this normalization and convention, then, we write $\phi(t)$ simply as

$$\phi(t) = e^{-(i/\hbar)Et} \tag{4.14}$$

The spatial part of Schrödinger's equation cannot, of course, be solved nearly so simply, and indeed a great deal of the body of quantum mechanics consists in the solving of Schrödinger's time-independent equation for various systems. Inspection of Eq. (4.8) reveals that solving Schrödinger's time-independent equation is entirely equivalent to solving for the eigenfunctions and eigenvalues of the Hamiltonian operator. The various values of the constant E for which solutions exist are called the *eigenenergies* of the system, and the various eigenfunctions of the Hamiltonian operator are called the *stationary states* of the system.

We can readily demonstrate why the eigenfunctions of the Hamiltonian operator (still for $V(\mathbf{r})$ not depending on time) are called the *stationary states* of the system. Suppose we have obtained one of the eigenfunctions of the Hamiltonian operator $\psi_n(\mathbf{r})$ and its associated eigenvalue E_n. Then the state function for the system, if it is in this eigenstate, is

$$\Psi_n(\mathbf{r},t) = \psi_n(\mathbf{r})e^{-(i/\hbar)E_n t} \qquad (4.15)$$

Let us look at the probability density associated with this state function:

$$\begin{aligned}
P(\mathbf{r},t) &= \Psi_n^*(\mathbf{r},t)\Psi_n(\mathbf{r},t) \\
&= \psi_n^*(\mathbf{r})\psi_n(\mathbf{r})e^{+(i/\hbar)E_n t}e^{-(i/\hbar)E_n t} \\
&= \psi_n^*(\mathbf{r})\psi_n(\mathbf{r}) \qquad (4.16)
\end{aligned}$$

We see immediately that the probability density *does not change with time* for such an eigenstate. The expectation value of position will not change with time, and the result of a measurement of $\langle r \rangle$ (an ensemble average) will not depend upon the time at which the measurement was made.

4.2 A MORE GENERAL FORMULATION OF THE HAMILTONIAN OPERATOR

The Hamiltonian operator was formed in the preceding section by following a particularly simple procedure:

1. Write the classical Hamiltonian for the system.
2. Make a straightforward literal substitution of operators for their dynamical equivalents wherever they appear.

Such a simple and straightforward procedure unfortunately often leads to ambiguous or incorrect formulation of the Hamiltonian operator unless certain pitfalls are avoided. These pitfalls all have their origin in the fact that conjugate variables commute in the classical Hamiltonian, whereas their associated operators do not. For instance, the term $x^2p_x^2$ in a classical Hamiltonian could be written equivalently as $x^2p_x^2,\ xp_xxp_x,\ p_xx^2p_x$ or in any other permutation without altering the results of any classical computation involving these terms; however, the associated operators $-\hbar^2x^2\dfrac{\partial^2}{\partial x^2}$, $-\hbar^2 x\dfrac{\partial}{\partial x}\left(x\dfrac{\partial}{\partial x}\right)$, $-\hbar^2\dfrac{\partial}{\partial x}\left(x^2\dfrac{\partial}{\partial x}\right)$, etc., are not at all equivalent.

Consider, for instance, the classical Hamiltonian for the free particle, written in cylindrical coordinates:

$$H = \frac{p_r^2}{2m} + \frac{1}{r^2}\frac{p_\phi^2}{2m} + \frac{p_z^2}{2m} + V(\mathbf{r}) \qquad (4.17)$$

Making the literal substitution of associated operators into Eq. (4.17) according to the general rule

$$p_k = \frac{\hbar}{i}\frac{\partial}{\partial q_k} \qquad (4.18)$$

we obtain a Hamiltonian operator:

$$H_{op} = -\frac{\hbar^2}{2m}\left(\frac{\partial^2}{\partial r^2} + \frac{1}{r^2}\frac{\partial^2}{\partial \phi^2} + \frac{\partial^2}{\partial z^2}\right) + V(\mathbf{r}) \qquad (4.19)$$

Suppose, on the other hand, we had formed the Hamiltonian operator first in cartesian coordinates, as in Eq. (4.5), and subsequently had transformed the operator ∇^2 into cylindrical coordinates in its properly invariant form. We would then have had

$$H_{op} = -\frac{\hbar^2}{2m}\left(\frac{\partial^2}{\partial r^2} + \frac{1}{r}\frac{\partial}{\partial r} + \frac{1}{r^2}\frac{\partial^2}{\partial \phi^2} + \frac{\partial^2}{\partial z^2}\right) + V(\mathbf{r}) \qquad (4.20)$$

which differs from Eq. (4.19) by the presence of an additional term.

The resolution of the paradox lies in the words *properly invariant*. Though the potential $V(\mathbf{r})$ may be of any symmetry, and will have different apparent forms for different orientations of the coordinate frame in which it is written, the operator ∇^2 should not change form as the coordinate frame in which it is written is rotated. This should be true whether the coordinate frame be cartesian, cylindrical, or whatever. For every coordinate scheme (cylindrical, spherical, etc.) there exists a unique rotationally invariant form of ∇^2, and that is the form which should be used in forming the Hamiltonian operator. The Appendix treats in some further detail the formation of the Hamiltonian operator in coordinates other than cartesian. Cartesian coordinates possess certain simple transformation properties which make the ∇^2 operator automatically invariant. If in doubt, we can always form the Hamiltonian operator in cartesian coordinates and subsequently transform to a more convenient coordinate scheme.

A second pitfall occurs if the potential is not conservative but contains both $\mathbf{r}$ and $\mathbf{p}$ terms. Again the ambiguity arises from the noncommutativity of the operators. In the classical Hamiltonian

$$f(q_j)p_j = p_j f(q_j) \qquad (4.21)$$

and the sequence of writing the factors is of no significance. For the associated operators, sequence is very important, and we must derive some rules for handling the sequencing problem. The general rule is to form the symmetrized sum of operators, for example,

$$f(q_j)p_j \rightarrow \tfrac{1}{2}[f(Q_j)P_j + P_j f(Q_j)] \qquad (4.22)$$

We will find that in many instances the symmetrizing has already entered the classical Hamiltonian and need not be accomplished *ad hoc*. If we look back at the classical Hamiltonian for a charged particle in the nonconservative magnetic field, we recall that

$$H = \frac{[\mathbf{p} - (q/c)\mathbf{A}]^2}{2m} + V(\mathbf{r}) \qquad (4.23)$$

The expanded form

$$H = \frac{1}{2m}\left[\mathbf{p}^2 - \frac{q}{c}(\mathbf{p} \cdot \mathbf{A} + \mathbf{A} \cdot \mathbf{p}) + \frac{q^2}{c^2}\mathbf{A}^2\right] + V(\mathbf{r}) \qquad (4.24)$$

contains the troublesome terms in an already symmetrized form.

4.3 THE EIGENFUNCTIONS OF THE HAMILTONIAN AS BASIS WAVE

FUNCTIONS   It was pointed out at some length in Chap. 3 that the eigenfunctions of _any_ of the Hermitian operators of quantum mechanics
provided a satisfactory basis system for describing the state function of
any system. In practice, however, it is almost invariably the eigenfunctions
of the Hamiltonian which are used as the basis for state-function expansions. We shall now examine why this should be the case.

p 39, 41

In Sec. 4.1 we observed that if a system was in an eigenstate of the
Hamiltonian operator, the associated probability density was invariant
with time, i.e., was a stationary state. Now since we know very well that
particles and systems in general do move and do change their probability
distributions with time, we will generally expect that most physical
systems will not be in pure eigenstates of the Hamiltonian but in more
complicated states which must be described by a superposition of many
eigenstates. Let us write such a general state for a conservative system
where $V(\mathbf{r},t) = V(\mathbf{r})$:

$$\Psi(\mathbf{r},t) = \sum_n c_n(t)\Psi_n(\mathbf{r},t)$$
$$= \sum_n c_n(t)\psi_n(\mathbf{r})e^{-(i/\hbar)E_n t} \qquad (4.25)$$

If we substitute the state-function expansion back into Schrödinger's
equation, we obtain

$$H_{\text{op}} \sum_n c_n(t)\psi_n(\mathbf{r})e^{-(i/\hbar)E_n t} = -\frac{\hbar}{i}\frac{\partial}{\partial t}\sum_n c_n(t)\psi(\mathbf{r})e^{-(i/\hbar)E_n t} \qquad (4.26)$$

Since $\psi_n(\mathbf{r})$ is an eigenfunction of H_{op} belonging to the eigenvalue E_n, we
may rewrite Eq. (4.26), after taking the partial derivative with respect to
time indicated on the right, in the form

$$\sum_n c_n(t)E_n\psi_n(\mathbf{r})e^{-(i/\hbar)E_n t} = -\frac{\hbar}{i}\sum_n \dot{c}_n(t)\psi_n(\mathbf{r})e^{-(i/\hbar)E_n t}$$
$$+ \sum_n c_n(t)E_n\psi_n(\mathbf{r})e^{-(i/\hbar)E_n t} \qquad (4.27)$$

or, canceling the equal terms on both sides,

$$-\frac{\hbar}{i} \sum_n \dot{c}_n(t)\psi_n(\mathbf{r})e^{-(i/\hbar)E_n t} = 0 \qquad (4.28)$$

This equation can be true for all $\mathbf{r}$ and t only if

$$\dot{c}_n(t) = 0 \qquad (4.29)$$

The expansion coefficients $c_n(t)$ are not time varying, but are constants independent of the time:

$$c_n(t) = c_n(t_0) \qquad (4.30)$$

If the expansion coefficients are established at some time t_0, they will remain the same ever after, and we can specify the state function completely and permanently by simply specifying the list of expansion coefficients $c_n(t_0)$.

The expansion coefficients of a general state function will not be constants independent of time if the eigenfunctions of some other arbitrary operator are used as a basis system. The privileged position of the eigenfunctions of the Hamiltonian in quantum mechanics is due largely to their excellent qualification as a set of basis wave functions.

There are many classical analogs of the expansion of a general quantum-mechanical state function in the eigenfunctions of the Hamiltonian. If, for instance, we establish the normal modes of vibration of a mechanical system, a general vibration of the system can be described as a superposition of the several normal modes, and, ignoring friction, the amplitude of each normal mode is constant with time. The normal modes correspond to the eigenfunctions, the mode amplitudes to the expansion coefficients, and indeed the frequencies of the normal modes are analogous to the eigenenergies. Similarly, the electromagnetic disturbance inside a microwave cavity can be described as a superposition of oscillations in the several normal electromagnetic modes of the cavity, and, except for damping effects, the amplitudes of each of the normal modes remain constant with time. The intensity of the electric field at any given point may vary in a complex way with time, but a spectral analysis of the intensity would show that the components at various frequencies were constant with time and that their addition was responsible for the complicated total behavior.

4.4 THE TIME VARIATION OF EXPECTATION VALUES Since we observe not state functions but expectation values of observables, we are ultimately interested not in the time dependence of expansion coefficients but in the variation with time of expectation values. Let us calculate the time variation of the expectation value $\langle a \rangle$. By definition

$$\langle a(t) \rangle = \langle \Psi(\mathbf{r},t), A\Psi(\mathbf{r},t) \rangle$$

$$= \int \psi^*(\mathbf{r},t) A\Psi(\mathbf{r},t) \, d\mathbf{r} \qquad (4.31)$$

Therefore

$$\frac{d}{dt}\langle a(t) \rangle = \int \left[\frac{\partial^*(\mathbf{r},t)}{\partial t} A\Psi(\mathbf{r},t) + \Psi^*(\mathbf{r},t) \frac{\partial A}{\partial t} \Psi(\mathbf{r},t) \right.$$

$$\left. + \Psi^*(\mathbf{r},t) A \frac{\partial \Psi(\mathbf{r},t)}{\partial t} \right] d\mathbf{r} \quad (4.32)$$

From Schrödinger's equation and its complex conjugate, we know that

$$\frac{\partial \Psi(\mathbf{r},t)}{\partial t} = -\frac{i}{\hbar} H\Psi(\mathbf{r},t)$$

$$\frac{\partial \Psi^*(\mathbf{r},t)}{\partial t} = \frac{i}{\hbar} H^* \Psi^*(\mathbf{r},t) \qquad (4.33)$$

p 53, postulate 4 [handwritten marginal note]

Substituting these expressions into Eq. (4.32) yields

$$\frac{d}{dt}\langle a(t) \rangle = \int \left(\frac{i}{\hbar} H^* \Psi^* A\Psi + \Psi^* \frac{\partial A}{\partial t} \Psi - \frac{i}{\hbar} \Psi^* A H\Psi \right) d\mathbf{r}$$

$$= \int \left(\frac{i}{\hbar} \Psi^* HA\Psi + \Psi^* \frac{\partial A}{\partial t} \Psi - \frac{i}{\hbar} \Psi^* A H\Psi \right) d\mathbf{r}$$

$$= \int \Psi^* \left[\frac{i}{\hbar}(HA - AH) + \frac{\partial A}{\partial t} \right] \Psi \, d\mathbf{r}$$

$$= -\frac{i}{\hbar} \langle [A,H] \rangle + \left\langle \frac{\partial A}{\partial t} \right\rangle \qquad (4.34)$$

The argument of $\Psi(\mathbf{r},t)$ has been suppressed as clearly understood; the second step is allowed because of the Hermiticity of H; and the remainder is straightforward manipulation.

Many of the formulas and expressions of quantum mechanics have analogs in classical dynamics, and indeed the existence of such parallelism helped guide the formulation of quantum mechanics. The parallelism which precipitates the present remark is that between Eq. (4.34), which gives the expression for the time rate of change of a quantum-mechanical expectation value, and Eq. (2.51) of Chap. 2,

$$\frac{dF}{dt} = \frac{\partial F}{\partial t} + \{F,H\} \qquad (2.51)$$

Once again the Poisson bracket of classical mechanics has been literally replaced by the commutator bracket of quantum mechanics.

If the operator A does not contain the time explicitly (and most operators, such as those associated with position, momentum, energy flow, etc., do not), the total rate of change of the expectation value $\langle a \rangle$ is determined by the expectation value of the commutator of A and H, the Hamiltonian. If A commutes with the Hamiltonian and does not contain time explicitly, the expectation value of $\langle a \rangle$ will be a constant for any state of the system, no matter how complicated that state may be. The observable a is then called *a constant of the motion*, a term borrowed from classical mechanics. Constants of the motion occur frequently in both quantum and classical dynamics. For instance, the angular momentum of a planet (or comet) about the sun is constant, even though the orbit be very eccentric and the velocity of the planet strongly dependent on its orbital position.

If we knew that an observable A commuted with the Hamiltonian, we might have arrived at the conclusion that $\langle a \rangle$ was a constant by a quite different but equally valid line of reasoning, which goes as follows: A and H commute, so they must share a set of eigenfunctions. If we expand $\Psi(\mathbf{r},t)$ in these eigenfunctions, the expansion coefficients will be constant (as shown in Sec. 4.3). The expectation value $\langle a \rangle$ is given by the weighted average of eigenvalues a_n, where the weighting factor is the expansion coefficient required:

$$\langle a \rangle = \sum_n |c_n|^2 a_n \tag{4.35}$$

Since, for this special case, neither the c_n nor the a_n is a function of time (A does not contain time explicitly), then the weighted average $\langle a \rangle$ must be independent of time.

Summary

Important points to remember from Chapter 4:

The Hamiltonian operator may be formed from the classical Hamiltonian of the system in question by a literal substitution of operators for dynamical quantities, providing certain commutativity problems are avoided.

Schrödinger's equation is simply

$$H_{\text{op}}\Psi(\mathbf{r},t) = -\frac{\hbar}{i}\frac{\partial}{\partial t}\Psi(\mathbf{r},t) \tag{4.1}$$

If the potential $V(\mathbf{r},t)$ in the Hamiltonian does not contain time explicitly, the solutions of Schrödinger's equation may be factored into a time function and a space function:

$$\Psi(\mathbf{r},t) = \psi(\mathbf{r})\phi(t) \tag{4.2}$$

which are solutions of the equations

$$\left[-\frac{\hbar^2}{2m} \nabla^2 + V(\mathbf{r}) \right] \psi(\mathbf{r}) = E\psi(\mathbf{r}) \tag{4.8}$$

and

$$-\frac{\hbar}{i} \frac{\partial}{\partial t} \varphi(t) = E\varphi(t) \tag{4.9}$$

where the separation constant E is the total energy of the system

$$\varphi(t) = e^{-(i/\hbar)Et} \tag{4.14}$$

Equation (4.8) is Schrödinger's time-independent equation. Its eigenfunctions $\psi_n(\mathbf{r})$ are stationary states of the system, that is, are states of constant probability distribution. Its eigenvalues E_n are the eigenenergies of the system.

If $V(\mathbf{r},t) = V(\mathbf{r})$ (is time invariant) and any general state function is expanded in the eigenfunctions $\psi_n(\mathbf{r})$ of the Hamiltonian, then the expansion coefficients are constants independent of time.

The time variation of an expectation value $\langle a(t) \rangle$ is given by

$$\frac{d}{dt} \langle a(t) \rangle = -\frac{i}{\hbar} \langle [A,H] \rangle + \left\langle \frac{\partial A}{\partial t} \right\rangle \tag{4.34}$$

Problems

4.1 A system consists of two particles of masses M_1 and M_2 moving in an unbounded region of constant potential. Their interaction can be described by means of a potential that is a function only of the distance between the particles.

  a Write the Hamiltonian for the system in terms of $\mathbf{r}_1$ and $\mathbf{r}_2$, the position vectors of the two particles.

  b Introduce new coordinates: $\mathbf{R}$, the position vector of the center of mass of the system and $\mathbf{r}$, the position of particle 2 relative to particle 1. Show that the Schrödinger equation can be separated in these new coordinates.

4.2 The ammonia molecule NH_3 has a pyramidal structure with the nitrogen atom at the apex of the tetrahedron. The ammonia molecule is an example of a symmetric rotor. It has one unique moment of inertia about an axis through the nitrogen and the center of the equilateral triangle formed by the hydrogens, and two equal moments of inertia about any pair of axes perpendicular to the unique axis and to each other. The unique axis is also called the *symmetry axis*, since it is an axis of threefold symmetry.

  a Regarding the molecule as rigid, write its classical Hamiltonian.

  b Write Schrödinger's equation, including the time.

c Separate Schrödinger's equation into one equation containing all time-dependent functions and two time-independent equations, one involving center-of-mass coordinates only and the other involving angular variables only.

4.3 Write the Hamiltonian operator for the two-dimensional harmonic oscillator in cartesian and in polar coordinates. Write the Hamiltonian operator for the three-dimensional harmonic oscillator in cartesian and in spherical coordinates.

Bibliography

Schrödinger's equation is the focal point of most introductory books on quantum mechanics, and is developed in any of the several books below:

Rojansky, V. B.: "Introductory Quantum Mechanics," chap. 3, Prentice-Hall, Inc., Englewood Cliffs, N.J., 1938.

Schiff, L. I.: "Quantum Mechanics," 2nd ed., chap. 2, McGraw-Hill Book Company, New York, 1955.

Dicke, R. H., and J. P. Wittke: "Introduction to Quantum Mechanics," chap. 3, Addison-Wesley Publishing Company, Inc., Reading, Mass., 1960.

Pauling, L., and E. B. Wilson: "Introduction to Quantum Mechanics," chap. 3, McGraw-Hill Book Company, New York, 1935.

Messiah, A.: "Quantum Mechanics," vol. 1, chap. 2, Interscience Publishers, Inc., New York, 1961.

Eisberg, R. M.: "Fundamentals of Modern Physics," chap. 7, John Wiley & Sons, Inc., New York, 1961.

Sproull, R. L.: "Modern Physics," 2nd ed., chap. 5, John Wiley & Sons, Inc., New York, 1963.

Merzbacher, E.: "Quantum Mechanics," chap. 3, John Wiley & Sons, Inc., New York, 1961.

CHAPTER 5

The Harmonic Oscillator, Schrödinger Treatment

5.1   THE HARMONIC OSCILLATOR: PHONONS, PHOTONS, AND MAGNONS   We will devote a great deal of attention in the next several chapters, and indeed throughout this book, to the harmonic oscillator, and the reader might well wonder why so much attention is devoted to what appears to be such an academic example of a dynamic system. Actually the harmonic oscillator affords an excellent model for many real physical systems of real technical interest. The essential reason for the applicability of the model is that all systems in stable equilibrium will execute simple harmonic motion about that equilibrium for small disturbances from equilibrium.

The simple harmonic oscillator is characterized by having a restoring force which is proportional to the displacement away from the equilibrium position. For a one-dimensional system this force would be written

$$F = -kx \tag{5.1}$$

Such a force is a conservative force and is derivable from a potential energy of the form

$$V = \tfrac{1}{2}kx^2 \tag{5.2}$$

Consider now a real physical system, perhaps a solid consisting of many atoms bound together by the cohesive forces of the solid. This many-body system has many "normal modes" of vibration. Suppose we assign one of our generalized coordinates q_j to each normal mode. The potential energy of the system is then some function of these generalized coordinates:

$$V(\mathbf{r}) = V(q_1, q_2, q_3, \ldots, q_N) \tag{5.3}$$

At equilibrium, each of the generalized coordinates has some value q_{j0}.

We may expand the potential in a Taylor's series about the equilibrium positions.

$$V(\mathbf{r}) = V_0 + \sum_j \left(\frac{\partial V}{\partial q_j}\right)_0 (q_j - q_{j0}) + \frac{1}{2}\sum_i \sum_j \left(\frac{\partial^2 V}{\partial q_i\,\partial q_j}\right)_0 (q_i - q_{j0})(q_j - q_{j0})$$
$$+ \text{ higher-order derivatives} \quad (5.4)$$

The subscript zero in Eq. (5.4) means that a quantity is evaluated at the equilibrium position. In Eq. (5.4), V_0 is a constant which simply specifies the reference point for the zero of energy, $(\partial V/\partial q_j)_0$ must be zero for all q_j by the definition of an equilibrium position, and, if we have truly chosen the normal coordinates of our system, all the <u>cross</u> derivatives will vanish in the term quadratic in displacements from equilibrium. For each normal mode then, we will have a potential whose leading term is of the form

$$V_j(\mathbf{r}) = \frac{1}{2}\left(\frac{\partial^2 V}{\partial q_j^2}\right)_0 (q_j - q_{j0})^2 \qquad (5.5)$$

The restoring force will again be proportional to the displacement [see Eqs. (5.2) and (5.1)], and the normal mode of vibration will be a simple harmonic motion about the equilibrium configuration. It is therefore possible and accurate to describe the thermal and acoustic properties of a solid, insofar as they arise from atomic vibrations, in terms of the degree of excitation of a set of simple harmonic oscillators. The term *phonon* has been coined to describe one quantum of excitation (terms we will define more clearly later) of these lattice harmonic oscillators.

Similarly, it is possible to cast the whole body of electromagnetic radiation theory into a form which treats electromagnetic disturbances as excitations of a set of electromagnetic simple harmonic oscillators. The word *photon* has been coined to denote one quantum of excitation of one of these electromagnetic oscillators. The concept of a photon maintains validity for electromagnetic radiation of any frequency, not only for oscillations whose wavelength places them in the visible portion of the electromagnetic spectrum. The broad subject of quantum electrodynamics, upon which we will touch only occasionally in this book, is based upon the characterization of electromagnetic fields in terms of a set of simple harmonic oscillators.

For the reasons outlined earlier in this section, disturbances of any system about its equilibrium configuration can be rephrased in terms of normal modes of simple harmonic character. For magnetic systems the harmonic modes are called *spin waves*, and the term *magnon* refers to the quantum of excitation of a spin wave. Many of the subtle but important effects in solids—lifetimes of excited optical states, origin of magneto-elastic effects, noise in quantum oscillators—are most effectively discussed in the language of simple harmonic oscillator eigenstates and eigenenergies. Knowing, then, that the properties of the simple harmonic oscillator will be of considerable significance subsequently, we now launch into the quantum-mechanical treatment of this prototype system.

5.2 THE SOLUTION OF SCHRÖDINGER'S EQUATION FOR THE ONE DIMENSIONAL HARMONIC OSCILLATOR To understand the general properties of the harmonic oscillator, we will study first the simplest prototype, the one-dimensional simple harmonic oscillator. We will solve Schrödinger's equation for this oscillator, and in so doing will illustrate how the boundary conditions of the problem introduce discrete eigenvalues and eigenfunctions.

The classical Hamiltonian for the one-dimensional harmonic oscillator is

$$H = \frac{p_x^2}{2m} + \frac{1}{2} kx^2 \tag{5.6}$$

Making the appropriate operator substitutions, we obtain Schrödinger's equation for this system:

$$\left(-\frac{\hbar^2}{2m} \frac{\partial^2}{\partial x^2} + \frac{1}{2} kx^2 \right) \Psi(x,t) = -\frac{\hbar}{i} \frac{\partial}{\partial t} \Psi(x,t) \tag{5.7}$$

Since the potential energy does not contain the time explicitly, we may perform a separation of variables:

$$\Psi(x,t) = \psi(x)\varphi(t) \tag{5.8}$$

The time-independent Schrödinger's equation for the one-dimensional harmonic oscillator is then

$$\frac{\hbar^2}{2m} \frac{d^2}{dx^2} \psi(x) + (E - \tfrac{1}{2}kx^2)\psi(x) = 0 \tag{5.9}$$

with a time-dependent function $\varphi(t)$

$$\varphi(t) = e^{-(i/\hbar)Et} \tag{5.10}$$

associated also with each value of the separation constant E.

We now seek the solutions $\psi(x)$ which satisfy Eq. (5.7) and meet the requirements imposed generally on state functions ψ, namely, that they be single valued, continuous, continuous in their first derivatives, and normalizable in the sense of Eq. (3.16):

$$\int_{-\infty}^{+\infty} \psi^*(x)\psi(x)\, dx = 1 \tag{5.11}$$

Equation (5.11) is also a statement of the requirement of square integrability of the state function. For the one-dimensional simple harmonic oscillator, we can guarantee that $\psi(x)$ is square integrable if we require that $\psi(x)$ be everywhere finite and that $\psi(x) \to 0$ as $x \to \pm\infty$ more rapidly than $x^{-\frac{1}{2}}$. These requirements ensure that the integral of Eq. (5.11) converges. This very mild set of boundary conditions is all that is required to produce discrete eigenvalues and eigenfunctions for the one-dimensional harmonic oscillator.

The first step in solving Eq. (5.9) is to introduce some notational substitutions which simplify the form of the equation. We therefore define the parameters λ and α:

$$\lambda = \frac{2mE}{\hbar^2}$$

$$\alpha^2 = \frac{mk}{\hbar^2} \tag{5.12}$$

which reduce Eq. (5.9) to the form

$$\frac{d^2}{dx^2}\psi(x) + (\lambda - \alpha^2 x^2)\psi(x) = 0 \tag{5.13}$$

There are many methods for the solution of Eq. (5.13), and we will adopt a technique known as the *polynomial method*. We know that the expression

$$x^n e^{-cx^2} \tag{5.14}$$

vanishes at infinity for any finite number n because the negative exponential term overwhelms x^n for very large x, however large n may be. The expression of Eq. (5.14) is in fact square integrable for finite n over the total range of x from $-\infty$ to $+\infty$. If such a term is square integrable, so is a sum of such terms. We therefore look for a solution of Schrödinger's equations, Eq. (5.13), of the form

$$\psi(x) = f(x)e^{-\alpha x^2/2} \tag{5.15}$$

where $f(x)$ is a polynomial in x terminating after a finite number of terms at a finite power of x. If $f(x)$ does not terminate after a finite number of terms, or contains infinitely high powers of x, it can be shown that the integral of Eq. (5.11) does not converge, and such solutions cannot correspond to realizable state functions.

We now examine the requirements upon $f(x)$ generated by the constraint that $\psi(x)$ must be a solution to Schrödinger's equation. Taking the derivatives of $\psi(x)$ with respect to x, we obtain

$$\frac{d^2\psi(x)}{dx^2} = e^{-\alpha x^2/2}\left[\frac{d^2f(x)}{dx^2} - 2\alpha x \frac{df(x)}{dx} - \alpha f(x) + \alpha^2 x^2 f(x)\right] \tag{5.16}$$

Substituting this identity into Eq. (5.13), we find that the terms in $\alpha^2 x^2$ cancel and, after dividing through by $e^{-\alpha x^2/2}$, we have a differential equation for $f(x)$:

$$\frac{d^2}{dx^2}f(x) - 2\alpha x \frac{df(x)}{dx} + (\lambda - \alpha)f(x) = 0 \qquad (5.17)$$

We have converted our original problem, that of seeking a general function $\psi(x)$ which had certain properties, into one of finding a finite polynomial in x, $f(x)$, which will satisfy Eq. (5.17). Before substituting trial polynomials, we convert to a dimensionless variable

$$\xi = \sqrt{\alpha}\, x \qquad (5.18)$$

and, making the identification

$$H(\xi) \equiv f(x) \qquad (5.19)$$

we can write the differential equation for $H(\xi)$.

$$\frac{d^2 H(\xi)}{d\xi^2} - 2\xi \frac{dH(\xi)}{d\xi} + \left(\frac{\lambda}{\alpha} - 1\right) H(\xi) = 0 \qquad (5.20)$$

By the identity of Eq. (5.19), we mean: Substitute $\xi/\sqrt{\alpha}$ for x wherever x appears in $f(x)$, and call $H(\xi)$ the resulting polynomial in ξ.

We now write our trial polynomial,

$$H(\xi) = \sum_{v=0} a_v \xi^v \qquad (5.21)$$

take the appropriate derivatives,

$$\frac{dH(\xi)}{d\xi} = \sum_{v=0}^{n} v a_v \xi^{v-1}$$

$$\frac{d^2 H(\xi)}{d\xi^2} = \sum_{v=0}^{n} (v - 1)(v) a_v \xi^{v-2} \qquad (5.22)$$

and substitute these into the characteristic equation (5.20). There results a polynomial in ξ whose coefficients are functions of the a_v. Writing a general term in this polynomial, we find it looks like

$$\cdots + \left[(v + 1)(v + 2)a_{v+2} + \left(\frac{\lambda}{\alpha} - 1 - 2v\right)a_v \right]\xi^v + \cdots = 0 \qquad (5.23)$$

For the expression in ξ to be equal to zero for arbitrary ξ, as Eq. (5.23) demands, it is necessary for the coefficients of the various powers of ξ to vanish separately. We obtain, therefore, a "recursion relation" between the coefficients a_v and a_{v+2}.

$$a_{v+2} = -\frac{(\lambda/\alpha - 1 - 2v)}{(v + 1)(v + 2)} a_v \qquad (5.24)$$

Note that the recursion relation in this instance couples only the coefficients of powers of ξ differing by 2. The coefficients of even powers of ξ are all related by Eq. (5.24) and those of odd powers are interrelated, but the coefficients of even powers are not interrelated with those of odd powers.

The physical requirement that $\psi(x)$ vanish at infinity was reduced earlier to the requirement that $H(\xi)$ be a finite polynomial in ξ. The polynomial must terminate after a finite number of terms. We can see from the recursion relation of Eq. (5.24) that we can terminate $H(\xi)$ at ξ^n by making

$$\frac{\lambda}{\alpha} - 1 - 2n = 0 \qquad (5.25)$$

which forces a_{n+2} and all successive a_{n+2k} to be zero.

Let us underscore this result strongly. The polynomial $H(\xi)$ will terminate after a finite number of terms (n terms), and

$$\psi(x) = e^{-\alpha x^2/2} H(\sqrt{\alpha}\, x) \qquad (5.26)$$

will be a physically admissible solution to Schrödinger's equation for the harmonic oscillator if, and only if, the condition of Eq. (5.25) is met. This equation establishes a definite numerical relation between the parameters λ and α. Rewriting Eq. (5.25), we have

$$\lambda = (2n + 1)\alpha \qquad (5.27)$$

where n is an integer. The parameter λ involved the separation constant E, corresponding to the total energy of the system. Recalling the definitions of λ and α, we have the quantum condition on energy:

$$E_n = (n + \tfrac{1}{2})\hbar \left(\frac{k}{m}\right)^{1/2} \qquad (5.28)$$

The eigenvalues of the Hamiltonian of the simple harmonic oscillator are given by Eq. (5.28), where n is any integer. *The eigenvalues are discrete and nondegenerate*, there being one $f(x)$ and therefore one $\psi(x)$ associated with each value of n.

Note that n is either even or odd, but cannot be both. It is therefore possible to terminate the odd terms in $f(x)$ at a finite number, or the even terms, but not both. The requirement of square integrability implies then that there will be two sets of solutions to Schrödinger's equation, one where $f(x)$ is a finite polynomial containing only even powers of x ($a_1 \equiv 0$ and all succeeding odd coefficients identically zero by the recursion relation) and the other where $f(x)$ is a finite polynomial containing only odd powers of x ($a_0 \equiv 0$, all succeeding even coefficients identically zero by the recursion relations). These solutions are said to be of even or odd parity, respectively. We will discuss more fully the concept of parity in a later section.

5.3 THE EIGENENERGIES AND EIGENFUNCTIONS OF THE HARMONIC OSCILLATOR The harmonic oscillator has provided us with an excellent example of the operator eigenvalue equation. We have an operator equation

$$Au_n = a_n u_n \qquad (5.29)$$

where A is an operator, u_n is a function, and a_n is a number, the separation constant of a partial differential equation. Upon examining the operator equation for the solutions u_n, consistent with certain boundary requirements forced by considerations of the physical interpretation of u_n, we find that "satisfactory" u_n may exist only for certain discrete values of a_n. It is not true that *all* operator equations have only discrete solutions, but many important ones, and especially those representing bound states of systems, *do* have discrete solutions. The u_n are called the *eigenfunctions of the operator*, and the a_n with which they are associated are the eigenvalues of the equation.

The eigenvalues of the Hamiltonian operator are the eigenenergies E_n of the system. For the harmonic oscillator

$$E_n = (n + \tfrac{1}{2})\hbar \left(\frac{k}{m}\right)^{\tfrac{1}{2}} \qquad (5.30)$$

We have introduced the subscript on E_n to label the eigenvalue, and in this case n also has the significance of being the highest power of ξ in $H_n(\xi)$, the polynomial associated with E_n. The classical angular frequency of the harmonic oscillator is given by

$$\omega_0 = \left(\frac{k}{m}\right)^{\tfrac{1}{2}} \qquad (5.31)$$

So the eigenenergies of the quantum oscillator can also be written

$$E_n = (n + \tfrac{1}{2})\hbar\omega_0 \qquad (5.32)$$

The E_n therefore form a ladder of equally spaced energy levels, as drawn in Fig. 5.1.

$$E_{n+1} - E_n = \hbar\omega_0 = h\nu_0 \qquad (5.33)$$

When a harmonic oscillator interacts with radiation, as we will subsequently see, it may make a "transition" from one eigenstate to an
immediately adjacent state, releasing or absorbing a quantum of energy
equal to $\hbar\omega_0$, the same frequency as would be observed for the corresponding classical harmonic oscillator.

   An important feature of the quantum-mechanical harmonic oscillator,
as compared to the classical harmonic oscillator, is that the *minimum*
energy of the system is <u>not</u> <u>zero</u> but $\frac{1}{2}\hbar\omega_0$. Associated with this minimum
energy state is the "<u>zero-point motion</u>" of the particle; the particle does
not settle down to zero excursion about the origin but remains spread out
as though in a state of small but finite agitation. The zero-point motion

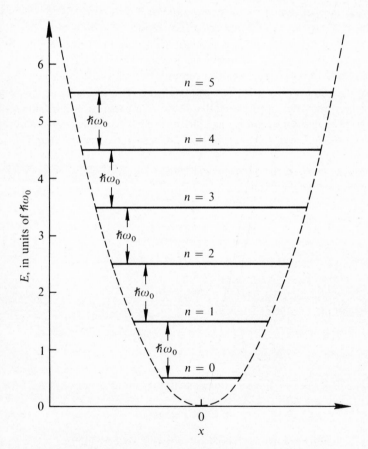

Fig. 5.1 *Energy levels of the harmonic oscillator. The parabola gives the
potential energy of the particle.*

predicted by quantum mechanics is not a mathematical artifact but a real physical effect, .and its existence explains a number of small but bothersome experimental facts inexplicable on a classical model.

Let us look now at the eigenfunctions of the Hamiltonian of the one-dimensional harmonic oscillator. From the previous section, we know the eigenfunctions may be written

$$\psi_n(x) = A_n e^{-\alpha x^2/2} H_n(\sqrt{\alpha}\, x)$$

$$= A_n e^{-\xi^2/2} H_n(\xi) \tag{5.34}$$

where A_n is a normalization constant yet to be defined and $H_n(\xi)$ is a polynomial of ξ of degree n. We can generate H_n for any n since we know the recursion relation between successive coefficients in the polynomial,

TABLE 5.1

Some Hermite Polynomials

$H_0(\xi) = 1$
$H_1(\xi) = 2\xi$
$H_2(\xi) = -2 + 4\xi^2$
$H_3(\xi) = -12\xi + 8\xi^3$
$H_4(\xi) = 12 - 48\xi^2 + 16\xi^4$
$H_5(\xi) = 120\xi - 160\xi^3 + 32\xi^5$
$H_6(\xi) = 120 - 720\xi^2 + 480\xi^4 - 64\xi^6$
$H_7(\xi) = -1680\xi + 3360\xi^3 - 1344\xi^5 + 128\xi^7$
$H_8(\xi) = 1680 - 13440\xi^2 + 13440\xi^4 - 3584\xi^6 + 256\xi^8$

and may choose the first constant arbitrarily [allowing the constant A_n to restore the normalization of $\psi_n(x)$]. However, we do not have to resort to computing the polynomials from the recursion relation ourselves, because Eq. (5.20) was thoroughly studied by mathematicians of the nineteenth century. Using solution techniques much more elegant than our polynomial method, they obtained the solutions $H_n(\xi)$, as well as many integral and differential relations among the $H_n(\xi)$. The $H_n(\xi)$ are in fact known as the *Hermite polynomials*, and the first few of them are listed in Table 5.1.

Among the integral and differential relations of the Hermite polynomials derived by the early mathematicians are several which we will find convenient to use:

$$\int_{-\infty}^{+\infty} e^{-\xi^2} H_n(\xi) H_m(\xi)\, d\xi = 2^n n!\, \sqrt{\pi}\, \delta_{nm} \tag{5.35}$$

where δ_{nm} is again Kronecker's delta, and two recursion relations among the Hermite polynomials,

$$\frac{dH_n(\xi)}{d\xi} = 2nH_{n-1}(\xi) \tag{5.36}$$

and

$$2\xi H_n(\xi) = H_{n+1}(\xi) + 2nH_{n-1}(\xi) \tag{5.37}$$

From the first of these, we may calculate immediately the normalization constant A_n of Eq. (5.34):

$$
\begin{aligned}
\int_{-\infty}^{+\infty} \psi_n^*(x)\psi_n(x)\, dx &= 1 \\
\int_{-\infty}^{+\infty} A_n^2 H_n(\xi)^2 e^{-\xi^2}\, dx &= 1 \\
\frac{A_n^2}{\sqrt{\alpha}} \int_{-\infty}^{+\infty} H_n(\xi)^2 e^{-\xi^2}\, d\xi &= 1 \\
\frac{A_n^2}{\sqrt{\alpha}} 2^n n!\, \sqrt{\pi} &= 1
\end{aligned}
\tag{5.38}
$$

giving

$$A_n = \left[\frac{1}{2^n n!}\left(\frac{\alpha}{\pi}\right)^{1/2}\right]^{1/2} \tag{5.39}$$

With A_n so defined,

$$\int_{-\infty}^{+\infty} \psi_n^*(x)\psi_m(x)\, dx = \delta_{nm} \tag{5.40}$$

and the eigenfunction $\psi_n(x)$ are seen indeed to be an orthonormal set of basis functions.

It is of some considerable interest to plot $\psi_n(x)$ and $\psi_n(x)\psi_n(x)$ for a few of the lower-order solutions (Fig. 5.2) and compare the results with the classical harmonic oscillator. Our first reaction is that there is very little resemblance, at least for the lower-order solutions. The classically oscillating particle moves rapidly through the origin, slows as it reaches the extremes of its excursion, and has zero velocity at the turnaround point. The probability of finding the classical particle in any interval dx is inversely proportional to its velocity at that point, so is inversely proportional to $\cos(x/x_{\max})$. The probability distribution $|\psi_n(\xi)|^2$ is plotted in Fig. 5.3 for $n = 0$ and $n = 10$, together with the classical probability distribution. For $n = 0$, we see virtually no resemblance, since the quantum-mechanical probability maximizes right where the classical probability minimizes. The plots are for particles of the same energy, which for $\psi_0(\xi)$ is the minimum energy state quantum-mechanically, but not classically. For the classical oscillator, the amplitude of excursion may diminish to zero and the classical probability distribution would then be a delta function at $x = 0$. For $n = 10$, the classical probability and the quantum-mechanical probability distribution do show some resemblance, a resemblance which continues to increase as n increases. The quantum-mechanical distribution differs, of course, in having rapidly alternating nodes and antinodes, whereas the classical distribution is smooth. As n increases, the nodes become increasingly more closely spaced. For a laboratory harmonic oscillator, such as we might make with a weight of several grams on a spring, the value of n corresponding to an oscillation of a few centimeters excursion would be on the order of 10^{26}. The 10^{26} nodes of the quantum-mechanical distribution would be so closely spaced as to defy observation, and a measurement of the probability would yield only the envelope of $\psi_n^*(x)\psi_n(x)$, which would be indistinguishable from the classical distribution.

The classical harmonic oscillator has turnaround points at the displacement for which the potential energy of the particle is equal to the

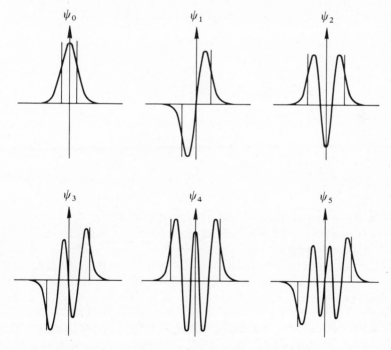

Fig. 5.2 $\psi_n(\xi)$ *vs. x for the first six harmonic-oscillator solutions. The vertical lines mark the classical turnaround points.*

total energy. This turnaround point is given by $x_{\max} = \sqrt{2E/k}$. If we look
at our quantum-mechanical probability distribution, we note that there is
a point of inflection at the classical turnaround value of x. At the inflection
point

$$\frac{\partial^2}{\partial x^2}\,\psi_n(x) = 0 \tag{5.41}$$

We have already associated $\partial/\partial x$ with the P_x and $\partial^2/\partial x^2$ with P_x^2, a measure
of the particle kinetic energy. It is not surprising then to find $(\partial^2/\partial x^2)\psi = 0$
at the point where T, the kinetic energy, is zero. It is surprising, however,
to find that there is a finite probability of finding the particle at $x > x_{\max}$
(classical), in a region where the total energy, on the classical model,

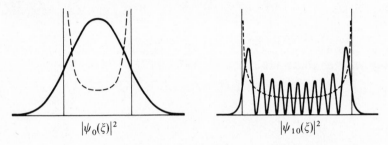

$$|\psi_0(\xi)|^2 \qquad\qquad\qquad\qquad |\psi_{10}(\xi)|^2$$

Fig. 5.3 $|\psi_0(\xi)|^2$ *and* $|\psi_{10}(\xi)|^2$ *for the harmonic oscillator (solid line). The
classical probability distribution for a particle of the same energy is
shown in each case by the dashed line.*

would be negative. Such is indeed the case here, and in many quantum-
mechanical cases. Quantum mechanics frequently predicts that particles
can be found in classically "forbidden" regions, as we will see repeatedly
in later examples.

**5.4 EXPECTATION VALUES OF SOME OBSERVABLES FOR PURE AND
MIXED STATES**   Now that we know explicitly the eigenfunctions of the
Hamiltonian, we may calculate the expectation values of various operators
for various states of the system. We will consider here some "pure" states
and some "mixed" states. By a "pure" state we mean here an eigenstate
of the Hamiltonian; by a "mixed" state we mean a state which is a superposition of several eigenstates of the Hamiltonian. Note that we are
implicitly assigning a privileged position to the eigenfunctions of the
Hamiltonian operator (as compared with those of any other arbitrary
operator) when we define "pure" and "mixed" in terms of the eigenfunctions of this operator. This privileged position arises from the

considerations of Sec. 4.3 and from the consideration that each dynamical system has its own Hamiltonian, specific to that system, whereas operators, like linear momentum, are quite general and not peculiar to one system or another.

Let us first calculate the expectation value $\langle x \rangle$ for an eigenstate $\Psi_n(x,t)$.

$$\langle x \rangle = \int_{-\infty}^{+\infty} \Psi_n^*(x,t) X \Psi_n(x,t) \, dx$$

$$= \int_{-\infty}^{+\infty} \psi_n^*(x) e^{+(i/\hbar)E_n t} x \psi_n(x) e^{-(i/\hbar)E_n t} \, dx$$

$$= \int_{-\infty}^{+\infty} \psi_n(x) x \psi_n(x) \, dx \qquad (5.42)$$

We note first that the time dependence cancels out, so that $\langle x \rangle$ does not vary with time. This is what we expect for a "stationary state."

We may readily evaluate the integral of Eq. (5.42) by using the recursion relation on Hermite polynomials of Eq. (5.37):

$$\langle x \rangle = \int_{-\infty}^{+\infty} \psi_n^*(x) x \psi_n(x) \, dx$$

$$= A_n^2 \int_{-\infty}^{+\infty} e^{-\xi^2/2} H_n(\xi) \left(\frac{\xi}{\sqrt{\alpha}} \right) e^{-\xi^2/2} H_n(\xi) \, dx$$

$$= \frac{A_n^2}{\sqrt{\alpha}} \int_{-\infty}^{+\infty} e^{-\xi^2} H_n(\xi) \xi H_n(\xi) \, dx \qquad (5.43)$$

Invoking the recursion relation which relates $\xi H_n(\xi)$ to $H_{n+1}(\xi)$ and $H_{n-1}(\xi)$, we obtain

$$\langle x \rangle = \frac{1}{2} \frac{A_n^2}{\sqrt{\alpha}} \int_{-\infty}^{+\infty} e^{-\xi^2} H_n(\xi) H_{n+1}(\xi) \, dx + n \frac{A_n^2}{\sqrt{\alpha}} \int_{-\infty}^{+\infty} e^{-\xi^2} H_n(\xi) H_{n-1}(\xi) \, dx$$

$$(5.44)$$

Both integrals of Eq. (5.44) we know to be zero from the orthogonality of the Hermite polynomials, whence we get

$$\langle x \rangle = 0 \qquad (5.45)$$

The resulting expectation value $\langle x \rangle = 0$ tells us that we are just as likely to find the particle with a positive x coordinate as with a negative coordinate, and indeed that the probability distribution $\psi_n^*(x)\psi_n(x)$ must be symmetric about the origin, the point of suspension.

To obtain an idea of the breadth of the distribution, we compute the expectation value $\langle x^2 \rangle$, for which the cancellation at positive and negative coordinates will not occur.

$$\langle x^2 \rangle = \int_{-\infty}^{+\infty} \psi_n^*(x) x^2 \psi_n(x)\, dx = \frac{A_n^2}{\alpha} \int_{-\infty}^{+\infty} e^{-\xi^2} H_n(\xi) \xi^2 H_n(\xi)\, dx \quad (5.46)$$

Applying the recursion relation of Eq. (5.37) twice, we find that

$$\xi^2 H_n(\xi) = \tfrac{1}{4} H_{n+2}(\xi) + (n + \tfrac{1}{2}) H_n(\xi) + n(n - 1) H_{n-2}(\xi) \quad (5.47)$$

We again know from the orthogonality of the $H_n(\xi)$ that the integrals involving $H_n(\xi) H_{n+2}(\xi)$ and $H_n(\xi) H_{n-2}(\xi)$ will be zero, so we are left with

$$\langle x^2 \rangle = \frac{n + \tfrac{1}{2}}{\alpha} A_n^2 \int_{-\infty}^{+\infty} e^{-\xi^2} H_n(\xi) H_n(\xi)\, dx = \frac{n + \tfrac{1}{2}}{\alpha} \quad (5.48)$$

Substituting for α, we obtain

$$\langle x^2 \rangle = (n + \tfrac{1}{2}) \frac{\hbar}{(mk)^{1/2}} \quad (5.49)$$

Comparing with the classical case, we find that

$$\langle x^2 \rangle = \tfrac{1}{2} x_{\max}^2 = \overline{x^2} \quad \text{(classical)} \quad (5.50)$$

The momentum expectation values may be calculated in an analogous fashion:

$$\langle p_x \rangle = \int_{-\infty}^{+\infty} \psi_n^*(x) \frac{\hbar}{i} \frac{d}{dx} \psi_n(x)\, dx$$
$$= \frac{\hbar}{i} A_n^2 \sqrt{\alpha} \int_{-\infty}^{+\infty} e^{-\xi^2/2} H_n(\xi) \frac{d}{d\xi} e^{-\xi^2/2} H_n(\xi)\, dx \quad (5.51)$$

Performing the derivative operation, we obtain

$$\frac{d}{d\xi} e^{-\xi^2/2} H_n(\xi) = -\xi e^{-\xi^2/2} H_n(\xi) + e^{-\xi^2/2} \frac{dH_n(\xi)}{d\xi} \quad (5.52)$$

Using both recursion relations of Eqs. (5.35) and (5.37), we obtain, after a little algebra,

$$\frac{d}{d\xi} e^{-\xi^2/2} H_n(\xi) = e^{-\xi^2/2} [n H_{n-1}(\xi) - \tfrac{1}{2} H_{n+1}(\xi)] \quad (5.53)$$

whence

$$\langle p_x \rangle = \frac{\hbar}{2i} A_n^2 \sqrt{\alpha} \int_{-\infty}^{+\infty} e^{-\xi^2} H_n(\xi)[n H_{n-1}(\xi) - \tfrac{1}{2} H_{n+1}(\xi)]\, dx = 0 \quad (5.54)$$

because of the orthogonality of the $H_n(\xi)$ and $H_{n\pm1}(\xi)$. The result $\langle p_x \rangle = 0$ implies equal probability of the particle's momentum directed in the positive x direction and in the negative x direction.

Finally, let us calculate $\langle p_x^2 \rangle$.

$$\langle p_x^2 \rangle = A_n^2 \int_{-\infty}^{+\infty} \psi_n^*(x) \left(\frac{\hbar}{i} \frac{d}{dx} \right)^2 \psi_n(x)\, dx$$

$$= - \alpha \hbar^2 A_n^2 \int_{-\infty}^{+\infty} e^{-\xi^2/2} H_n(\xi) \frac{d^2}{d\xi^2} e^{-\xi^2/2} H_n(\xi)\, dx \qquad (5.55)$$

It can be readily demonstrated that

$$\frac{d^2}{d\xi^2} [e^{-\xi^2/2} H_n(\xi)] = e^{-\xi^2/2} [n(n-1) H_{n-2}(\xi) - (n + \tfrac{1}{2}) H_n(\xi) + \tfrac{1}{4} H_{n+2}(\xi)]$$

$$(5.56)$$

Only the terms in H_n will survive the integration, so

$$\langle p_x^2 \rangle = \alpha \hbar^2 A_n^2 \int_{-\infty}^{+\infty} e^{-\xi^2} H_n(\xi)\, (n + \tfrac{1}{2}) H_n(\xi)\, dx = (n + \tfrac{1}{2}) \alpha \hbar^2 \qquad (5.57)$$

Comparison with the classical case shows that

$$\langle p_x^2 \rangle = \tfrac{1}{2}(p_{max})^2 = \overline{p^2} \qquad \text{(classical)} \qquad (5.58)$$

Expectation values are statistical quantities, as we have commented earlier, and when we specify the expectation value of a statistical quantity it is also necessary to specify something about the statistical spread expected about the average value. The probability distribution may be sharply peaked about the most probable value or it may be badly spread about, and it is often important to know which situation prevails. We therefore seek a quantity which will be a measure of the statistical spread in the measurements to be expected. We might, for instance, specify the quantity $(q - \langle q \rangle)$, the deviation between any one measurement and the mean of a large set of measurements. By the very definition of $\langle q \rangle$, though, this parameter will vanish when averaged over the distribution, so it is not a useful criterion. We use, therefore, the square of the deviation, averaged over the distribution, as a measure of the probability spread:

$$\overline{(q - \langle q \rangle)^2} = \overline{q^2 - 2q\langle q \rangle + \langle q \rangle^2}$$

$$= \langle q^2 \rangle - \langle q \rangle^2 \qquad (5.59)$$

The parameter so defined is known in statistical theory as the *mean square deviation of q*, and is usually called in quantum mechanics simply the *uncertainty in q*, designated by the symbol Δq.

$$(\Delta q)^2 = \langle q^2 \rangle - \langle q \rangle^2 \qquad (5.60)$$

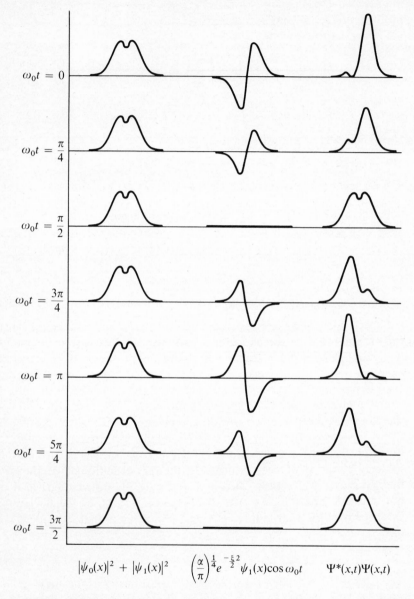

$$\omega_0 t = 0$$

$$\omega_0 t = \frac{\pi}{4}$$

$$\omega_0 t = \frac{\pi}{2}$$

$$\omega_0 t = \frac{3\pi}{4}$$

$$\omega_0 t = \pi$$

$$\omega_0 t = \frac{5\pi}{4}$$

$$\omega_0 t = \frac{3\pi}{2}$$

$$|\psi_0(x)|^2 + |\psi_1(x)|^2 \qquad \left(\frac{\alpha}{\pi}\right)^{\frac{1}{4}} e^{-\frac{\xi^2}{2}} \psi_1(x)\cos\omega_0 t \qquad \Psi^*(x,t)\Psi(x,t)$$

Fig. 5.4 *The probability density as a function of time of the mixed harmonic-oscillator state* $\Psi = \dfrac{1}{\sqrt{2}}(\Psi_0 + \Psi_1)$. *The various contributions to the probability density* [*see Eq.* (5.64)] *are shown separately, then their sum is shown.*

82

For the simple harmonic oscillator in an eigenstate $\Psi_n(x,t)$, we have

$$(\Delta x)^2 = \langle x^2 \rangle - \langle x \rangle^2 = \frac{n + \frac{1}{2}}{\alpha}$$

$$(\Delta p_x)^2 = \langle p_x^2 \rangle - \langle p_x \rangle^2 = (n + \frac{1}{2})\hbar^2\alpha$$
(5.61)

from which we obtain the "uncertainty product"

$$\Delta x \, \Delta p_x = (n + \frac{1}{2})\hbar$$
(5.62)

This is our first encounter in quantum mechanics with the uncertainty principle (which is not peculiar to quantum mechanics, occurring in classical theory as well). We will discuss the uncertainty principle at some length in Chap. 7; but for now we wish to make two points:

1. The uncertainty product $\Delta x \, \Delta p_x$ has a minimum (nonzero) value equal to $\hbar/2$, which occurs for the harmonic oscillator for the eigenstate $n = 0$.
2. The uncertainty product for a given state is completely calculable from the state function alone, with no reference to measuring equipment.

Let us now move on to calculate the expectation value of some observables for mixed states. Since for the pure states all probability distributions were stationary, and nothing "moved," we suspect quite correctly that mixed states will be required to describe systems of real interest, where indeed motion does take place.

We will examine a very simple mixed state

$$\Psi(x,t) = \frac{1}{\sqrt{2}} [\Psi_0(x,t) + \Psi_1(x,t)]$$
(5.63)

and find that it shows many of the features we ordinarily associate with simple harmonic motion. Let us calculate first the probability density associated with this state.

$$\Psi^*(x,t)\Psi(x,t) = \frac{1}{2}[A_0 e^{-\xi^2/2}H_0(\xi)e^{+i\omega_0 t/2} + A_1 e^{-\xi^2/2}H_1(\xi)e^{+3i\omega_0 t/2}]$$
$$\times [A_0 e^{-\xi^2/2}H_0(\xi)e^{-i\omega_0 t/2} + A_1 e^{-\xi^2/2}H_1(\xi)e^{-3i\omega_0 t/2}]$$
$$= \frac{1}{2}|\psi_0(x)|^2 + \frac{1}{2}|\psi_1(x)|^2$$
$$+ \frac{1}{2}A_0 A_1 e^{-\xi^2}H_0(\xi)H_1(\xi)(e^{i\omega_0 t} + e^{-i\omega_0 t})$$
$$= \frac{1}{2}|\psi_0(x)|^2 + \frac{1}{2}|\psi_1(x)|^2 + A_0 A_1 e^{-\xi^2}H_0(\xi)H_1(\xi) \cos \omega_0 t$$
$$= \frac{1}{2}|\psi_0(x)|^2 + \frac{1}{2}|\psi_1(x)|^2 + \left(\frac{\alpha}{\pi}\right)^{1/4} e^{-\xi^2/2}\psi_1(x) \cos \omega_0 t \quad (5.64)$$

The probability density distribution described by Eq. (5.64) may be pictured by reference to Fig. 5.4. The probability density is plotted at $\omega_0 t = 0$,

$\pi/4$, $\pi/2$, $3\pi/4$, π, $5\pi/4$, and $3\pi/2$. We note that the probability density is composed of a time-independent part $[\frac{1}{2}|\psi_0(x)|^2 + \frac{1}{2}|\psi_1(x)|^2]$ and a term varying harmonically with time at frequency ω_0. The oscillating part, an odd function of x, alternately adds to and subtracts from the constant part, giving a total probability distribution whose maximum oscillates about the origin with angular frequency ω_0.

It is also instructive to calculate the expectation values of E, x, and p for our present state function. The expectation value of energy is particularly easy to calculate, since the $\psi_n(x)$ are eigenfunctions of H.

$$\langle E \rangle = \langle \Psi(x,t), H\Psi(x,t) \rangle = \int_{-\infty}^{+\infty} \Psi^*(x,t) H\Psi(x,t)\, dx$$

$$= \frac{1}{2} \int_{-\infty}^{+\infty} [\psi_0^*(x)e^{+i\omega_0 t/2} + \psi_1(x)e^{+3i\omega_0 t/2}] H [\psi_0(x)e^{-i\omega_0 t/2}$$
$$+ \psi_1(x)e^{-3i\omega_0 t/2}]\, dx$$

$$= \frac{1}{2} \int_{-\infty}^{+\infty} [\psi_0^*(x)e^{+i\omega_0 t/2} + \psi_1(x)e^{+3i\omega_0 t/2}] \left[\frac{\hbar\omega_0}{2} \psi_0(x)e^{-i\omega_0 t/2} \right.$$
$$\left. + \frac{3\hbar\omega_0}{2} \psi_1(x)e^{-3i\omega_0 t/2} \right] dx$$

$$= \frac{1}{2} \left(\frac{\hbar\omega_0}{2} + \frac{3\hbar\omega_0}{2} \right) = \hbar\omega_0 \qquad (5.65)$$

The integral collapses to two terms because of the orthogonality of the $\psi_n(x)$, and the time variation exactly cancels out in the terms that are preserved. The expectation of energy $\langle E \rangle$ is then a constant, as we might have deduced in advance from Eq. (4.34) and from the observation that H commutes with itself. We note further that the expectation value of energy is not one of the eigenenergies of the system $(n + \frac{1}{2})\hbar\omega_0$, but something in between. This is characteristic of mixed states, and is the usual case rather than an exception.

Since neither X nor P_x commutes with the Hamiltonian, we should not expect either $\langle x \rangle$ or $\langle p \rangle$ to be generally time independent. Calculating first $\langle x \rangle$ for our simple mixed state function, we obtain

$$\langle x \rangle = \langle \Psi(x,t), X\Psi(x,t) \rangle = \int_{-\infty}^{+\infty} \Psi^*(x,t) X\Psi(x,t)\, dx$$

$$= \frac{1}{2} \int_{-\infty}^{+\infty} [\psi_0^*(x)e^{+i\omega_0 t/2} + \psi_1^*(x)e^{+3i\omega_0 t/2}] x [\psi_0(x)e^{-i\omega_0 t/2}$$
$$+ \psi_1(x)e^{-3i\omega_0 t/2}]\, dx$$

$$= \frac{1}{2} \int_{-\infty}^{+\infty} [\psi_0^*(x)x\psi_0(x) + \psi_1^*(x)x\psi_1(x) + \psi_0^*(x)x\psi_1(x)e^{-i\omega_0 t}$$
$$+ \psi_1^*(x)x\psi_0(x)e^{i\omega_0 t}]\, dx \qquad (5.66)$$

The first two terms of the above integral we know to integrate to zero, and the second two terms combine to give

$$\langle x \rangle = \frac{1}{\sqrt{2\alpha}} \cos \omega_0 t \tag{5.67}$$

The expectation value of x is no longer zero, but oscillates back and forth with the same frequency as the corresponding classical harmonic oscillator. In fact, it may be readily shown that any harmonic oscillator superposition state, however complex, will have this frequency, though the phase and amplitude of the excursion will, of course, differ for the various state functions.

We may calculate $\langle p \rangle$ by an exactly analogous process:

$$\langle p_x \rangle = \langle \Psi(x,t), P\Psi(x,t) \rangle = \int_{-\infty}^{+\infty} \Psi^*(x,t) \frac{\hbar}{i} \frac{d}{dx} \Psi(x,t)\, dx$$

$$= \frac{\sqrt{\alpha}\hbar}{2i} \int_{-\infty}^{+\infty} \left[\psi_0^*(x) \frac{d}{d\xi} \psi_0(x) + \psi_1^*(x) \frac{d}{d\xi} \psi_1(x) \right.$$

$$\left. + \psi_0^*(x) \frac{d}{d\xi} \psi_1(x)e^{-i\omega_0 t} + \psi_1^*(x) \frac{d}{d\xi} \psi_0(x)e^{i\omega_0 t} \right] dx \tag{5.68}$$

The first two terms in the integral again vanish upon integration, and the second two, after utilization of the recursion relations, combine to give

$$\langle p_x \rangle = -\sqrt{\frac{\alpha}{2}} \hbar \sin \omega_0 t \tag{5.69}$$

The expectation value of momentum is also periodic with frequency ω_0, and bears the same phase relation to the position as is the case for a classical harmonic oscillator.

The mixed state we have used is a particularly simple one, but the computational procedures utilized here are exactly those which would be used in obtaining the expectation values from more complex states and for other systems. The existence of recursion relations between the various eigenstates of the Hamiltonian make the calculation of expectation values especially straightforward in the Schrödinger scheme, and we invariably seek to establish such recursion relations for any system in order to facilitate subsequent calculations concerning the system. Since the eigenfunctions of the Hamiltonian in the Schrödinger formulation of quantum mechanics are the solutions of differential equations, such recursion relations usually exist.

5.5 DIGRESSION ON MEASUREMENT AND SPECIFICATION OF THE STATE FUNCTION In the preceding section we have arbitrarily postulated certain state functions for our system, then proceeded to calculate various expectation values consequent upon this choice of state function. The reader may well ask "How do we know what the state function of a given system actually is?" The answer is "Only by measurement."

The state function of a system is the statement of our knowledge of the system at that time. Suppose we write our state function and use the eigenfunctions of the Hamiltonian as a basis. A general state function may have many components (N, for example) in this basis system, and the coefficient of each component is complex; so there are $2N$ parameters to be specified to describe the state. At least $2N$ pieces of data are required to determine $2N$ parameters, and when each of these parameters is a statement of relative probability, many times $2N$ measurements are required to determine the $2N$ parameters.

Consider a system known to be a linear harmonic oscillator, and suppose that a large number of measurements of energy upon identically prepared systems invariably yields the result $E = \frac{1}{2}\hbar\omega_0$. We may then state that this preparation placed the system in the state $\Psi(x,t) = \Psi_0(x,t)$, its ground state, and for such a pure state the phase of the coefficient is unimportant, because it cancels out of any expectation value or scalar product. Suppose, on the other hand, that energy measurements had yielded the values $\frac{1}{2}\hbar\omega_0$ and $\frac{3}{2}\hbar\omega_0$ with equal probability. We could write our state function as

$$\Psi(x,t_0) = \frac{e^{i\delta_1}}{\sqrt{2}}[\Psi_0(x,t_0) + e^{i\delta_2}\Psi_1(x,t_0)] \qquad (5.70)$$

Two unknowns remain, δ_1 and δ_2. The first, δ_1, is again irrelevant since it cancels out of all scalar products, but the second, δ_2, the relative phase of two components, is indeed meaningful and can be determined by measurement. For instance, the state function of Eq. (5.70) yields the expectation values for $\langle x \rangle$ and $\langle p_x \rangle$ of

$$\langle x \rangle = \frac{1}{\sqrt{2\alpha}}\cos[\omega_0(t - t_0) - \delta_2] \qquad (5.71)$$

and

$$\langle p_x \rangle = -\sqrt{\frac{\alpha}{2}}\,\hbar\sin[\omega_0(t - t_0) - \delta_2] \qquad (5.72)$$

so measurements of $\langle x \rangle$ or $\langle p_x \rangle$ would serve to establish the unknown phase constant δ_2.

We must, however, be careful to specify for what system our measurements have defined the wave function. Suppose we have a box full of identical noninteracting quantum-mechanical systems of identical dynamical history—a literal manifestation of the statistical ensemble. Suppose we extract from the box a number N of these systems, and at $t = t_0$ perform a measurement on each of these N systems (the same observable need not be measured for all N systems). The number N is presumed to be large, yet small compared to the number of systems originally in the box. Consider one of the N specimen systems, say number 43. When we make a measurement upon this system of some observable A, we obtain one of the eigenvalues a_n of A and know therefore that this particular system, immediately after the measurement, is in the eigenstate u_n of A. The state function of a system reflects our knowledge of that system; by making a measurement on system number 43, we have changed our state of knowledge about that particular system (we know that it exhibited the value a_n for the dynamical variable A), so we have changed the state function of that system. System number 43 now has a state function different from the particles remaining in the box unobserved, for its history contains one more preparative step than theirs—it has had a measurement made upon it.

If, however, we record the results of the measurements on all N sample systems, we can predict in a statistical fashion what we would expect to observe as the result of a measurement upon the $(N + 1)$th particle drawn from the box. By the composite of measurements on N particles, we have arrived at a state function which describes not one of the N particles observed, but rather the state function for the typical particle which *was not observed*.

The above procedure for determining a state function may seem to the reader ridiculously obtuse and not very realistically connected with the conduct of actual experiments. In point of fact the object of most experiments upon quantum-mechanical systems is not that of establishing the state of a system of known Hamiltonian but rather to determine what Hamiltonian is appropriate to the system, what interactions are present and with what relative strength. Then the performance of a measurement places the system in some known eigenstate, and the evolution of the system from this reference state is observed. When we have proceeded further with the quantum-mechanical description of several prototype systems, it will be possible to give a more meaningful development of the role of measurement in quantum mechanics. The present brief digression has been included since the reader has certainly begun, by this point in our development, to be curious about the arbitrary manner in which the state function has been specified for our several examples.

5.6 THE TWO-DIMENSIONAL HARMONIC OSCILLATOR AND DEGENERATE STATES The one-dimensional harmonic oscillator provided an excellent example of a nondegenerate quantum-mechanical system. By extending our discussion to the two-dimensional case, we can illustrate a number of features, both of harmonic oscillator behavior and of the quantum mechanics of slightly more complicated systems.

We may write the Hamiltonian of the two-dimensional harmonic oscillator in cartesian coordinates as

$$H = \frac{p_x^2}{2m} + \frac{p_y^2}{2m} + \tfrac{1}{2}k_1 x^2 + \tfrac{1}{2}k_2 y^2 \tag{5.73}$$

where we assign for the moment different "spring constants" k_1 and k_2 to the x and y directions, respectively. The associated Hamiltonian operator will be

$$H_{\mathrm{op}} = -\frac{\hbar^2}{2m}\left(\frac{\partial^2}{\partial x^2} + \frac{\partial^2}{\partial y^2}\right) + \tfrac{1}{2}k_1 x^2 + \tfrac{1}{2}k_2 y^2 \tag{5.74}$$

and the resultant Schrödinger equation is

$$\left[\frac{\hbar^2}{2m}\left(\frac{\partial^2}{\partial x^2} + \frac{\partial^2}{\partial y^2}\right) - \tfrac{1}{2}k_1 x^2 - \tfrac{1}{2}k_2 y^2\right]\Psi(x,y,t) = \frac{\hbar}{i}\frac{\partial}{\partial t}\Psi(x,y,t) \tag{5.75}$$

Since the potentials involved are not functions of time, we may again perform the separation of space variables from the time variable:

$$\Psi(x,y,t) = \psi(x,y)\varphi(t) \tag{5.76}$$

The time-independent Schrödinger equation is then

$$\frac{\hbar^2}{2m}\left(\frac{\partial^2}{\partial x^2} + \frac{\partial^2}{\partial y^2}\right)\psi(x,y) + (E - \tfrac{1}{2}k_1 x^2 - \tfrac{1}{2}k_2 y^2)\psi(x,y) = 0 \tag{5.77}$$

We observe now that the potential-energy term of this two-dimensional oscillator is separable in x and y and that the equation is therefore further separable into two equations, one involving x alone and the other involving y alone. Making the substitution

$$\psi(x,y) = \psi_x(x)\psi_y(y) \tag{5.78}$$

we can rearrange Eq. (5.77) into the form

$$\frac{1}{\psi_x(x)}\left[\frac{\hbar^2}{2m}\frac{\partial^2}{\partial x^2} + (E - \tfrac{1}{2}k_1 x^2)\right]\psi_x(x) + \frac{1}{\psi_y(y)}\left(\frac{\hbar^2}{2m}\frac{\partial^2}{\partial y^2} - \tfrac{1}{2}k_2 y^2\right)\psi_y(y) = 0 \tag{5.79}$$

Since the sum of the two functions must remain zero for arbitrary x and y, the functions in x and y must be separately equal to the same constant, which we will call E_y. Our fully separated equations are now

$$\left[\frac{\hbar^2}{2m}\frac{\partial^2}{\partial x^2} + (E - E_y - \tfrac{1}{2}k_1x^2)\right]\psi_x(x) = 0$$

$$\left[\frac{\hbar^2}{2m}\frac{\partial^2}{\partial y^2} + (E_y - \tfrac{1}{2}k_2y^2)\right]\psi_y(y) = 0 \tag{5.80}$$

$$-\frac{\hbar}{i}\frac{\partial}{\partial t}\varphi(t) = E\varphi(t)$$

If we define a further constant

$$E_x = E - E_y \tag{5.81}$$

we see that we may assign to E_x the physical significance of the energy of the system associated with the motion in the x direction, to E_y the significance of the energy of the system associated with motion in the y direction, and to E the significance of the total energy of the system:

$$E = E_x + E_y \tag{5.82}$$

The eigenenergies of the two-dimensional harmonic oscillator are therefore the sum of two one-dimensional oscillator eigenenergies, and the eigenfunctions of the two-dimensional harmonic oscillator are products of two one-dimensional eigenfunctions. To solve the two-dimensional problem, we need only the solutions to the one-dimensional problem.

$$\psi_{n_1 n_2}(x,y) = \psi_{n_1}(x)\psi_{n_2}(y) \tag{5.83}$$

where

$$\psi_{n_1}(x) = A_{n_1}e^{-\xi_1^2/2}H_{n_1}(\xi_1)$$

$$\psi_{n_2}(y) = A_{n_2}e^{-\xi_2^2/2}H_{n_2}(\xi_2) \tag{5.84}$$

and

$$\xi_1 = \sqrt{\alpha_1}\,x \qquad \alpha_1^2 = \frac{mk_1}{\hbar^2}$$

$$\xi_2 = \sqrt{\alpha_2}\,y \qquad \alpha_2^2 = \frac{mk_2}{\hbar^2} \tag{5.85}$$

The eigenenergies of the two-dimensional oscillator will be

$$E = E_{n_1 x} + E_{n_2 y} \tag{5.86}$$

where

$$E_{n_1 x} = (n_1 + \tfrac{1}{2})\hbar\omega_1$$

$$E_{n_2 y} = (n_2 + \tfrac{1}{2})\hbar\omega_2 \tag{5.87}$$

and

$$\omega_1 = \left(\frac{k_1}{m}\right)^{1/2} \qquad \omega_2 = \left(\frac{k_2}{m}\right)^{1/2} \tag{5.88}$$

If k_1 and k_2 are not equal, we still have a nondegenerate system, with one unique state associated with each eigenenergy E. There may occur accidental degeneracies, where the same total E may be attained by two different combinations of E_x and E_y, but such coincidences will presumably be rare. If, on the other hand, we have an *isotropic* two-dimensional oscillator

$$k_1 = k_2 = k \tag{5.89}$$

we will have a system displaying considerable degeneracy. If $k_1 = k_2 = k$, then $\omega_1 = \omega_2 = \omega$, and our total eigenenergy is given by

$$E = (n_1 + \tfrac{1}{2})\hbar\omega + (n_2 + \tfrac{1}{2})\hbar\omega$$
$$= (n_1 + n_2 + 1)\hbar\omega \tag{5.90}$$

The only nondegenerate state is the ground state $n_1 = n_2 = 0$:

$$\psi_{00}(x,y) = \psi_0(x)\psi_0(y) \qquad E_0 = \hbar\omega \tag{5.91}$$

For the first excited state

$$E_1 = 2\hbar\omega \tag{5.92}$$

we have the two possibilities

$$n_1 = 0 \qquad n_2 = 1$$
and $$n_1 = 1 \qquad n_2 = 0 \tag{5.93}$$

leading to the two degenerate eigenstates

$$\psi_{01}(x,y) = \psi_0(x)\psi_1(y)$$
$$\psi_{10}(x,y) = \psi_1(x)\psi_0(y) \tag{5.94}$$

These two states correspond to different distributions of probability and to different expectation values of various observables, but they correspond to the same total energy E_1.

For the higher excited states, the degeneracy becomes greater. For instance, for the next state

$$E_2 = 3\hbar\omega \tag{5.95}$$

we have the possibilities

$$n_1 = 0 \qquad n_2 = 2$$
$$n_1 = 1 \qquad n_2 = 1$$
$$n_1 = 2 \qquad n_2 = 0 \tag{5.96}$$

with the three distinct $\psi_{n_1 n_2}(x,y)$ associated. If we define a total quantum number

$$n = n_1 + n_2 \tag{5.97}$$

we find that the energy depends only upon n

$$E = (n + 1)\hbar\omega \tag{5.98}$$

and that each state is $(n + 1)$-fold degenerate.

We chose (arbitrarily) to write the Hamiltonian of our two-dimensional oscillator in cartesian coordinates. We might equally well have chosen two-dimensional polar coordinates r and φ. Then our equations and eigenfunctions would appear different but must correspond to the same probability distributions and yield the same eigenenergies, since the properties of the system cannot depend upon the coordinate scheme chosen for its description. For the isotropic oscillator, the potential function would involve r alone, and not φ, and Schrödinger's equation will be separable in r and φ. All energy eigenstates except the lowest will be degenerate. Within a degenerate manifold, the eigenfunctions $\psi_{n_1 n_2}(x,y)$ may be obtained as linear combinations of the $\psi_n(r,\varphi)$ belonging to the same eigenenergy, providing an example of the nonuniqueness of the orthogonal basis functions within a degenerate manifold. The connection between the two sets of eigenfunctions is explored further in the problems at the end of this chapter.

Summary

Things to remember from Chapter 5:

The harmonic oscillator provides a good approximation to many real physical systems, in particular to the characteristic oscillations of any system about an equilibrium state.

The very mild boundary condition of square integrability on the eigenfunctions is sufficient to lead to discrete eigenvalue spectra in some cases.

The one-dimensional simple harmonic oscillator has the eigenenergies

$$E_n = (n + \tfrac{1}{2})\hbar\omega$$

where n is an integer and ω is the classical frequency of the oscillator.

Recursion relations exist involving the various ψ_n which make relatively easy the direct calculation of expectation values for various observables.

The properties of more complex systems (such as the two-dimensional harmonic oscillator) may be simply related to the properties of simple systems (the one-dimensional harmonic oscillator).

Problems

5.1 Show that

$$\langle \text{Kinetic energy} \rangle = \langle \text{potential energy} \rangle = \frac{E_n}{2}$$

for any eigenstate of the Hamiltonian. Show further that for a general (super-position) state of the harmonic oscillator the above relation is not true except at certain times.

5.2 Measurement of the energy of an ensemble of linear harmonic oscillators invariably yields the result $\frac{1}{2}\hbar\omega$ or $\frac{3}{2}\hbar\omega$, and yields the two results with equal probability. We therefore know that the state function, at the measurement time, is

$$\Psi(x, t = t_0) = \frac{1}{\sqrt{2}} (\Psi_0 + e^{i\delta}\Psi_1)$$

We have included the phase factor because the energy measurements do not give the relative phase of the two components of Ψ.

How do $\langle x \rangle$, $\langle x^2 \rangle$, and $\langle p \rangle$ depend on δ?

What measurement or measurements are needed to establish δ?

5.3 A laboratory oscillator consists of a mass of 1 gram on a spring. The mass is displaced from its equilibrium position and released. The oscillator exhibits a period of 1 second and the mass passes through the zero displacement position with a velocity of 10 cm/sec.

    a Is this oscillator probably in an eigenstate of the Hamiltonian?

    b What is the order of magnitude of the quantum number n associated with the $\langle E \rangle$ of this system?

    c What is the average spacing between nodes of the probability density of an eigenstate with such a quantum number?

5.4 We wish to test the hypothesis that the nucleus of an atom contains harmonically bound electrons. We know that the radius of a typical nucleus is approximately 10^{-12} cm and that the binding energy per nucleon is typically 7 or 8 Mev.

What would be the zero-point energy of an electron bound with sufficient strength to confine its zero-point excursions to a nuclear diameter?

Is the hypothesis true or false?

5.5 Show that neither Δx nor Δp is generally constant (independent of time) for a general state of the harmonic oscillator. Prove that $(\Delta x)^2$ and $(\Delta p)^2$ are both of the form

$$(\Delta)^2 = A + B \cos^2 \omega t$$

5.6 The vibrational spectra of molecules are readily observed by the techniques of infrared spectroscopy. The spacing between vibrational eigenstates of the carbon monoxide (CO) molecule is 2,170 cm^{-1} (reciprocal centimeters—a unit of energy commonly used by spectroscopists). Taking the masses of carbon and oxygen to be 12 and 16 atomic mass units, respectively, compute the effective spring constant k, which is a measure of the bond stiffness between the atoms of the molecule.

5.7 Consider the Hermitian operator

$$G = (XP_y - YP_x)$$

    a Calculate $\langle g \rangle$ for the ground state $\Psi_{00}(x,y,t)$ of the isotropic two-dimensional harmonic oscillator.

    b Calculate $\langle g \rangle$ for

$$\Psi(x,y,t) = \frac{1}{\sqrt{2}}\left[\Psi_{10}(x,y,t) + \Psi_{01}(x,y,t)\right]$$

    c Calculate $\langle g \rangle$ for

$$\Psi(x,y,t) = \frac{1}{\sqrt{2}}\left[\Psi_{10}(x,y,t) + e^{i\pi/2}\Psi_{01}(x,y,t)\right]$$

    d Note that G is the operator associated with the component of angular momentum perpendicular to the plane of the oscillator. Knowing this, can you give a physical interpretation to the result of the above calculations?

5.8 Solve for the eigenfunctions and eigenvalues of the Hamiltonian of the two-dimensional isotropic harmonic oscillator in polar coordinates.

Bibliography

The harmonic oscillator is treated with the Schrödinger wave equation approach in the following books:

Merzbacher, E.: "Quantum Mechanics," chap. 5, John Wiley & Sons, Inc., New York, 1961.

Schiff, L. I.: "Quantum Mechanics," 2nd ed., chap. 4, McGraw-Hill Book Company, New York, 1955.

Eisberg, R. M.: "Fundamentals of Modern Physics," chap. 8, sec. 6, John Wiley & Sons, Inc., New York, 1961.

Pauling, L., and E. B. Wilson: "Introduction to Quantum Mechanics," chaps. 3 and 4, McGraw-Hill Book Company, New York, 1935.

Dicke, R. H., and J. P. Wittke: "Introduction to Quantum Mechanics," chap. 3, Addison-Wesley Publishing Company, Inc., Reading, Mass., 1960.

Bohm, D.: "Quantum Theory," chap. 13, Prentice-Hall, Inc., Englewood Cliffs, N.J., 1951.

CHAPTER 6

The Matrix Formulation of Quantum Mechanics: The Harmonic Oscillator

6.1 OPERATORS AS MATRICES The operators of quantum mechanics, as we have remarked extensively, are linear operators, and linear operators are always susceptible to representation as matrices. It is therefore possible to present the various equations and operations of quantum mechanics in matrix language. We will find that in many instances this form of representation is more elegant, more general, and more powerful than the Schrödinger representation.

Let us see how we typically arrive at a matrix representation for an operator. The first thing we need is a set of basis functions to provide the framework within which we may describe our state functions and the operations we perform upon them. Let us arbitrarily select as a basis the eigenfunctions $u_n(\mathbf{r})$ of the operator A. Consider the effect of operating upon one of these eigenfunctions $u_n(\mathbf{r})$ with some other arbitrary quantum-mechanical operator F:

$$Fu_n(\mathbf{r}) = \chi_n(\mathbf{r}) \tag{6.1}$$

We produce some other function $\chi_n(\mathbf{r})$ of the coordinates of the system. This function can certainly be expanded in the basis functions $u_n(\mathbf{r})$ since the basis functions constitute a complete set.

$$\chi_n(\mathbf{r}) = \sum_m f_{mn} u_m(\mathbf{r}) \tag{6.2}$$

The expansion coefficients f_{mn} are the projections upon the various basis vectors $u_m(\mathbf{r})$ of the new function $\chi_n(\mathbf{r})$ which we have generated through the action of F. The magnitude of these projections is given by the scalar product of $u_m(\mathbf{r})$ and $\chi_n(\mathbf{r})$.

$$f_{mn} = \langle u_m(\mathbf{r}), \chi_n(\mathbf{r}) \rangle$$

$$= \int u_m^*(\mathbf{r}) \chi_n(\mathbf{r}) \, d\mathbf{r}$$

$$= \int u_m^*(\mathbf{r}) F u_n(\mathbf{r}) \, d\mathbf{r} \qquad (6.3)$$

We may write these scalar products (generally complex) as a square array.

$$\begin{bmatrix}
f_{11} & f_{12} & f_{13} & f_{14} & \cdots & f_{1n} & \cdots \\
f_{21} & f_{22} & f_{23} & f_{24} & \cdots & f_{2n} & \cdots \\
f_{31} & f_{32} & f_{33} & f_{34} & \cdots & \cdots & \cdots \\
f_{41} & f_{42} & \cdots & \cdots & \cdots & \cdots & \cdots \\
\cdots & \cdots & \cdots & \cdots & \cdots & \cdots & \cdots \\
f_{m1} & f_{m2} & \cdots & \cdots & \cdots & f_{mn} & \cdots \\
\cdots & \cdots & \cdots & \cdots & \cdots & \cdots & \cdots
\end{bmatrix} \qquad (6.4)$$

The entries in the first column are the expansion coefficients of the function $\chi_1(\mathbf{r}) = F u_1(\mathbf{r})$ in the $u_m(\mathbf{r})$ basis functions; the entries in the second column are the expansion coefficients of the function $\chi_2(\mathbf{r}) = F u_2(\mathbf{r})$ in the same basis set; etc.

The square infinite array of numbers of Eq. (6.4) is the matrix of F in the u_n representation. The elements f_{mn} are the *matrix elements* of F in this representation. Note that the matrix of F depends explicitly upon the choice of basis functions; there is no such thing as *the* matrix of F. The matrix may, however, look simpler in some bases than in others. In particular, if we had chosen the eigenfunctions of F as a basis for the representation, the matrix of F would be diagonal, that is, would have zeros everywhere except along the main diagonal, and the entries on the diagonal would be the eigenvalues of F. If we have the matrix of F in any representation, we can obtain the eigenvalues of F by diagonalizing that matrix.

In this age of high-speed machine computation, the diagonalization of a matrix may in practice be a rapid route to the eigenvalues of an operator.

If we have the matrix F in some known basis, we may calculate the action of F upon any state function and the expectation value of F for any state function. Suppose we have some arbitrary state function $\psi(\mathbf{r})$ and we expand this state in the basis set $u_n(\mathbf{r})$:

$$\psi(\mathbf{r}) = \sum_n c_n u_n(\mathbf{r}) \qquad (6.5)$$

Then
$$\chi(\mathbf{r}) = F\psi(\mathbf{r})$$
$$= F \sum_n c_n u_n(\mathbf{r})$$
$$= \sum_m \sum_n f_{mn} c_n u_n(\mathbf{r}) \qquad (6.6)$$

and $\chi(\mathbf{r})$ is completely specified by the expansion coefficients f_{mn} and c_n. The double summation of Eq. (6.6) is compactly and conveniently expressed in matrix notation as

$$
\chi(\mathbf{r}) \;=\; \begin{bmatrix} \\ \\ \\ F \\ \\ \\ \\ \end{bmatrix} \begin{bmatrix} c_1 \\ c_2 \\ c_3 \\ c_4 \\ \cdot \\ \cdot \\ c_n \\ \cdot \\ \cdot \\ \cdot \end{bmatrix} \qquad (6.7)
$$

The general state function $\psi(\mathbf{r})$ appears in the matrix formulation of quantum mechanics as a *column* vector whose entries are the expansion coefficients of the state function in some basis system. The operation of the matrix F upon the vector $\psi(\mathbf{r})$ produces a new column vector $\chi(\mathbf{r})$. The conjugate state $\psi^*(\mathbf{r})$ appears in the matrix formulation of quantum mechanics as a *row* vector whose entries are the c_n^*. The scalar product of two states

$$\psi(\mathbf{r}) = \sum_n c_n u_n(\mathbf{r})$$
$$\chi(\mathbf{r}) = \sum_n d_n u_n(\mathbf{r}) \qquad (6.8)$$

is then written

$$
\langle \chi(\mathbf{r}), \psi(\mathbf{r}) \rangle = \begin{bmatrix} d_1^* & d_2^* & d_3^* & \cdots & d_n^* & \cdots \end{bmatrix} \begin{bmatrix} c_1 \\ c_2 \\ c_3 \\ \cdot \\ \cdot \\ \cdot \\ c_n \\ \cdot \\ \cdot \\ \cdot \end{bmatrix}
$$

$$= \sum_n d_n^* c_n \qquad (6.9)$$

The scalar product of a general state function with itself is

$$\langle \psi(\mathbf{r}), \psi(\mathbf{r}) \rangle = \begin{bmatrix} c_1^* & c_2^* & c_3^* & \cdots & c_n^* & \cdots \end{bmatrix} \begin{bmatrix} c_1 \\ c_2 \\ c_3 \\ \cdot \\ \cdot \\ \cdot \\ c_n \\ \cdot \\ \cdot \\ \cdot \end{bmatrix}$$

$$= \sum_n |c_n|^2 = 1 \tag{6.10}$$

The expectation value of the observable F for a system in state $\psi(\mathbf{r})$ is written

$$\langle \psi(\mathbf{r}), F\psi(\mathbf{r}) \rangle = \begin{bmatrix} c_1^* & c_2^* & c_3^* & \cdots & c_n^* & \cdots \end{bmatrix}$$

$$\times \begin{bmatrix} f_{11} & f_{12} & f_{13} & \cdots & f_{1n} & \cdots \\ f_{21} & f_{22} & \cdots & \cdots & \cdots & \cdots \\ f_{31} & \cdots & \cdots & \cdots & \cdots & \cdots \\ \cdots & \cdots & \cdots & \cdots & \cdots & \cdots \\ f_{m1} & \cdots & \cdots & \cdots & \cdots & \cdots \\ \cdots & \cdots & \cdots & \cdots & \cdots & \cdots \end{bmatrix} \begin{bmatrix} c_1 \\ c_2 \\ c_3 \\ \cdot \\ \cdot \\ c_m \\ \cdot \\ \cdot \end{bmatrix} \tag{6.11}$$

As will be demonstrated in the next section, such matrix manipulations can be very short and informative, especially when many of the f_{mn} or c_n are zero, as is frequently the case. Authors using the matrix formulation usually use notation for the scalar product as follows: The scalar product of two functions is noted simply

$$\langle \chi(\mathbf{r}) \mid \psi(\mathbf{r}) \rangle \tag{6.12}$$

The scalar product of one function with another resulting from the operation of some observable on yet a third is noted

$$\langle \chi(\mathbf{r}) \mid F\psi(\mathbf{r}) \rangle = \langle \chi(\mathbf{r})| \ F \ |\psi(\mathbf{r}) \rangle \tag{6.13}$$

where F is the operator and $\psi(\mathbf{r})$ is the function upon which it operates. The matrix elements f_{mn} are the scalar products

$$\langle u_m(\mathbf{r})|\, F\, |u_n(\mathbf{r})\rangle \tag{6.14}$$

which are easily seen to be a special case of Eq. (6.13). The scalar product f_{mn} is commonly called *the matrix element of F between the states* u_m *and* u_n.

6.2 OPERATOR MATRICES FOR THE HARMONIC OSCILLATOR We shall now illustrate the matrix formulation of quantum mechanics by generating some operator matrices, using the eigenfunctions of the Hamiltonian of the linear harmonic oscillator as basis functions. We recall that these eigenfunctions were of the form

$$\psi_n(x) = A_n e^{-\xi^2/2} H_n(\xi) \tag{6.15}$$

where ξ is a dimensionless variable linear in x, and $H_n(\xi)$ is the Hermite polynomial of order n. The $\psi_n(x)$ are eigenfunctions of the Hamiltonian of the linear harmonic oscillator belonging to the eigenvalue

$$E_n = (n + \tfrac{1}{2})\hbar\omega \tag{6.16}$$

where all symbols have been discussed earlier. The matrix for the Hamiltonian operator is therefore particularly simple. Its elements are

$$\langle \psi_m(x)|\, H\, |\psi_n(x)\rangle = (n + \tfrac{1}{2})\hbar\omega\, \delta_{nm} \tag{6.17}$$

and the matrix may be written

$$H = \begin{bmatrix} \tfrac{1}{2}\hbar\omega & 0 & 0 & 0 & 0 & 0 & 0 \\ 0 & \tfrac{3}{2}\hbar\omega & 0 & 0 & 0 & \cdots & \cdots \\ 0 & 0 & \tfrac{5}{2}\hbar\omega & \cdots & \cdots & \cdots & \cdots \\ 0 & 0 & 0 & \cdots & \cdots & \cdots & \cdots \\ 0 & \cdots & \cdots & \cdots & \cdots & 0 & \cdots \\ 0 & 0 & 0 & \cdots & 0 & (n + \tfrac{1}{2})\hbar\omega & 0 \\ 0 & \cdots & \cdots & \cdots & \cdots & 0 & \cdots \end{bmatrix} \tag{6.18}$$

The H matrix is diagonal, as will be the matrix for any operator in the representation of its own eigenfunctions.

Let us turn to a matrix we cannot derive in such a trivial fashion—that for X. We wish the matrix elements

$$x_{mn} = \langle \psi_m(x) | \, X \, | \psi_n(x) \rangle$$
$$= \int_{-\infty}^{+\infty} \psi_m^*(x) x \psi_n(x) \, dx \qquad (6.19)$$

Using the procedures developed in the preceding section, we invoke the recursion relations on the $H_n(\xi)$ to obtain $x\psi_n(x)$ as an expansion in the $H_{n'}(\xi)$, obtaining

$$x_{mn} = \frac{1}{2} \frac{A_m^* A_n}{\sqrt{\alpha}} \int_{-\infty}^{+\infty} e^{-\xi^2} H_m(\xi) H_{n+1}(\xi) \, dx$$
$$+ n \frac{A_m^* A_n}{\sqrt{\alpha}} \int_{-\infty}^{+\infty} e^{-\xi^2} H_m(\xi) \, H_{n-1}(\xi) \, dx \qquad (6.20)$$

From the orthogonality of the $H_n(\xi)$, we know that these integrals will vanish unless $n = m - 1$ (in which event the first integral survives) or unless $n = m + 1$ (in which event the second integral survives). Evaluating the nonvanishing integrals, we find

$$x_{m,m-1} = \left(\frac{m}{2\alpha}\right)^{\frac{1}{2}}$$
$$\qquad\qquad\qquad\qquad (6.21)$$
$$x_{m,m+1} = \left(\frac{m+1}{2\alpha}\right)^{\frac{1}{2}}$$

The matrix for X, in this representation, is then

$$X = [2\alpha]^{-\frac{1}{2}} \begin{bmatrix} 0 & \sqrt{1} & 0 & 0 & 0 & \cdots & \cdots & & \cdots & & \cdots \\ \sqrt{1} & 0 & \sqrt{2} & 0 & 0 & \cdots & \cdots & & \cdots & & \cdots \\ 0 & \sqrt{2} & 0 & \sqrt{3} & 0 & \cdots & \cdots & & \cdots & & \cdots \\ 0 & 0 & \sqrt{3} & 0 & \sqrt{4} & \cdots & \cdots & & \cdots & & \cdots \\ 0 & 0 & 0 & \sqrt{4} & 0 & \cdots & \cdots & & \cdots & & \cdots \\ \cdots & \cdots & \cdots & \cdots & \cdots & & & & & & \\ \cdots & \cdots & \cdots & \cdots & \cdots & \cdots & 0 & \sqrt{m} & 0 & \cdots \\ \cdots & \cdots & \cdots & \cdots & \cdots & \cdots & \sqrt{m} & 0 & \sqrt{m+1} & \cdots \\ \cdots & \cdots & \cdots & \cdots & \cdots & \cdots & 0 & \sqrt{m+1} & 0 & \cdots \\ \cdots & \cdots & \cdots & \cdots & \cdots & & & & & \end{bmatrix}$$

$$\qquad\qquad\qquad\qquad\qquad\qquad\qquad (6.22)$$

The matrix X is called *off diagonal by one*. It has nonzero entries just off the main diagonal, but nowhere else. We may calculate the matrix for X^2 in a similar fashion:

$$x^2_{mn} = \langle \psi_m(x)| \, X^2 \, |\psi_n(x)\rangle$$

$$= \int_{-\infty}^{+\infty} \psi_m(x) x^2 \psi_n(x) \, dx \qquad (6.23)$$

Using the recursion relation of Eq. (5.37) twice, we find that

$$x^2_{mn} = \frac{1}{4} \frac{A_m^* A_n}{\alpha} \int_{-\infty}^{+\infty} e^{-\xi^2} H_m(\xi) H_{n+2}(\xi) \, dx$$

$$+ \left(n + \frac{1}{2}\right) \frac{A_m^* A_n}{\alpha} \int_{-\infty}^{+\infty} e^{-\xi^2} H_m(\xi) H_n(\xi) \, dx$$

$$+ n(n - 1) \frac{A_m^* A_n}{\alpha} \int_{-\infty}^{+\infty} e^{-\xi^2} H_m(\xi) H_{n-2}(\xi) \, dx \quad (6.24)$$

Because of the orthogonality of the Hermite polynomials, the matrix element x^2_{mn} will then be zero unless $n = m$ or $n = m \pm 2$. Again evaluating the nonzero integrals, we obtain

$$x^2_{m,m-2} = \frac{\sqrt{m(m - 1)}}{2\alpha}$$

$$x^2_{m,m} = \frac{2m + 1}{2\alpha} \qquad (6.25)$$

$$x^2_{m,m+2} = \frac{\sqrt{(m + 1)(m + 2)}}{2\alpha}$$

The matrix for X^2 is shown on the opposite page.

The matrix X^2 of Eq. (6.26) was obtained here by direct computation from the basis functions. We could have obtained the same matrix much less laboriously by noting that since $X^2_{\text{op}} = X_{\text{op}} X_{\text{op}}$, then $X^2 = XX$. If we simply multiply X of Eq. (6.22) by itself, we will obtain the matrix X^2 of Eq. (6.26). The matrix for any operation which is a product of operations may be obtained by multiplying together (with proper respect for order) the matrices of the factor operations.

The matrices for P_x and P_x^2 may be obtained by procedures entirely analogous to those used to obtain the matrices for X and X^2. Omitting

$$X^2 = \frac{1}{2\alpha}\begin{bmatrix}
1 & 0 & \sqrt{2} & 0 & 0 & \cdots & \cdots & \cdots & \cdots & \cdots & \cdots & \cdots \\
0 & 3 & 0 & \sqrt{6} & 0 & \cdots & \cdots & \cdots & \cdots & \cdots & \cdots & \cdots \\
\sqrt{2} & 0 & 5 & 0 & \sqrt{12} & \cdots & \cdots & \cdots & \cdots & \cdots & \cdots & \cdots \\
0 & \sqrt{6} & 0 & 7 & 0 & \cdots & \cdots & \cdots & \cdots & \cdots & \cdots & \cdots \\
0 & 0 & \sqrt{12} & 0 & 9 & \cdots & \cdots & \cdots & \cdots & \cdots & \cdots & \cdots \\
\vdots & \vdots & \vdots & \vdots & \vdots & & & & & & & \\
& & & & & 2m-3 & 0 & \sqrt{m(m-1)} & 0 & 0 & 0 & \cdots \\
& & & & & 0 & 2m-1 & 0 & \sqrt{m(m-1)} & 0 & 0 & \cdots \\
& & & & & \sqrt{m(m-1)} & 0 & 2m+1 & 0 & \sqrt{m(m+1)} & 0 & \cdots \\
& & & & & 0 & \sqrt{m(m+1)} & 0 & 2m+3 & 0 & \sqrt{(m+1)(m+2)} & \cdots \\
& & & & & 0 & 0 & \sqrt{(m+1)(m+2)} & 0 & 2m+5 & 0 & \cdots \\
& & & & & \vdots & \vdots & \vdots & \vdots & \vdots & \vdots &
\end{bmatrix}$$

(6.26)

the algebra, we display here these matrices, again in the representation of the eigenfunctions of the Hamiltonian.

$$P_x = \hbar\left(\frac{\alpha}{2}\right)^{1/2} \begin{bmatrix} 0 & -i\sqrt{1} & 0 & 0 & \cdots & \cdots & \cdots & & \cdots & \cdots \\ i\sqrt{1} & 0 & -i\sqrt{2} & 0 & \cdots & \cdots & \cdots & & \cdots & \cdot\cdot \\ 0 & i\sqrt{2} & 0 & -i\sqrt{3} & \cdots & \cdots & \cdots & & \cdots & \cdots \\ 0 & 0 & i\sqrt{3} & 0 & \cdots & \cdots & \cdots & & \cdots & \cdots \\ \cdots & \cdots & \cdots & \cdots & \cdots & 0 & -i\sqrt{m} & & 0 & \cdots \\ \cdots & \cdots & \cdots & \cdots & \cdots & i\sqrt{m} & 0 & & -i\sqrt{m+1} & \cdots \\ \cdots & \cdots & \cdots & \cdots & \cdots & 0 & i\sqrt{m+1} & & 0 & \cdots \end{bmatrix}$$

(6.27)

Note that P_x is off diagonal by one, as was X, and that it contains imaginary entries.

The matrices P_x and P_x^2 (see opposite page) are similar to the matrices X and X^2 in the magnitude and position of the entries, but differ significantly through the presence of factors of ± 1 and $\pm i$.

We are now in a position to calculate some expectation values of these observables, for the same states as we considered in Sec. 5.4. First we calculate $\langle x \rangle$ for a pure state $\Psi_n(x,t)$. We restore time to the problem at this point; our matrices are time-independent arrays of numbers obtained by evaluating all elements at the same fixed time, implicitly $t = 0$ for the present case. The pure state $\Psi_n(x,t)$ is represented in the matrix formulation as a column vector with zero entries at all positions but one—the nth row.

$$\Psi_n(x,t) = \begin{bmatrix} 0 \\ 0 \\ \cdot \\ \cdot \\ \cdot \\ 0 \\ e^{-(i/\hbar)E_n t} \\ 0 \\ \cdot \\ \cdot \\ \cdot \\ 0 \end{bmatrix}$$

(6.29)

$$P_x^2 = \frac{h^2\alpha}{2}
\begin{bmatrix}
1 & 0 & -\sqrt{2} & 0 & 0 & \cdots & \cdots & \cdots & \cdots & \cdots & \cdots \\
0 & 3 & 0 & -\sqrt{6} & 0 & \cdots & \cdots & \cdots & \cdots & \cdots & \cdots \\
-\sqrt{2} & 0 & 5 & 0 & -\sqrt{12} & \cdots & \cdots & \cdots & \cdots & \cdots & \cdots \\
0 & -\sqrt{6} & 0 & 7 & 0 & \cdots & \cdots & \cdots & \cdots & \cdots & \cdots \\
0 & 0 & -\sqrt{12} & 0 & 9 & \cdots & \cdots & \cdots & \cdots & \cdots & \cdots \\
\vdots & \vdots & \vdots & \vdots & \vdots & \ddots & & & & & \\
\cdots & \cdots & \cdots & \cdots & \cdots & \cdots & 2m-1 & 0 & -\sqrt{m(m-1)} & \cdots & \cdots \\
\cdots & \cdots & \cdots & \cdots & \cdots & \cdots & 0 & 2m+1 & 0 & -\sqrt{m(m+1)} & \cdots \\
\cdots & \cdots & \cdots & \cdots & \cdots & \cdots & -\sqrt{m(m+1)} & 0 & 2m+3 & 0 & -\sqrt{(m+1)(m+2)} \\
\cdots & \cdots & \cdots & \cdots & \cdots & \cdots & \cdots & -\sqrt{(m+1)(m+2)} & \cdots & \cdots & \cdots \\
\vdots & \vdots & \vdots & \vdots & \vdots & & \vdots & \vdots & \vdots & \vdots & \vdots
\end{bmatrix}
\tag{6.28}$$

103

Evaluating our expectation value through the matrix product

$$\langle x \rangle = \overline{0 \quad 0 \quad 0 \quad \cdot \quad \cdot \quad \cdot \quad e^{+(i/\hbar)E_n t} \quad \cdot \cdot \cdot \quad 0}$$

$$\times \left(\frac{1}{2\alpha}\right)^{1\!/\!2} \begin{bmatrix} 0 & \sqrt{1} & 0 & & & \\ \sqrt{1} & 0 & \sqrt{2} & & & \\ 0 & \sqrt{2} & 0 & & & \\ & & & 0 & & \\ & & & & 0 & \\ & & & & & 0 \end{bmatrix} \begin{bmatrix} 0 \\ 0 \\ \cdot \\ \cdot \\ e^{-(i/\hbar)E_n t} \\ 0 \\ \cdot \\ \cdot \\ \cdot \\ 0 \end{bmatrix} \qquad (6.30)$$

we see immediately that $\langle x \rangle = 0$ for a pure state since all the diagonal entries of X are identically zero. By an identical argument we can quickly establish that $\langle p_x \rangle = 0$ for a pure state also. Turning to $\langle x^2 \rangle$ and $\langle p_x^2 \rangle$, we see that for the pure state $\psi_n(x,t)$

$$\langle x^2 \rangle = x_{nn}^2 = \frac{2n+1}{2\alpha} = (n + \tfrac{1}{2})/\alpha$$

$$\langle p_x^2 \rangle = p_{nn}^2 = \frac{\hbar^2 \alpha}{2}(2n+1) = (n + \tfrac{1}{2})\hbar\alpha \qquad (6.31)$$

The computational virtues of the matrix formulation begin to emerge.
Let us now turn to the mixed state treated in Sec. 5.4:

$$\Psi(x,t) = \frac{1}{\sqrt{2}}[\Psi_0(x,t) + \Psi_1(x,t)]$$

$$= \frac{1}{\sqrt{2}}\psi_0(x)e^{-i\omega t/2} + \frac{1}{\sqrt{2}}\psi_1(x)e^{-3i\omega t/2} \qquad (6.32)$$

For the energy, we obtain the expectation value of energy.

$$\langle E \rangle = \begin{bmatrix} \dfrac{1}{\sqrt{2}}e^{i\omega t/2} & \dfrac{1}{\sqrt{2}}e^{3i\omega t/2} & 0 & 0 & \cdots \end{bmatrix}$$

$$\times \begin{bmatrix} \dfrac{\hbar\omega}{2} & 0 & 0 & \cdots \\ 0 & \dfrac{3\hbar\omega}{2} & 0 & \cdots \\ 0 & 0 & \dfrac{5\hbar\omega}{2} & \cdots \\ & \cdots & & \end{bmatrix} \begin{bmatrix} \dfrac{1}{\sqrt{2}}e^{-i\omega t/2} \\ \dfrac{1}{\sqrt{2}}e^{-3i\omega t/2} \\ 0 \\ \vdots \end{bmatrix}$$

$$= \begin{bmatrix} \dfrac{1}{\sqrt{2}}e^{i\omega t/2} & \dfrac{1}{\sqrt{2}}e^{3i\omega t/2} & 0 & 0 & \cdots \end{bmatrix} \begin{bmatrix} \dfrac{\hbar\omega}{2}\dfrac{1}{\sqrt{2}}e^{-i\omega t/2} \\ \dfrac{3\hbar\omega}{2}\dfrac{1}{\sqrt{2}}e^{-3i\omega t/2} \\ 0 \\ 0 \\ \vdots \end{bmatrix}$$

$$= \frac{1}{2}\frac{\hbar\omega}{2} + \frac{1}{2}\frac{3\hbar\omega}{2} = \hbar\omega \tag{6.33}$$

Next we evaluate $\langle x \rangle$.

$$\langle x \rangle = \begin{bmatrix} \frac{1}{\sqrt{2}} e^{i\omega t/2} & \frac{1}{\sqrt{2}} e^{3i\omega t/2} & 0 & \cdots \end{bmatrix}$$

$$\times \left(\frac{1}{2\alpha}\right)^{1/2} \begin{bmatrix} 0 & \sqrt{1} & 0 & \cdots \\ \sqrt{1} & 0 & \sqrt{2} & \cdots \\ 0 & \sqrt{2} & 0 & \cdots \\ \cdots & \cdots & \cdots & \cdots \end{bmatrix} \begin{bmatrix} \frac{1}{\sqrt{2}} e^{-i\omega t/2} \\ \frac{1}{\sqrt{2}} e^{-3i\omega t} \\ 0 \\ 0 \\ \vdots \end{bmatrix}$$

$$= \begin{bmatrix} \frac{1}{\sqrt{2}} e^{i\omega t/2} & \frac{1}{\sqrt{2}} e^{3i\omega t/2} & 0 & \cdots \end{bmatrix} \left(\frac{1}{2\alpha}\right)^{1/2} \begin{bmatrix} \frac{1}{\sqrt{2}} e^{-3i\omega t/2} \\ \frac{1}{\sqrt{2}} e^{-i\omega t/2} \\ e^{-3i\omega t/2} \\ 0 \\ 0 \\ \vdots \end{bmatrix}$$

$$= \frac{1}{2}\left(\frac{1}{2\alpha}\right)^{1/2}(e^{-i\omega t} + e^{+i\omega t}) = \left(\frac{1}{2\alpha}\right)^{1/2} \cos \omega t \tag{6.34}$$

Finally, we evaluate $\langle p_x \rangle$ for the same state.

$$\langle p_x \rangle = \boxed{\frac{1}{\sqrt{2}} e^{i\omega t/2} \quad \frac{1}{\sqrt{2}} e^{3i\omega t/2} \quad 0 \quad \cdots} \, h\left(\frac{\alpha}{2}\right)^{\frac{1}{2}} \begin{bmatrix} 0 & -i\sqrt{1} & 0 & \cdots \\ i\sqrt{1} & 0 & -i\sqrt{2} & \cdots \\ 0 & i\sqrt{2} & 0 & \cdots \\ \multicolumn{4}{c}{\cdots\cdots\cdots\cdots\cdots} \end{bmatrix} \begin{bmatrix} \frac{1}{\sqrt{2}} e^{-i\omega t/2} \\ \frac{1}{\sqrt{2}} e^{-3i\omega t/2} \\ 0 \\ \vdots \end{bmatrix}$$

$$= \boxed{\frac{1}{\sqrt{2}} e^{i\omega t/2} \quad \frac{1}{\sqrt{2}} e^{3i\omega t/2} \quad 0 \quad \cdots} \, h\left(\frac{\alpha}{2}\right)^{\frac{1}{2}} \begin{bmatrix} \frac{-i}{\sqrt{2}} e^{-3i\omega t/2} \\ +\frac{i}{\sqrt{2}} e^{-i\omega t/2} \\ +ie^{-3i\omega t/2} \\ 0 \\ \vdots \end{bmatrix}$$

$$= \frac{\hbar}{2}\left(\frac{\alpha}{2}\right)^{\frac{1}{2}} (-ie^{-i\omega t} + ie^{i\omega t}) = -\hbar\left(\frac{\alpha}{2}\right)^{\frac{1}{2}} \sin \omega t \qquad (6.35)$$

We observe that in all instances we obtain the same result as we did by a straightforward Schrödinger calculation, as we might well expect since we have done essentially the same calculation, concealing most of the labor in the matrix element. We will shortly show, however, that it is not necessary to go through the Schrödinger calculation to obtain the matrix elements, that we can in fact bypass the solution of a differential equation entirely. We first digress to discuss a few of the properties of matrices in general and of the special kinds with which we will meet in particular.

6.3 SOME MATRIX DEFINITIONS AND GENERAL PROPERTIES We have already presumed a certain degree of familiarity with matrices and their manipulation. Before we proceed further, however, it is desirable to establish a certain level of familiarity with the formal properties of matrices and the nomenclature appropriate to certain special classes of matrices. We therefore state here some of these matrix properties (including some of the simple properties with which we are already conversant).

A matrix is a rectangular $m \times n$ array of numbers for which certain algebraic operations are defined. Two matrices are equal when their corresponding elements are equal:

$$A = B \qquad (6.36)$$

if $\qquad\qquad a_{mn} = b_{mn} \qquad$ for all m,n

For two matrices to be equal it is therefore necessary for their dimensions m and n to be the same.

Two matrices can be added, giving a new matrix whose elements are sums of the corresponding elements of the component matrices:

$$C = A + B \qquad (6.37)$$

means $\qquad\qquad c_{mn} = a_{mn} + b_{mn} \qquad$ for all m,n

For addition to be defined it is necessary for the two matrices involved to have the same dimensions.

A matrix can be multiplied by a constant, giving a new matrix whose elements are all multiplied by the constant:

$$B = kA \qquad (6.38)$$

means $\qquad\qquad b_{mn} = ka_{mn} \qquad$ for all m,n

Two matrices can be multiplied together to give a third matrix, according to the following rule:

$$C = AB \qquad (6.39)$$

means $\qquad\qquad c_{mn} = \sum_k a_{mk} b_{kn}$

We see that the element c_{mn} is obtained by summing together the binary products of elements from the mth row of A with the nth column of B. For the product to be defined, there must be as many elements in the mth row of A as there are elements in the nth column of B. The matrix A must then have as many columns as B has rows, so the dimensionality of our matrices will be

$$C(m \times n) = A(m \times l) \times B(l \times n) \qquad (6.40)$$

If A and B are square matrices, the product BA is defined as well as the product AB. In general these products are not equal, and the matrices A and B do not, in general, commute.

The *trace* of a matrix is the sum of the diagonal elements of a matrix.

$$\text{Tr } A = \sum_n a_{nn} \qquad (6.41)$$

A matrix which has all off-diagonal elements zero is called a *diagonal matrix*. Its elements may be written

$$a_{ij} = a_{ii} \delta_{ij} \qquad (6.42)$$

A special case of the diagonal matrix is the unit matrix I, for which all the diagonal elements are unity.

$$(I)_{ij} = \delta_{ij} \tag{6.43}$$

A matrix A may or may not have an inverse A^{-1} defined by

$$A^{-1}A = AA^{-1} = I \tag{6.44}$$

If a matrix possesses an inverse it is called a *nonsingular matrix*; if a matrix has no inverse it is called a *singular matrix*.

The transpose $\tilde{A}$ of a matrix A is defined by

$$(\tilde{A})_{mn} = (A)_{nm} \tag{6.45}$$

that is, rows and columns have been interchanged. If $\tilde{A} = A$, the matrix is called *symmetric*. If $\tilde{A} = -A$, the matrix is called *antisymmetric*. Obviously a matrix can be symmetric or antisymmetric only if it is square.

The Hermitian adjoint $A^\dagger$ of a matrix A is defined by

$$(A^\dagger)_{mn} = (A)^*_{nm} \tag{6.46}$$

Rows and columns have been interchanged and then the complex conjugate of each element taken. Note that the row vector $\psi^*(\mathbf{r})$ is the Hermitian adjoint of the column vector $\psi(\mathbf{r})$.

The two classes of matrices of primary importance to quantum mechanics are *Hermitian* matrices and *unitary* matrices.

A Hermitian matrix is defined as a matrix equal to its own Hermitian adjoint. The matrix A is Hermitian if

$$A = A^\dagger \tag{6.47}$$
$$a_{mn} = a^*_{nm}$$

A unitary matrix is a matrix whose inverse is equal to its Hermitian adjoint. The matrix A is unitary if

$$A^{-1} = A^\dagger \tag{6.48}$$

or, equivalently,
$$AA^\dagger = I \tag{6.49}$$

Hermitian matrices occur regularly in quantum mechanics because the operators associated with observables are always Hermitian. The matrix representing a Hermitian operator is, not surprisingly, a Hermitian matrix. We may readily check that the matrices for X, P_x, etc., derived earlier in this chapter satisfy element by element the requirement of Eq. (6.47).

In the Schrödinger language, the Hermiticity of an operator was described as

$$\int \psi^* A\psi \, d\mathbf{r} = \int [A^*\psi^*]\psi \, d\mathbf{r}$$

$$= \int [A\psi]^*\psi \, d\mathbf{r} \qquad (3.49)$$

indicating that A could be allowed to operate on ψ^* rather than on ψ if it were first complex-conjugated. In the matrix multiplication

$$\boxed{\chi^*} \begin{bmatrix} A \end{bmatrix} \begin{bmatrix} \psi \end{bmatrix} \qquad (6.50)$$

the sequence of multiplication is immaterial. We may multiply together $\overrightarrow{\chi^*}[A]$ and then multiply $[\psi]$ by the resulting row vector, or we may equivalently multiply together $[A][\psi]$ and multiply the resulting column vector by $\overrightarrow{\chi^*}$. A may be regarded as operating on $\overrightarrow{\chi^*}$ from the right or on $[\psi]$ from the left. The Hermiticity of A implies that we may also allow it to multiply $\overrightarrow{\chi^*}$ from the left, if we replace A with $A^\dagger$. The matrix equivalent of Eq. (3.49), describing the Hermiticity of A, is

$$\boxed{\chi^*} \begin{bmatrix} A \end{bmatrix} \begin{bmatrix} \psi \end{bmatrix} = \left\{ \begin{bmatrix} A^\dagger \end{bmatrix} \begin{bmatrix} \chi \end{bmatrix} \right\}^\dagger \begin{bmatrix} \psi \end{bmatrix}$$

$$= \left\{ \begin{bmatrix} A \end{bmatrix} \begin{bmatrix} \chi \end{bmatrix} \right\}^\dagger \begin{bmatrix} \psi \end{bmatrix} \qquad (6.51)$$

We may write the matrix for the Hermitian operator in any of a number of basis systems, and in any of these basis systems A will be Hermitian. We may convert A and the state vectors ψ from one representation to another by a linear transformation which is a unitary transformation and which is representable therefore by a unitary matrix. The importance of the unitary matrix in quantum mechanics arises from exactly this property; it allows us to switch from one basis system, one representation, to another. Let us consider therefore some of the properties of a unitary transformation.

When a matrix S operates upon a vector $\mathbf{V}$ (which is an $n \times 1$ matrix), it transforms $\mathbf{V}$ into a new vector $\mathbf{V}'$. The new vector $\mathbf{V}'$ is in general stretched or compressed and rotated with respect to the original vector $\mathbf{V}$.

Consider the transformation of two vectors $\mathbf{V}_1$ and $\mathbf{V}_2$:

$$SV_1 = V_1' \tag{6.52}$$
$$SV_2 = V_2'$$

If S is unitary, then

$$\langle V_1' \mid V_1' \rangle = \langle V_1 \mid V_1 \rangle$$
$$\langle V_2' \mid V_2' \rangle = \langle V_2 \mid V_2 \rangle \tag{6.53}$$
$$\langle V_1' \mid V_2' \rangle = \langle V_1 \mid V_2 \rangle$$

The lengths of vectors are not changed by a unitary transformation, nor are the angles between vectors. In particular, orthogonal unit vectors remain orthogonal unit vectors. A unitary transformation represents a sort of n-dimensional rigid rotation in Hilbert space. (The reader may readily verify that the matrices representing rigid rotations in ordinary three-dimensional space are unitary.) The transformation connecting two different sets of orthonormal basis functions spanning the same space (e.g., the eigenfunctions of two different Hermitian operators) will be a unitary transformation.

Before examining specifically the transformation between different bases of state-function space, we shall look at a few more general properties of matrix operations and matrix equations.

When we transform the vectors and matrices involved in a matrix equation, we might well suppose that the appearance of the equation will be radically altered. Let us examine this supposition. As a test case we start with the simple vector equation

$$F\psi = \chi \tag{6.54}$$

and operate upon both sides of this equation from the left with the transformation matrix S.

$$SF\psi = S\chi \tag{6.55}$$

If we further specify that S be nonsingular, that there exists a transformation S^{-1} which "undoes" the transformation S, then we may insert the identity matrix $I = S^{-1}S$ between F and ψ without disturbing the equality:

$$SFS^{-1}S\psi = S\chi \tag{6.56}$$

We see then that if $F\psi$ and χ obeyed Eq. (6.54), then their transformed counterparts

$$F' = SFS^{-1}$$
$$\psi' = S\psi \tag{6.57}$$
$$\chi' = S\chi$$

will obey an equation

$$F'\psi' = \chi' \tag{6.58}$$

which is identical in form with the original Eq. (6.54). The form of a matrix equation is preserved under a nonsingular transformation. This is true whether or not S is unitary. If, in addition, S is unitary, we have a theorem from linear algebra concerning the transformed matrices which is important for quantum mechanics:

MATRIX THEOREM 1   *If A is Hermitian and S is unitary then $A' = SAS^{-1}$ is also Hermitian.*

Since the various eigenfunction sets which span state-function space are all connected by unitary transformations, we may recognize that the above general theorem is the basis for our earlier assertion that the matrix of a Hermitian operator will be Hermitian in any such representation.

Linear algebra also supplies us with a second theorem, an existence theorem, important to quantum mechanics:

MATRIX THEOREM 2   *For any Hermitian matrix A there exists a unitary transformation S which will cause $A' = SAS^{-1}$ to be diagonal. Further, the transformed matrix A' is unique except for the order of its diagonal elements.*

As we have remarked earlier, the matrix of an operator in the representation provided by its own eigenfunctions as a basis will be diagonal. Matrix theorem 2 is logically equivalent to the statement that every Hermitian operator does indeed generate a complete set of eigenfunctions. The diagonalized form of an operator matrix is of special interest because the diagonal entries are the eigenvalues of the operator. These diagonal entries will be real, as eigenvalues must be, because the requirement $a_{mn} = a_{nm}^*$ forces the diagonal entries of Hermitian matrices always to be real.

When we come to the solution of actual problems we will often find it necessary or convenient to change from one basis, or representation, to another. We will therefore develop here some of the machinery associated with such a change of basis.

Let us imagine that we have a set of operator matrices A, B, C, etc., written in the representation generated by the set of basis functions u_1, u_2, u_3, ..., u_n ..., and wish to express these matrices in a different representation, that generated by an alternate set of basis functions v_1, v_2,

$v_3, \ldots, v_n \ldots$ We may expand each of our original basis functions u_n in the set of new basis functions v_m

$$u_n = \sum_m s_{mn} v_m \qquad (6.59)$$

Each of the expansion coefficients is, as before, the projection of one basis vector upon the other, and may be obtained from the scalar product of the two vectors:

$$s_{mn} = \langle v_m \mid u_n \rangle \qquad (6.60)$$

The array of coefficients s_{mn} comprise a transformation matrix S. The matrices A, B, C, etc., are transformed from the u representation into the v representation (indicated here by primes) by

$$A' = SAS^{-1}$$
$$B' = SAS^{-1} \qquad (6.61)$$
$$\cdot\ \cdot\ \cdot\ \cdot\ \cdot\ \cdot$$

State vectors ψ_a or ψ_b are transformed from the u representation to the v (primed) representation according to

$$\psi'_a = S\psi_a$$
$$\psi'_b = S\psi_b \qquad (6.62)$$
$$\cdot\ \cdot\ \cdot\ \cdot\ \cdot$$

We must at this point distinguish between the transformation which carries a vector expressed in one basis into the same vector expressed in a different basis system and the transformation which carries one set of basis vectors into another. The matrix S transforms a vector expressed in the u basis into the same vector expressed in the v basis. If we examine Eq. (6.59) carefully, we note that the convention we have followed for the expansion of u_n in terms of a set of basis functions v_m is not compatible with regarding the function u_n as resulting from the matrix multiplication of the matrix S times the set of functions v_n, treated as components of a vector; the subscripts on the s_{mn} are in the wrong order to correspond to matrix multiplication. The expansion convention was chosen deliberately so that Eqs. (6.61) and (6.62) would have the form they do, i.e., so that matrices and vectors expressed in the various representations would transform according to the rules of regular matrix multiplication. If we wish to obtain the functions u_n, regarded as components of a vector, from the functions v_m, also regarded as components of a vector, we must multiply the v_m by the transpose of S, by $\tilde{S}$. Conversely, to obtain the v_m from the u_n we must multiply the u_n by $\tilde{S}^{-1} = S^*$.

The reader will recognize that the need to distinguish between the transformation properties of the components of a vector and the transformation properties of the basis vectors themselves is not peculiar to quantum mechanics. In cases where the quantities involved are all real, the distinctions between S and S^* and between $\tilde{S}$ and S^{-1} are lost, so components and basis vectors transform in the same manner, but whenever complex quantities are involved the distinctions must be maintained.

6.4 PURE MATRIX TREATMENT OF THE SIMPLE HARMONIC OSCILLATOR In the matrices we have encountered so far, each entry has been computed directly by the use of explicit basis functions obtained from the solution of a differential equation. It would seem at this point that a matrix represents merely a compact notation for the results of Schrödinger wave-mechanical calculations. We shall show in this section that we may obtain all the matrices of Sec. 6.2 without ever solving a differential equation or obtaining an explicit wave function. In point of fact, the matrix formulation of quantum mechanics was developed by Born and Heisenberg largely to eliminate explicit wave functions, themselves not observable, from quantum mechanics.

Our starting point in the matrix treatment of the linear harmonic oscillator is again the classical Hamiltonian of the system.

$$H = \frac{p_x^2}{2m} + \tfrac{1}{2}kx^2 \tag{6.63}$$

which we convert into operator form

$$H_{\mathrm{op}} = \frac{P^2}{2m} + \tfrac{1}{2}kX^2 \tag{6.64}$$

where we have dropped the subscript x on P, the x being understood. The Hamiltonian operator can be put in somewhat cleaner form if we substitute for P and X new operators $\mathscr{P}$ and $\mathfrak{X}$ which differ from P and X only by scalar multipliers involving m, k, and $\hbar$.

$$\mathscr{P} = (m\hbar\omega)^{-1/2}P$$

$$\mathfrak{X} = \left(\frac{m\omega}{\hbar}\right)^{1/2}X \tag{6.65}$$

$$\omega = \left(\frac{k}{m}\right)^{1/2}$$

In terms of these new operators

$$H_{\text{op}} = \tfrac{1}{2}\hbar\omega(\mathscr{P}^2 + \mathfrak{X}^2) = \hbar\omega\mathscr{H}_{\text{op}} \qquad (6.66)$$

where

$$\mathscr{H}_{\text{op}} = \tfrac{1}{2}(\mathscr{P}^2 + \mathfrak{X}^2) \qquad (6.67)$$

Since the operators P and X had the commutation property

$$[X,P] = i\hbar \qquad (6.68)$$

the new operators will have the commutation rule

$$\begin{aligned}
[\mathfrak{X},\mathscr{P}] &= \left(\frac{m\omega}{\hbar}\right)^{1/2}\left(\frac{1}{m\omega\hbar}\right)^{1/2}[X,P] \\
&= \frac{1}{\hbar}\,i\hbar \\
&= i \qquad (6.69)
\end{aligned}$$

We now define two further operators a and $a^\dagger$ such that

$$a = \frac{1}{\sqrt{2}}(\mathfrak{X} + i\mathscr{P}) \qquad a^\dagger = \frac{1}{\sqrt{2}}(\mathfrak{X} - i\mathscr{P}) \qquad (6.70)$$

The motivation for inventing these operators must certainly be obscure at this point, but suffice it to say that a and $a^\dagger$ will turn out to be the annihilation and creation operators (or demotion and promotion operators) so very important in all theories of the interaction of radiation with matter. Note that $a^\dagger$ is indeed the Hermitian adjoint of a, but that $a^\dagger$ does not equal a, so these operators are not Hermitian and cannot correspond to observables. If we form the product operators

$$aa^\dagger = \tfrac{1}{2}[\mathfrak{X}^2 - i(\mathfrak{X}\mathscr{P} - \mathscr{P}\mathfrak{X}) + \mathscr{P}^2] \qquad (6.71)$$

and

$$a^\dagger a = \tfrac{1}{2}[\mathfrak{X}^2 + i(\mathfrak{X}\mathscr{P} - \mathscr{P}\mathfrak{X}) + \mathscr{P}^2]$$

we observe that

$$\tfrac{1}{2}(aa^\dagger + a^\dagger a) = \tfrac{1}{2}(\mathfrak{X}^2 + \mathscr{P}^2) = \mathscr{H}_{\text{op}} \qquad (6.72)$$

and we have obtained the Hamiltonian operator of the harmonic oscillator in terms of the a and $a^\dagger$ operators. Further, we note that

$$\begin{aligned}
aa^\dagger - a^\dagger a &= (\tfrac{1}{2})(-2i)(\mathfrak{X}\mathscr{P} - \mathscr{P}\mathfrak{X}) \\
&= -i[\mathfrak{X},\mathscr{P}] \\
&= (-i)(i) \qquad (6.73) \\
[a,a^\dagger] &= 1
\end{aligned}$$

and the a and $a^\dagger$ operators obey a particularly simple commutation relation. Since, from this commutation rule

$$aa^\dagger = 1 + a^\dagger a \tag{6.74}$$

the modified Hamiltonian operator may be rewritten

$$\begin{aligned}
\mathcal{H}_{\text{op}} &= \tfrac{1}{2}(aa^\dagger + a^\dagger a) \\
&= \tfrac{1}{2}(2a^\dagger a + 1) \\
&= (a^\dagger a + \tfrac{1}{2})
\end{aligned} \tag{6.75}$$

Defining a new operator N such that

$$N = a^\dagger a \tag{6.76}$$

the Hamiltonian operator for the harmonic oscillator becomes

$$H_{\text{op}} = (N + \tfrac{1}{2})\hbar\omega \tag{6.77}$$

We do not yet know the eigenvalues of the operator N; if we did we would know the eigenenergies of the harmonic oscillator. Certainly H_{op} does have eigenfunctions and eigenvalues, so let us adopt some arbitrary symbol for the eigenfunctions and see what relations the Hamiltonian operator of Eq. (6.75) implies between these eigenfunctions. Let us denote by $|v\rangle$ the eigenfunction such that

$$N\,|v\rangle = v\,|v\rangle \tag{6.78}$$

We are in essence labeling the eigenfunctions by the eigenvalues with which they are associated. For the one-dimensional oscillator, only one eigenvalue is necessary in order to label the eigenfunction completely. For a more complicated system, a large number of eigenvalues is necessary in order to specify the eigenfunction completely. Such an eigenfunction might be noted

$$|\alpha,\beta,\gamma, \ldots, v \ldots\rangle \tag{6.79}$$

where the α, β, etc., are the eigenvalues of the various relevant operators. We are adopting here the *Dirac* notation. The symbol $|\ \rangle$ is called a *ket;* its dual $\langle\ |$ is called a *bra*. Together, the two symbols define a scalar product Dirac calls a *bracket* $\langle\ |\ \rangle$. The expectation value of an operator is, in the Dirac notation, $\langle\ |\ F\ |\ \rangle$, just as in our earlier notation [see Eq. (6.13)].

At present we have no knowledge of v except that it is an eigenvalue; it must be real but it need not be an integer or even a rational fraction. It is possible, however, to derive the allowed values of v by examining the relations between eigenfunctions implied by the Hamiltonian equation (6.75) and by the commutation relation between a and $a^\dagger$ [Eq. (6.73)]. To develop this relation between eigenfunctions, we need first to develop two operator equalities involving Na and $Na^\dagger$.

$$
\begin{aligned}
Na &= a^\dagger aa \\
&= (aa^\dagger - 1)a \\
&= aa^\dagger a - a \\
&= a(a^\dagger a - 1) \\
&= a(N - 1) \tag{6.80}
\end{aligned}
$$

and

$$
\begin{aligned}
Na^\dagger &= a^\dagger aa^\dagger \\
&= a^\dagger(a^\dagger a + 1) \\
&= a^\dagger(N + 1) \tag{6.81}
\end{aligned}
$$

Consider now the vector $a\,|v\rangle$ obtained by operating on $|v\rangle$ with a. Is $a\,|v\rangle$ an eigenvector of N? To answer this question we let N operate on $a\,|v\rangle$. Using the identity of Eq. (6.80), we find that

$$
\begin{aligned}
Na\,|v\rangle &= a(N - 1)\,|v\rangle \\
&= a(v - 1)\,|v\rangle \\
&= (v - 1)a\,|v\rangle \tag{6.82}
\end{aligned}
$$

The quantity $v - 1$ is a scalar and can be brought through the operator a. Equation (6.82) tells us that

$$
N[a\,|v\rangle] = (v - 1)[a\,|v\rangle] \tag{6.83}
$$

or that $a\,|v\rangle$ is an eigenvector of N belonging to the eigenvalue $v - 1$.

$$
a\,|v\rangle = A_v\,|(v - 1)\rangle \tag{6.84}
$$

We have included the scalar A_v in Eq. (6.84) to describe what a has done to the normalization of $|v\rangle$ while converting it to the eigenvector $|(v - 1)\rangle$.

Similarly

$$
\begin{aligned}
Na^\dagger\,|v\rangle &= a^\dagger(N + 1)\,|v\rangle \\
&= a^\dagger(v + 1)\,|v\rangle \\
&= (v + 1)a^\dagger\,|v\rangle \tag{6.85}
\end{aligned}
$$

or

$$
N[a^\dagger\,|v\rangle] = (v + 1)[a^\dagger\,|v\rangle] \tag{6.86}
$$

implying

$$
a^\dagger\,|v\rangle = A_v^\dagger\,|(v + 1)\rangle \tag{6.87}
$$

We see now why a and $a^\dagger$ are called the *demotion* and *promotion* operators. a operating on the eigenfunction $|v\rangle$ demotes it to the eigenfunction belonging to the eigenvalue $v - 1$, and $a^\dagger$ operating on $|v\rangle$ promotes it to the eigenfunction belonging to the eigenvalue $v + 1$. Given any eigenfunction $|v\rangle$ (where v may not itself be integral), we can now generate a ladder of eigenvalues whose spacing is integral.

We ask now if there is any limit to the number of times we may repeat the promotion or demotion operation. The answer is "yes" because of the physical interpretation of our eigenvalues. Since v is an eigenvalue of N, $(v + \frac{1}{2})\hbar\omega$ is an eigenenergy of the system. For this particular system we cannot have negative eigenenergies since the total energy is quadratic in both position and momentum coordinates. There exists, therefore, some minimum v, which we call v_{min}, such that the demotion operation upon $|v_{min}\rangle$ produces a null vector:

$$a\,|v_{min}\rangle = 0 \qquad (6.88)$$

If Eq. (6.88) is true, so also is

$$a^\dagger a\,|v_{min}\rangle = 0$$
$$N\,|v_{min}\rangle = 0 \qquad (6.89)$$
$$v_{min}\,|v_{min}\rangle = 0$$

and

$$\langle v_{min}|\,N\,|v_{min}\rangle = 0$$
$$v_{min}\langle v_{min}\mid v_{min}\rangle = 0 \qquad (6.90)$$

Since $|v_{min}\rangle$ was an existent eigenfunction by prior assumption,

$$\langle v_{min}\mid v_{min}\rangle = 1 \qquad (6.91)$$

and therefore

$$v_{min} = 0$$

The minimum value for the eigenvalue v is therefore 0. Operating on this minimum value successively with $a^\dagger$ will generate the ladder of eigenvalues 0, 1, 2, ..., n, ... Knowing this, and knowing that the eigenvalues of H_{op} are $(v + \frac{1}{2})\hbar\omega$, we may immediately write the Hamiltonian operator matrix:

$$H_{op} = \begin{bmatrix} \dfrac{\hbar\omega}{2} & 0 & 0 & 0 & \cdots & 0 \\[1ex] 0 & \tfrac{3}{2}\hbar\omega & 0 & 0 & \cdots & 0 \\[1ex] 0 & 0 & \tfrac{5}{2}\hbar\omega & 0 & \cdots & 0 \\[1ex] 0 & 0 & 0 & \cdots & \cdots & 0 \\[1ex] \cdots & \cdots & \cdots & \cdots & \cdots & \cdots \\[1ex] \cdots & \cdots & \cdots & \cdots & \cdots & (n + \tfrac{1}{2})\hbar\omega \end{bmatrix} \qquad (6.92)$$

This matrix is called the *matrix of H in the N representation*.

We may also obtain quite directly, and again without writing any explicit wave functions, the matrices for X and P. Since

$$a \mid v\rangle = A_v\,|(v - 1)\rangle \qquad (6.84)$$

then

$$\langle (v - 1)|\,a\,|v\rangle = A_v\langle (v - 1)\mid (v - 1)\rangle$$
$$a_{v-1,\,v} = A_v \qquad (6.93)$$

and we may identify the matrix element $a_{v-1,\,v}$, off diagonal by one, with A_v. Similarly,

$$a^\dagger |v\rangle = A_v^\dagger |(v+1)\rangle \qquad (6.87)$$

Whence
$$\langle (v+1)| a^\dagger |v\rangle = A_v^\dagger \langle (v+1) | (v+1)\rangle$$
$$a^\dagger_{v+1,\,v} = A_v^\dagger \qquad (6.94)$$

and we may identify the matrix element $a^\dagger_{v+1,\,v}$, also off diagonal by one, with $A_v^\dagger$. Operating successively with the demotion and promotion operators returns us to our starting eigenfunction, except for normalizing constants.

$$a^\dagger a |v\rangle = a^\dagger A_v |(v-1)\rangle = A_v a^\dagger |(v-1)\rangle$$
$$N |v\rangle = A_v A_{v-1}^\dagger |v\rangle \qquad (6.95)$$

or
$$\langle v| N |v\rangle = A_v A_{v-1}^\dagger \langle v | v\rangle$$
$$v\langle v | v\rangle = a_{v-1,v} a^\dagger_{v,\,v-1} \langle v | v\rangle \qquad (6.96)$$
$$v = a_{v-1,v} a^\dagger_{v,\,v-1}$$

Inasmuch as $a^\dagger$ is the Hermitian adjoint of a,

$$a_{v-1,v} = (a^\dagger_{v,v-1})^* $$
$$a^\dagger_{v,\,v-1} = (a_{v-1,v})^* \qquad (6.97)$$

and
$$v = |a_{v-1,v}|^2 = |a^\dagger_{v,v-1}|^2 \qquad (6.98)$$

Taking the a_{ij} to be real, for lack of any motivation to preserve an arbitrary phase factor, we now have the matrix elements of the matrices for a and $a^\dagger$:

$$a_{v-1,v} = a^\dagger_{v,v-1} = \sqrt{v} \qquad (6.99)$$

and the matrices are, respectively,

$$a = \begin{bmatrix} 0 & \sqrt{1} & 0 & 0 & \cdots & \cdots & \cdots & \cdots & \cdots & \cdots \\ 0 & 0 & \sqrt{2} & 0 & \cdots & \cdots & \cdots & \cdots & \cdots & \cdots \\ 0 & 0 & 0 & \sqrt{3} & \cdots & \cdots & \cdots & \cdots & \cdots & \cdots \\ 0 & 0 & 0 & 0 & \cdots & \cdots & \cdots & \cdots & \cdots & \cdots \\ \cdots & & & & & & & & & \\ \cdots & \cdots & \cdots & \cdots & \cdots & 0 & \sqrt{n-1} & 0 & 0 & \cdots \\ \cdots & \cdots & \cdots & \cdots & \cdots & 0 & 0 & \sqrt{n} & 0 & \cdots \\ \cdots & \cdots & \cdots & \cdots & \cdots & 0 & 0 & 0 & \sqrt{n+1} & \cdots \\ \cdots & \cdots & \cdots & \cdots & \cdots & 0 & 0 & 0 & 0 & \cdots \end{bmatrix}$$

$$(6.100)$$

$$a^\dagger = \begin{bmatrix} 0 & 0 & 0 & 0 & \cdots & \cdots & \cdots & \cdots & \cdots \cdots \\ \sqrt{1} & 0 & 0 & 0 & \cdots & \cdots & \cdots & \cdots & \cdots \cdots \\ 0 & \sqrt{2} & 0 & 0 & \cdots & \cdots & \cdots & \cdots & \cdots \cdots \\ 0 & 0 & \sqrt{3} & 0 & \cdots & \cdots & \cdots & \cdots & \cdots \cdots \\ \cdots & \cdots & \cdots & \cdots & \cdots & 0 & 0 & 0 & 0 & \cdots \\ \cdots & \cdots & \cdots & \cdots & \cdots & \sqrt{n-1} & 0 & 0 & 0 & \cdots \\ \cdots & \cdots & \cdots & \cdots & \cdots & 0 & \sqrt{n} & 0 & 0 & \cdots \\ \cdots & \cdots & \cdots & \cdots & \cdots & 0 & 0 & \sqrt{n+1} & 0 & \cdots \end{bmatrix}$$

$$(6.101)$$

Looking back to Eqs. (6.65) and (6.70), we find that we can write the X and P matrices in terms of a and $a^\dagger$.

$$X = \left(\frac{\hbar}{2m\omega}\right)^{1/2}(a + a^\dagger) = \left(\frac{1}{2\alpha}\right)^{1/2}(a + a^\dagger) \tag{6.102}$$

$$P = i\left(\frac{m\hbar\omega}{2}\right)^{1/2}(a^\dagger - a) = i\hbar\left(\frac{\alpha}{2}\right)^{1/2}(a^\dagger - a) \tag{6.103}$$

Comparison with X and P of Eqs. (6.22) and (6.27) shows that these expressions lead to the identical matrices obtained by the use of the explicit Schrödinger wave functions for the various $|v\rangle$. From the matrices for X and P, we may construct those for X^2, P^2, or any other $f(X,P)$ we may desire.

In this section we have demonstrated the matrix technique for the solution of a quantum-mechanical problem. The approach was typical of the matrix attack upon a problem: First, using the Hamiltonian operator and commutation relations, establish some sort of a recursion relation among the eigenfunctions, some ladder of eigenvalues; second, fix one rung of the ladder by physical argument. The uniqueness of the solution can usually be proved quite directly.

Summary

Important points to remember from Chap. 6 are:

The linear operator associated with an observable may be represented by a matrix. This matrix will look different in various basis function sets, but will always be *Hermitian*.

The matrix of an operator in the representation of its own eigenfunctions will be a diagonal matrix, and the diagonal entries (all real for a Hermitian matrix) will be the eigenvalues of the operator.

The state function ψ appears in the matrix formulation as a column vector whose entries are the expansion coefficients of the state function in the basis system of the representation.

We may go from one representation to another through the utilization of a transformation matrix S which is *unitary*. If A is an operator and ψ a state function in one representation, then

$$A' = SAS^{-1}$$

and

$$\psi' = S\psi$$

give the operator matrix and state function in the new representation. The matrix S is obtained from the expansion of the old basis functions in terms of the new, and represents a kind of rigid rotation in Hilbert space.

The matrix for the compound operator $A^m B^n$ may be obtained simply from the matrices for A and B by matrix multiplication.

In the representation provided by the eigenfunctions of the Hamiltonian of the one-dimensional harmonic oscillator, the matrices for X and P_x are off diagonal by one.

It is possible to define for the linear harmonic oscillator useful non-Hermitian operators a and $a^\dagger$, called the *demotion* and *promotion* operators, respectively, which have the properties

$$a\,|v\rangle = \sqrt{v}\,|v - 1\rangle$$
$$a^\dagger\,|v\rangle = \sqrt{v + 1}\,|v + 1\rangle$$

Using these operators and the assertion that $p^2/2m + \frac{1}{2}kx^2$ must be positive, it is possible to derive all the matrices associated with the harmonic oscillator without ever solving explicitly Schrödinger's equation to obtain explicit eigenfunctions. Knowing these matrices, all required expectation values (scalar products) may be calculated, again by matrix multiplication.

Problems

6.1 Prove that if A is Hermitian and S is unitary then

$$A' = SAS^{-1}$$

is also Hermitian.

6.2 Prove that the trace of a matrix is invariant under a unitary transformation, that is,

$$\mathrm{Tr}\,SBS^{-1} = \mathrm{Tr}\,B$$

6.3   Consider the unitary matrix S and the vectors $\mathbf{F}_1$ and $\mathbf{F}_2$. Prove that

$$\langle \mathbf{F}_1 \mid \mathbf{F}_2 \rangle = \langle \mathbf{F}_1' \mid \mathbf{F}_2' \rangle$$

where $\mathbf{F}_1' = S\mathbf{F}_1$ and $\mathbf{F}_2' = S\mathbf{F}_2$

6.4   If A and B are Hermitian prove that
   a AB is not generally Hermitian.
   b $AB + BA$ is Hermitian.
   c $AB - BA$ is not Hermitian, and in fact has purely imaginary eigenvalues.

6.5   Obtain by matrix methods alone $\langle x \rangle$, $\langle p \rangle$, and Δp for the simple harmonic oscillator superposition state

$$\Psi(x,t) = \frac{1}{2}\Psi_3(x,t) + \frac{1}{\sqrt{2}}\Psi_4(x,t) + \frac{1}{2}\Psi_5(x,t)$$

Compare (mentally) the amount of effort required to obtain these results by matrix methods with the amount involved in direct Schrödinger sandwich calculations.

6.6   Write the matrices for E and X for the two-dimensional isotropic harmonic oscillator. Note that the basis functions are now product wave functions.

6.7   Do Prob. 5.7 by matrix techniques.

6.8   Consider the two-dimensional harmonic oscillator whose Hamiltonian is

$$H = \frac{p_x^2}{2m} + \frac{1}{2}kx^2 + \frac{p_y^2}{2m} + \frac{1}{2}ky^2$$

   a   Write this Hamiltonian in terms of the promotion and demotion operators a_1, $a_1^\dagger$, a_2 and $a_2^\dagger$, where the subscripts 1 and 2 refer to the x and y coordinates, respectively.
   b   Write the angular-momentum operator

$$L_z = XP_y - YP_x$$

in terms of the promotion and demotion operators.
   c   Prove (in the matrix notation) that L_z commutes with the Hamiltonian.
   d   What do we now know about the eigenfunctions of L_z?
   e   In Sec. 5.6 we showed that the eigenfunctions of the two-dimensional harmonic oscillator belonging to the eigenenergy

$$E = (n + 1)\hbar\omega$$

where $n = n_1 + n_2$ were $(n + 1)$-fold degenerate and could be written

$$\psi_{n_1,n_2}(x,y) = \psi_{n_1}(x)\psi_{n_2}(y)$$

Denote the above wave function by $|n_1,n_2\rangle$. Consider the two eigenfunctions $|0,1\rangle$ and $|1,0\rangle$ belonging to the first excited state ($n = 1$) of the oscillator. Are they eigenfunctions of L_z? Document your answer by showing the result of operating on these wave functions with L_z (in $a_1,a_1^\dagger$ and $a_2,a_2^\dagger$ form).
   f   Reconcile the answers obtained for parts **d** and **e** above.

Bibliography

Useful references on linear algebra and matrices in general are:

Nering, E. D.: "Linear Algebra and Matrix Theory," John Wiley & Sons, Inc., New York, 1963.

Braae, R.: "Matrix Algebra for Electrical Engineers," Addison-Wesley Publishing Company, Inc., Reading Mass., 1963.

The matrix formulation of quantum mechanics is treated in—

Rojansky, V. B.: "Introductory Quantum Mechanics," chaps. 9 and 10, Prentice-Hall, Inc., Englewood Cliffs, N.J., 1938.

Schiff, L. I.: "Quantum Mechanics," 2nd ed., chap. 6, McGraw-Hill Book Company, New York, 1955.

Louisell, W. H.: "Radiation and Noise in Quantum Mechanics," chap. 1, McGraw-Hill Book Company, New York, 1964.

Dicke, R. H., and J. P. Wittke: "Introduction to Quantum Mechanics," chap. 11, Addison-Wesley Publishing Company, Inc., Reading, Mass., 1960.

Messiah, A.: "Quantum Mechanics," vol. 1, chap. 7, Interscience Publishers, Inc., New York, 1961.

Bohm, D.: "Quantum Theory," chap. 16, Prentice-Hall, Inc., Englewood Cliffs, N.J., 1951.

Merzbacher, E.: "Quantum Mechanics," chap. 14, John Wiley & Sons, Inc., New York, 1961.

The harmonic oscillator is treated in matrix form in—

Messiah, A.: "Quantum Mechanics," vol. 1, chap. 12, Interscience Publishers, Inc., New York, 1961.

Merzbacher, E.: "Quantum Mechanics," chap. 15, sec. 7, John Wiley & Sons, Inc., New York, 1961.

Louisell, W. H.: "Radiation and Noise in Quantum Electronics," part 1, chap. 2, McGraw-Hill Book Company, New York, 1964.

CHAPTER 7

The Uncertainty Principle, Momentum Representation, and Wave Packets

7.1 THE UNCERTAINTY PRINCIPLE: FORMAL PROOF The harmonic oscillator eigenfunctions displayed the property of having a nonvanishing uncertainty product

$$\Delta x \, \Delta p_x = (n + \tfrac{1}{2})\hbar \tag{7.1}$$

which has a minimum value of $\hbar/2$. The existence of this minimum uncertainty product, while not peculiar to quantum mechanics, is certainly one of the best known and most highly advertised features of quantum mechanics. It is also perhaps one of the most widely misunderstood features of quantum mechanics. Before launching our formal discussion of the uncertainty principle, we wish first to point out that the existence of the uncertainty product does *not* remove causality from quantum mechanics. The Schrödinger equation predicts exactly the evolution with time of $\Psi(\mathbf{r},t)$, given $\Psi(\mathbf{r},t_0)$, and hence predicts exactly the evolution with time of expectation values. The uncertainty principle does limit the precision with which certain observables can be simultaneously determined.

The uncertainty principle can be demonstrated in a form which is independent of the particular eigenfunctions or state functions involved. The proof of the existence of a minimum uncertainty product commences with Schwarz's inequality:

$$\int |f|^2 \, d\tau \int |g|^2 \, d\tau \geq \left| \int f^* g \, d\tau \right|^2 \tag{7.2}$$

where f and g are any two functions and the integral is over all variables in the arguments of f and g. We shall not prove this inequality; we shall treat it as intuitively obvious. The equivalent theorem in three-dimensional vector space would be

$$(\mathbf{V}_1 \cdot \mathbf{V}_1)(\mathbf{V}_2 \cdot \mathbf{V}_2) \geq (\mathbf{V}_1 \cdot \mathbf{V}_2)^2 \tag{7.3}$$

whose validity is apparent. We may also see in the simple three-dimensional case that the equality sign (rather than the "greater than" sign) holds only if $V_2 = \lambda V_1$, that is, if one vector is a scalar multiple of the other. The equivalent condition holds for the more general form of Schwarz's inequality.

$$\left(\int |f|^2 \, d\tau \right) \left(\int |g|^2 \, d\tau \right) = \left| \int f^*g \, d\tau \right|^2 \tag{7.4}$$

only if
$$g = \lambda f$$

Let now

$$f = (Q - \langle q \rangle)\psi \qquad g = (P - \langle p \rangle)\psi \tag{7.5}$$

where Q is the operator associated with a generalized coordinate and P is the operator associated with a generalized momentum which may or may not be the momentum conjugate to Q. Schwarz's inequality then becomes

$$(\Delta q)^2 (\Delta p)^2 \geq \left| \int \psi^*(Q - \langle q \rangle)(P - \langle p \rangle)\psi \, d\tau \right|^2 \tag{7.6}$$

We may rewrite the integrand of Eq. (7.6) as

$$\int \psi^*(QP - \langle q \rangle P - \langle p \rangle Q + \langle p \rangle \langle q \rangle)\psi \, d\tau = \int \psi^*[\tfrac{1}{2}(QP + PQ)$$

$$- \langle q \rangle P - \langle p \rangle Q + \langle p \rangle \langle q \rangle]\psi \, d\tau + \int \psi^* \tfrac{1}{2}(QP - PQ)\psi \, d\tau \tag{7.7}$$

The operator in square brackets is Hermitian (the reader should verify that $QP + PQ$ is Hermitian if P and Q are Hermitian, though QP and PQ separately are not), so its expectation value must be real. Call this bracketed operator F and its expectation value $\langle f \rangle$. Schwarz's inequality has now become

$$(\Delta q)^2 (\Delta p)^2 \geq |\langle f \rangle + \tfrac{1}{2}\langle [Q,P] \rangle|^2 \tag{7.8}$$

where $\langle f \rangle$ is real, and may be zero for some ψ.

If Q and P are canonically conjugate variables,

$$[Q,P] = i\hbar \tag{7.9}$$

and
$$(\Delta q)^2 (\Delta p)^2 \geq \langle f \rangle^2 + \frac{\hbar^2}{4} \geq \frac{\hbar^2}{4} \tag{7.10}$$

or
$$(\Delta q)(\Delta p) \geq \frac{\hbar}{2} \tag{7.11}$$

The uncertainty product $\Delta q \, \Delta p$ has a minimum value no matter what ψ may be.

The minimum uncertainty-product arises ultimately from the failure of Q and P to commute. The proof above may, in fact, be generalized to any two observables a and b with the result

$$(\Delta a)(\Delta b) \geq \tfrac{1}{2} |\langle [A,B] \rangle| \tag{7.12}$$

If the operators A and B (or Q and P) commute, the uncertainty product $\Delta a \, \Delta b$ may vanish, though it does not necessarily do so for all ψ.

7.2 MOMENTUM EIGENFUNCTIONS, THE MOMENTUM REPRESENTA-TION, AND THE UNCERTAINTY PRINCIPLE   The significance of the uncertainty principle and its physical interpretation can be illuminated by considering the relation between some Schrödinger wave function $\psi(\mathbf{r})$ and the representation of that same state function in the eigenfunctions of the momentum operator P. We recall from Chap. 3 that the eigenvalue equation for the momentum operator may be written

$$\frac{\hbar}{i} \nabla u(\mathbf{r}) = \mathbf{p} u(\mathbf{r}) \tag{7.13}$$

We have written Eq. (7.13) as a vector equation; it might equally well have been written as three scalar equations in the three orthogonal components of $\mathbf{p}$. An obviously satisfactory solution of the eigenvalue equation is

$$u(\mathbf{r}) = e^{(i/\hbar)\mathbf{p} \cdot \mathbf{r}} \tag{7.14}$$

The eigenfunctions of the momentum operator obviously are a continuous set, since the function of Eq. (7.14) is a satisfactory solution of the eigenvalue equation [Eq. (7.13)] for any arbitrary value of $\mathbf{p}$. The function $u(\mathbf{r})$ is not normalized as written, and in fact we come to grief if we attempt to arrive at a normalization constant by the straightforward calculation of $\int u^*(\mathbf{r}) \, u(\mathbf{r}) \, d\mathbf{r} = \int 1 \, d\mathbf{r}$ over all space. We shall normalize the momentum eigenfunction immediately after the next paragraphs through use of the irregular δ function touched upon earlier in Sec. 3.5. If the reader is uneasy about the appearance of this difficulty, he may draw some solace from the observation that there exists an exact analog in electromagnetic theory in the plane wave, which if extended through all space must contain infinite energy unless of vanishing amplitude. The difficulty is in both cases purely formalistic rather than real, since realizable state functions are not going to have appreciable amplitude throughout all space any more than real electromagnetic plane waves will extend undiminished to infinity in all directions. Both the momentum eigenfunction and the infinite plane wave are limiting cases of an idealized concept, very useful for many analytic purposes, but not truly realizable states.

Ignoring for the moment our normalization problem, let us expand some arbitrary state function $\psi(\mathbf{r})$ in the eigenfunctions $u(\mathbf{r})$ of Eq. (7.14).

$$\psi(\mathbf{r}) = \int_0^\infty c(\mathbf{p})e^{(i/\hbar)\mathbf{p}\cdot\mathbf{r}}d\mathbf{p} \tag{7.15}$$

where the integral is over all momentum space—all directions and magnitudes of $\mathbf{p}$. The expansion coefficients $c(\mathbf{p})$, now a continuous function of $\mathbf{p}$, are given as usual by the projection of the eigenfunction $u(\mathbf{r})$ upon the state function $\psi(\mathbf{r})$.

$$c(\mathbf{p}) = \int_0^\infty \psi(\mathbf{r})e^{-(i/\hbar)\mathbf{p}\cdot\mathbf{r}}\,d\mathbf{r} \tag{7.16}$$

An examination of Eqs. (7.15) and (7.16) reveals that $\psi(\mathbf{r})$ and $c(\mathbf{p})$ are almost, but not quite, Fourier transforms of each other. They fail of being accurate Fourier transforms of each other only by a multiplicative constant involving 2π and $\hbar$. If we redefine our eigenfunctions slightly by introducing the multiplicative constant $(2\pi\hbar)^{-3/2}$ (which does not destroy their status as eigenfunctions of the momentum operator),

$$u'(\mathbf{r}) = (2\pi\hbar)^{-3/2}e^{(i/\hbar)\mathbf{p}\cdot\mathbf{r}} \tag{7.17}$$

we arrive at a function $\varphi(\mathbf{p})$ which plays the same role as the expansion coefficient $c(\mathbf{p})$ but which is now also the exact Fourier transform of $\psi(\mathbf{r})$:

$$\begin{aligned}\psi(\mathbf{r}) &= (2\pi\hbar)^{-3/2}\int_0^\infty \varphi(\mathbf{p})e^{(i/\hbar)\mathbf{p}\cdot\mathbf{r}}\,d\mathbf{p} \\ \varphi(\mathbf{p}) &= (2\pi\hbar)^{-3/2}\int_0^\infty \psi(\mathbf{r})e^{-(i/\hbar)\mathbf{p}\cdot\mathbf{r}}\,d\mathbf{r}\end{aligned} \tag{7.18}$$

$\varphi(\mathbf{p})$ is the transform of $\psi(\mathbf{r})$ into momentum space. $\psi(\mathbf{r})$ is called the *state function in configuration space*, and $\varphi(\mathbf{p})$ is called the *state function in momentum space*, or the *state function in the momentum representation*. The product $\varphi^*(\mathbf{p})\varphi(\mathbf{p})$ is a probability density in momentum space; it is the probability of finding the system with momentum between $\mathbf{p}$ and $\mathbf{p} + d\mathbf{p}$. The state function is specified completely by either $\psi(\mathbf{r})$ or $\varphi(\mathbf{p})$; all the information implicitly contained in one representation is equally contained in the other. In particular, the statistical spread $\Delta\mathbf{r}$ in the probability density $\psi^*(\mathbf{r})\,\psi(\mathbf{r})$ in configuration space implies unambiguously the statistical spread $\Delta\mathbf{p}$ of the probability density $\varphi^*(\mathbf{p})\varphi(\mathbf{p})$ in momentum space. The two quantities are interrelated through the Fourier transform and therefore may not be independently specified. This necessary interrelation underlies the uncertainty principle, which is simply a statement of the interdependence of $\Delta \mathbf{p}$ and $\Delta \mathbf{r}$.

Let us illustrate the connection between $\Delta \mathbf{r}$ and $\Delta \mathbf{p}$ by looking at these quantities for a few simple state functions. Consider first a system known to have a momentum of exactly $\mathbf{p_0}$. The state function is then the momentum eigenfunction belonging to the eigenvalue $\mathbf{p_0}$,

$$\psi(\mathbf{r}) = A_0 e^{(i/\hbar)\mathbf{p_0} \cdot \mathbf{r}} \tag{7.19}$$

where A_0 is our elusive normalization constant which we are finally about to determine. The transform of the $\psi(\mathbf{r})$ into momentum space is

$$\varphi(\mathbf{p}) = (2\pi\hbar)^{-3/2} A_0 \int e^{(i/\hbar)\mathbf{p_0} \cdot \mathbf{r}} e^{(-i/\hbar)\mathbf{p} \cdot \mathbf{r}} d\mathbf{r}$$

$$= (2\pi\hbar)^{-3/2} A_0 \int e^{(i/\hbar)(\mathbf{p_0} - \mathbf{p}) \cdot \mathbf{r}} d\mathbf{r}$$

$$= (2\pi\hbar)^{+3/2} A_0 \, \delta(\mathbf{p_0} - \mathbf{p}) \tag{7.20}$$

where $\delta(\mathbf{p_0} - \mathbf{p})$ is the Dirac delta function having the property

$$\delta(\mathbf{p_0} - \mathbf{p}) = \begin{cases} 0 & \text{if } \mathbf{p} \neq \mathbf{p_0} \\ \infty & \text{if } \mathbf{p} = \mathbf{p_0} \end{cases} \tag{7.21}$$

$$\int_0^\infty \delta(\mathbf{p_0} - \mathbf{p}) \, d\mathbf{p} = 1$$

The momentum eigenfunction belonging to the eigenvalue $\mathbf{p_0}$ is represented in momentum space by a single point at momentum $\mathbf{p_0}$. This point has vanishingly small extent, so for this state $\Delta \mathbf{p} = 0$. The normalization of the state function in momentum space requires that

$$A_0 = (2\pi\hbar)^{-3/2} \tag{7.22}$$

since the area under the delta function is itself unity. We have normalized our state function through the back door, as it were, and henceforth write our momentum eigenfunctions, normalized, as

$$u'(\mathbf{r}) = (2\pi\hbar)^{-3/2} e^{(i/\hbar)\mathbf{p} \cdot \mathbf{r}} \tag{7.17}$$

The normalization constant turns out to be just that constant required to make $u'(\mathbf{r})$ the proper basis functions for our Fourier transform expansion.

As remarked above, $\Delta \mathbf{p}$ for this state is zero. Let us look, on the other hand, at $\Delta \mathbf{r}$. Now

$$\psi^*(\mathbf{r})\psi(\mathbf{r}) = (2\pi\hbar)^{-3} e^{-(i/\hbar)\mathbf{p_0} \cdot \mathbf{r}} e^{+(i/\hbar)\mathbf{p_0} \cdot \mathbf{r}}$$

$$= (2\pi\hbar)^{-3} \tag{7.23}$$

so the probability density in configuration space is a constant, independent of $\mathbf{r}$. We have no more expectation of finding the particle in one place than in any other. The uncertainty in $\mathbf{r}$ is $\Delta\mathbf{r} = \infty$. By confining our state function to an arbitrarily small region in $\mathbf{p}$ space, we have caused it to be spread out indefinitely in configuration space. Similarly, if we were to consider the state function $\psi(\mathbf{r}) = \delta(\mathbf{r} - \mathbf{r_0})$, placing the particle at $\mathbf{r_0}$ with $\Delta\mathbf{r} = 0$, we would find that the transform into $\mathbf{p}$ space was a constant function spread equally throughout momentum space, giving $\Delta\mathbf{p} = \infty$.

Rather than considering further these somewhat pathological cases involving delta functions and uniform distributions, let us look at some finite, localized distribution corresponding more closely to physically realizable state functions. In Fig. 7.1 are drawn several one-dimensional state functions, probability amplitudes, in both configuration space and momentum space. Since the Fourier transform is reciprocal, we may

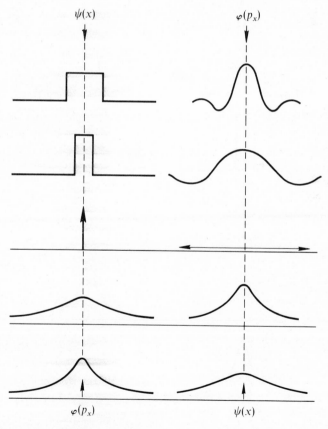

Fig. 7.1 *Corresponding probability amplitudes in configuration space and in momentum space.*

regard the left-hand column as the state function in configuration space $\psi(x)$ and the right-hand column as the state function $\varphi(p_x)$ in momentum space, or we may equally well regard the left-hand column as a possible $\varphi(p_x)$ and the right-hand column as the corresponding $\psi(x)$. The column labels at the top and at the bottom of the figure correspond, respectively, to these two interpretations. In Fig. 7.2 are drawn the corresponding probability densities in configuration space and in momentum space. The first three state functions are rectangular distributions of different width with their Fourier transforms, $\sin \pi x / \pi x$; the last two functions are exponential functions of different width with their Fourier transforms, which are also exponential functions. Note that in all cases a narrowing of one function implies a spreading out of its transform. Localization in x space implies delocalization in p_x space.

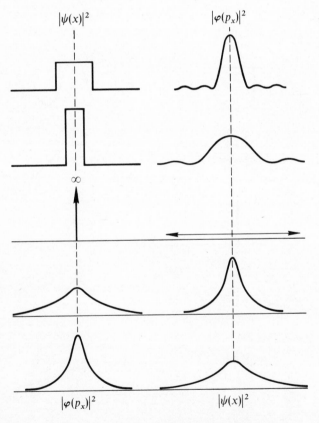

Fig. 7.2 *Corresponding probability densities in configuration space and in momentum space.*

Such a transform relation between variables occurs in many other instances in science and engineering, and the reader has undoubtedly encountered this relation in many guises. Perhaps the most familiar is the relation between the *time* distribution of an electromagnetic signal and the *spectral* (frequency) distribution of the same signal.

Consider a signal absolutely monochromatic at f_0. Such a spectral distribution can be accomplished only by a continuous wave of constant amplitude extending from $t = -\infty$ to $t = +\infty$. Varying the signal amplitude or cutting it off at any time other than $\pm\infty$ introduces sidebands into the spectrum, in violation of the assumption of pure monochromaticity. Conversely, if a signal is highly localized in time—a short pulse of radiation—its spectral distribution is very broad, containing many frequencies. In amplifier design we know that the bandpass of the amplifier determines the minimum width of a pulsed signal which the amplifier can handle without excessive degradation of form. The frequency "representation" and the time "representation" of the electromagnetic radiation are interconnected by precisely the same Fourier transform relation which interconnects coordinate and momentum representation in quantum mechanics:

$$F(\omega) = \frac{1}{(2\pi)^{1/2}} \int_{-\infty}^{+\infty} f(t)e^{-i\omega t}\, dt$$

$$f(t) = \frac{1}{(2\pi)^{1/2}} \int_{-\infty}^{+\infty} F(\omega)e^{+i\omega t}\, d\omega \tag{7.24}$$

Suppose we have an oscillator whose characteristic frequency is ω_0 and which is excited in such a fashion as to give out a pulse of gaussian shape. We can write the expression for the oscillator's output as a function of time as

$$E(t) = \exp\left[-\frac{(t-t_0)^2}{2(\Delta t)^2}\right]e^{i\omega_0 t} \tag{7.25}$$

The pulse of radiation is centered at $t = t_0$ and has a spread in time of Δt measured at the half-amplitude points of the pulse. If we calculate the spectral distribution of this same signal, we find

$$E(\omega) = \frac{1}{(2\pi)^{1/2}} \int_{-\infty}^{+\infty} E(t)e^{-i\omega t}\, dt$$

$$= \frac{1}{(2\pi)^{1/2}} \int_{-\infty}^{+\infty} \exp\left[-\frac{(t-t_0)^2}{2(\Delta t)^2}\right]\exp\left[i(\omega_0 - \omega)t\right] dt$$

$$= \frac{1}{\Delta t}\exp\left[\frac{(\Delta t)^2(\omega_0 - \omega)^2}{2}\right]e^{i\omega_0 t_0}e^{-i\omega t_0} \tag{7.26}$$

We see that $E(\omega)$ is a gaussian distribution of frequencies centered about $\omega = \omega_0$ and with a spectral spread

$$\Delta\omega = \frac{1}{\Delta t} \qquad (7.27)$$

If Eq. (7.27) is rewritten as

$$\Delta\omega\,\Delta t = 1 \qquad (7.28)$$

we have an expression greatly resembling Heisenberg's uncertainty principle. If we make the literal substitution $E = \hbar\omega$ into Eq. (7.28), we obtain $\Delta E\,\Delta t = \hbar$, suggesting that time and energy somehow play the role of conjugate, noncommuting operators in quantum mechanics. This is indeed the case. Before discussing this point, let us note, however, that we have in Eq. (7.28) an "uncertainty product" occurring in a purely classical situation.

Time is not an observable in nonrelativistic quantum mechanics [in the sense that $\langle t \rangle$ is calculated from Eq. (3.42)], but time is a parameter. Nonetheless, the operators "multiply by t" and "take the derivative with respect to t" are fully defined. The commutator of the above operators is clearly nonzero, and we can in fact make the following sequence of associations. First we have the commutation relation, verifiable by direct calculations,

$$\left[t, \frac{\hbar}{i}\frac{\partial}{\partial t}\right] = i\hbar \qquad (7.29)$$

From Postulate 4 connecting the Hamiltonian with the time derivative, we have

$$[t, -H] = i\hbar \qquad (7.30)$$

and, finally, from the identification of the Hamiltonian with the total energy of the system, we may write

$$[t, -E] = i\hbar \qquad (7.31)$$

Given this commutation rule, the derivation of the uncertainty relation given earlier yields

$$\Delta t\,\Delta E \geq \frac{\hbar}{2} \qquad (7.32)$$

the quantum-mechanical analog of Eq. (7.28)

The physical interpretation of Eq. (7.32) may be stated as follows: If only a finite time Δt is devoted to the measurement of the energy of a system, a finite uncertainty ΔE is introduced into the measurement of the energy E. The *exact* measurement of the energy of an eigenstate of the harmonic oscillator, for instance, would require the infinite time for which the state is stationary. (For a more detailed discussion of this point, the reader is referred to the excellent discussion in Messiah, "Quantum Mechanics," vol. 1, pp. 135–138 and 319–320.)

7.3 MEASUREMENT AND THE UNCERTAINTY PRINCIPLE In the entire discussion of the uncertainty principle so far, no mention has been made of the interaction of measuring apparatus with the quantum system involved. Just as it is not necessary to discuss the bandwidth of the spectrum analyzer nor the sweep rate of the display scheme to understand the relation between spectral width and temporal distribution of radio signals, so also is it not necessary to discuss the properties of the quantum-mechanical detectors to understand the relation between Δp and Δx. As long as a spatial distribution of probability is connected to a momentum distribution of probability by a transform relation, the uncertainty product $\Delta p \, \Delta x$ can be calculated for any state function without reference to the proposed apparatus for measuring p or x. Two observables p and q will be connected by a Fourier transform relation whenever $[Q,P] = i\hbar$, because a satisfactory set of operators for such a noncommuting pair will always be q and $\dfrac{\hbar}{i} \dfrac{\partial}{\partial q}$ with eigenfunctions of the form $e^{(i/\hbar)pq}$. If the observables commute, as do, say, x and p_z (or p_y), there is not a transform relation between the state function in x space and the state function in p_z (or p_y) space; the distribution in x space does not explicitly determine the state function and probability distribution in p_z space, and no minimum uncertainty-product $\Delta x \, \Delta p_z$ is implied.

The reader may find surprising or disturbing the statements immediately above in which it is asserted that the uncertainty product for any state can be exactly calculated without any reference to proposed measuring apparatus. He has probably been introduced to the uncertainty principle at some earlier stage of his education by a quite different route, namely, through a discussion of several experimental schemes for measuring simultaneously two conjugate variables, such as x and p_x. Typically, a number of schemes are proposed which appear to have promise of violating the uncertainty principle, and all are shown to fail of this objective because of their interaction with the measured system. In the absence of any successful schemes for violating the uncertainty principle, the principle is taken to be universally applicable. The student is left with the suspicion that all that has been demonstrated is insufficient cleverness in devising an experiment.

We wish to show now that although the system perturbations during measurement have not been overtly introduced into the development of the previous section, it is nonetheless this interaction with the measuring system which is the physical mechanism underlying the uncertainty principle. The essential point is that if there were not a minimum interaction between measuring system and measured system, there would not exist the transform relation between momentum and coordinate representation.

The minimum interaction between systems is measured by $\hbar$, which has the dimensions of action. If we were to allow this minimum interaction to become arbitrarily small, formally equivalent to making $\hbar$ arbitrarily small, conjugate variables would fail to commute by an increasingly smaller amount. In the limit that $\hbar \to 0$, conjugate variables would commute, we could not make the derivative operator associations we now make, and the mathematical framework of quantum mechanics, including the transform relations, would collapse. The quantum interaction of measuring apparatus and measuring system is plugged into the formulation of quantum mechanics with the postulating of the commutation relations of Eq. (3.11). It is therefore true that the uncertainty principle has its roots in the finite interaction between the subject system and the measurement apparatus.

The making of a measurement upon a system has a profound effect upon the state function over and above any minimum interaction and uncertainty effects. The state function is, in the last analysis, a statement of our knowledge concerning a system, and we alter that state of knowledge by making a measurement. If we measure at t_0 the value of an observable A for a system (obtaining by Postulate 2 an eigenvalue a_n of the associated operator), and then make a second measurement immediately thereafter upon the same system, we will always obtain, within the precision of our measuring apparatus, the same value for the observable. The result obtained for the first measurement might be any one of the values consistent with the state function of the system at the time of the first measurement; the result of the second measurement is determined by the first. It is in this sense that we say the measurement "forces" a new state function on the system.

If the second measurement follows the first by some finite interval of time, we cannot be so specific about the expected result of the second measurement. The state function will have evolved since the measurement according to $H\Psi = -\dfrac{\hbar}{i}\dfrac{\partial\Psi}{\partial t}$, and we must consider the statistical properties of an ensemble of systems, all of which have been subjected to a common preparative treatment: the measurement of observable A at time t_0 with the result a_n. As the wave function evolves with time, the observable A will develop a statistical spread of eigenvalues which might be obtained from a measurement, and we can no longer expect to obtain unambiguously the value a_n.

7.4   THE MINIMUM UNCERTAINTY WAVE PACKET   The harmonic oscillator eigenfunctions all displayed an uncertainty product greater than $\hbar/2$, except the ground state. The general proof of the uncertainty principle of Sec. 7.1 showed that the uncertainty product was in general *equal to* or *greater than $\hbar/2$*. Let us ask the question "What sort of wave function is associated with the minimum uncertainty product?"

We may extract a minimum uncertainty wave function from the same expressions used in the formal proof of the uncertainty principle of Sec. 7.1. Referring to that section, we observe that the uncertainty product was shown to be

$$(\Delta q)^2 (\Delta p)^2 \geq \langle f \rangle^2 + \frac{\hbar^2}{4} \tag{7.10}$$

The uncertainty product can take on its minimum value only if (1) the equality rather than the inequality sign holds in Schwarz's inequality, and (2) the expectation value $\langle f \rangle = 0$. As was remarked in Sec. 7.1, the condition under which Schwarz's inequality becomes an equality is that the two functions involved differ only by a scalar multiplier. For the uncertainty product, we may write this condition [combining Eqs. (7.4) and (7.5)] as

$$(P - \langle p \rangle)\psi = \lambda (Q - \langle q \rangle)\psi \tag{7.33}$$

If we can choose λ such that $\langle f \rangle \equiv 0$, we may substitute this λ into Eq. (7.33) and have an equation which, solved for ψ, will yield a minimum uncertainty wave function. We therefore now seek that λ which will cause $\langle f \rangle = 0$. First we recall the definition of $\langle f \rangle$ [see Eq. (7.7)]:

$$\begin{aligned}
\langle f \rangle &= \langle \tfrac{1}{2}(QP + PQ) - \langle q \rangle P - \langle p \rangle Q + \langle p \rangle \langle q \rangle \rangle \\
&= \langle \tfrac{1}{2}(QP + PQ) - \langle p \rangle \langle q \rangle \rangle
\end{aligned} \tag{7.34}$$

Operating now on Eq. (7.33) from the left with $(P - \langle p \rangle)$ and taking expectation values, we obtain

$$\begin{aligned}
(\Delta p)^2 &= \lambda \langle (P - \langle p \rangle)(Q - \langle q \rangle) \rangle \\
&= \lambda \langle PQ - \langle p \rangle \langle q \rangle \rangle
\end{aligned} \tag{7.35}$$

or

$$\langle PQ - \langle p \rangle \langle q \rangle \rangle = \frac{(\Delta p)^2}{\lambda} \tag{7.36}$$

Operating on Eq. (7.33) from the left with $(Q - \langle q \rangle)$ and taking expectation values gives

$$\begin{aligned}
\langle (Q - \langle q \rangle)(P - \langle p \rangle) \rangle &= \lambda (\Delta q)^2 \\
\langle QP - \langle q \rangle \langle p \rangle \rangle &= \lambda (\Delta q)^2
\end{aligned} \tag{7.37}$$

Subtracting Eq. (7.37) from Eq. (7.36) yields

$$\langle QP - PQ \rangle = \lambda(\Delta q)^2 - \frac{1}{\lambda}(\Delta p)^2$$

$$i\hbar = \lambda(\Delta q)^2 - \frac{1}{\lambda}(\Delta p)^2 \qquad (7.38)$$

From which we obtain the information

$$\frac{1}{\lambda}(\Delta p)^2 = \lambda(\Delta q)^2 - i\hbar \qquad (7.39)$$

On the other hand, adding Eq. (7.37) and Eq. (7.36) gives

$$\langle QP + PQ - 2\langle p \rangle \langle q \rangle \rangle = \lambda(\Delta q)^2 + \frac{1}{\lambda}(\Delta p)^2$$

$$2\langle f \rangle = \lambda(\Delta q)^2 + \frac{1}{\lambda}(\Delta p)^2 \qquad (7.40)$$

Inserting now into Eq. (7.40) the value of $(\Delta p)^2/\lambda$ given by Eq. (7.39), we obtain

$$2\langle f \rangle = 2\lambda(\Delta q)^2 - i\hbar \qquad (7.41)$$

If, then, we choose λ such that

$$\lambda = \frac{i\hbar}{2(\Delta q)^2} \qquad (7.42)$$

we may be assured that $\langle f \rangle = 0$, and the second of our conditions for the minimum uncertainty product is fulfilled. Substituting this value of λ back into Eq. (7.33), we obtain as the equation to be solved to yield a minimum uncertainty wave function

$$(P - \langle p \rangle)\psi = \frac{i\hbar}{2(\Delta q)^2}(Q - \langle q \rangle)\psi \qquad (7.43)$$

Let us now solve this equation for ψ, particularizing to the one-dimensional case, where we will take the coordinate to be x and understand that by p we mean p_x. Equation (7.43) then becomes

$$\left(\frac{\hbar}{i}\frac{d}{dx} - \langle p \rangle\right)\psi(x) = \frac{i\hbar}{2(\Delta x)^2}(x - \langle x \rangle)\psi(x) \qquad (7.44)$$

This equation can be rearranged into the form

$$\frac{d}{dx}\psi(x) = \left(-\frac{x - \langle x \rangle}{2(\Delta x)^2} + \frac{i}{\hbar}\langle p \rangle\right)\psi(x) \qquad (7.45)$$

which can, in turn, be directly integrated to give

$$\psi(x) = c \exp\left[-\frac{(x - \langle x\rangle)^2}{4(\Delta x)^2} + \frac{i}{\hbar}\langle p\rangle x\right] \tag{7.46}$$

where the normalizing constant c is given by

$$c = [2\pi(\Delta x)^2]^{-\frac{1}{4}} \tag{7.47}$$

We have now our minimum uncertainty-product state function $\psi(x)$ given by Eq. (7.46). The associated probability density is

$$\psi^*(x)\psi(x) = [2\pi(\Delta x)^2]^{-\frac{1}{2}} \exp\left[-\frac{(x - \langle x\rangle)^2}{2(\Delta x)^2}\right] \tag{7.48}$$

The minimum uncertainty wave function gives a probability density which is a *gaussian distribution about $\langle x\rangle$ with a width* Δx. We note that the ground state of the harmonic oscillator had this same shape, and was therefore a minimum uncertainty wave function.

What is the probability distribution in momentum space corresponding to the minimum uncertainty wave function $\psi(x)$? This is easily computed:

$$\varphi(p) = \frac{1}{(2\pi\hbar)^{\frac{1}{2}}} \int_{-\infty}^{+\infty} \psi(x)e^{-(i/\hbar)px}\, dx$$

$$= \frac{c}{(2\pi\hbar)^{\frac{1}{2}}} \int_{-\infty}^{+\infty} \exp\left[-\frac{(x - \langle x\rangle)^2}{4(\Delta x)^2}\right] \exp\left[-\frac{i}{\hbar}(p - \langle p\rangle)x\right] dx$$

$$= \frac{c}{(2\pi\hbar)^{\frac{1}{2}}} \exp\left[-\frac{i}{\hbar}(p - \langle p\rangle)\langle x\rangle\right] \int_{-\infty}^{+\infty} \exp\left[-\frac{(x - \langle x\rangle)^2}{4(\Delta x)^2}\right]$$

$$\times \exp\left[-\frac{i}{\hbar}(p - \langle p\rangle)(x - \langle x\rangle)\right] d(x - \langle x\rangle)$$

$$= c' \exp\left[-\frac{i}{\hbar}(p - \langle p\rangle)\langle x\rangle\right] \exp\left[-(\Delta x)^2\left(\frac{p - \langle p\rangle}{\hbar}\right)^2\right] \tag{7.49}$$

where c' is again a normalizing constant. Remembering that $(\Delta x)^2 = \hbar^2/4(\Delta p)^2$ for the minimum uncertainty case, we may write $\varphi(p)$ in a form symmetric to $\psi(x)$:

$$\varphi(p) = c' \exp\left[-\frac{(p - \langle p\rangle)^2}{4(\Delta p)^2}\right] \exp\left[-\frac{i}{\hbar}(p - \langle p\rangle)\langle x\rangle\right] \tag{7.50}$$

where

$$c' = [2\pi(\Delta p)^2]^{-\frac{1}{4}} \tag{7.51}$$

The associated probability density in momentum space is

$$\varphi^*(p)\varphi(p) = [2\pi(\Delta p)^2]^{-\frac{1}{2}} \exp\left[-\frac{(p - \langle p\rangle)^2}{2(\Delta p)^2}\right] \tag{7.52}$$

The minimum uncertainty wave function gives a probability distribution in momentum space which is *gaussian about $\langle p \rangle$ with a width $\langle \Delta p \rangle$*.

The distributions in both momentum space and coordinate space are gaussian. The exact width Δx for the minimum uncertainty gaussian distribution is not specified. Width in coordinate space Δx and width in momentum space, Δp, may be traded off against each other without altering the uncertainty product if the probability distributions remain gaussian.

7.5 THE FREE PARTICLE We are now in a position to discuss the appropriate state function for a free particle. This state function must describe the motion of fairly localized probability density if it is to correspond to our knowledge of a particle's behavior in the classical limit.

First we note that the Hamiltonian of the free particle is

$$H = \frac{p^2}{2m} \tag{7.53}$$

Since this Hamiltonian commutes with the momentum $\mathbf{p}$, it must, by the theorems of Sec. 3.7, share eigenfunctions with the momentum operator:

$$\psi(\mathbf{r}) = A_p e^{(i/\hbar)\mathbf{p} \cdot \mathbf{r}} \tag{7.54}$$

We might, of course, obtain these same eigenfunctions from the solution of Schrödinger's equation for the free particle:

$$\frac{\hbar^2}{2m} \nabla^2 \Psi(\mathbf{r},t) = \frac{\hbar}{i} \frac{\partial}{\partial t} \Psi(\mathbf{r},t) \tag{7.55}$$

Schrödinger's equation is separable in $\mathbf{r}$ and t, with the solutions

$$\Psi(\mathbf{r},t) = A_p e^{(i/\hbar)\mathbf{p} \cdot \mathbf{r}} e^{-(i/\hbar)Et} \tag{7.56}$$

where
$$E = \frac{p^2}{2m} \tag{7.57}$$

and where A_p is a normalization constant. The eigenfunctions and eigenvalues form a continuous set, since any value of $\mathbf{p}$ gives a solution to the Schrödinger equation. These solutions have the form of plane waves of frequency $E/\hbar$ and propagation vector $\mathbf{k} = \mathbf{p}/\hbar$. Each eigenfunction belonging to a specific value of $\mathbf{p}$ ($\mathbf{p}_0$, for example) describes a state which is completely localized in momentum space but is completely delocalized in coordinate space. As we saw earlier in this chapter, the probability density $\psi^*(\mathbf{r}) \, \psi(\mathbf{r})$ is constant throughout space.

The plane-wave eigenfunctions of the free particle seem particularly unparticlelike in their behavior. Even if we can conquer the normalization problem by one artifice or another, the completely delocalized plane wave is the complete antithesis of the highly localized entity we think of as a particle.

Consider, however, the minimum uncertainty wave function

$$\psi(\mathbf{r}) = [2\pi(\Delta\mathbf{r})^2]^{-3/4} \exp\left[-\frac{(\mathbf{r} - \langle\mathbf{r}\rangle)^2}{4(\Delta\mathbf{r})^2}\right] \exp\left(\frac{i}{\hbar}\langle\mathbf{p}\rangle \cdot \mathbf{r}\right)$$

$$\varphi(\mathbf{p}) = [2\pi(\Delta\mathbf{p})^2]^{-3/4} \exp\left[-\frac{(\mathbf{p} - \langle\mathbf{p}\rangle)^2}{4(\Delta\mathbf{p})^2}\right] \exp\left[-\frac{i}{\hbar}(\mathbf{p} - \langle\mathbf{p}\rangle) \cdot \langle\mathbf{r}\rangle\right]$$

(7.58)

We see that $\psi(\mathbf{r})$ consists of a free particle (or momentum) eigenfunction multiplied by a function (of $\mathbf{r}$) of the form of a gaussian envelope. The probability density is localized in space, and the wave function vanishes at infinity, so is readily normalized. Looking at the momentum representation of this state, we see that it is built out of a package of momentum eigenfunctions, a package which is centered on $\langle\mathbf{p}\rangle$ and which weights the component members in a gaussian fashion as $\mathbf{p}$ departs from $\langle\mathbf{p}\rangle$.

Physically, the state function represents a highly localized particle moving with momentum $\langle\mathbf{p}\rangle$. This is exactly what we need to represent the free particle. It is a special case of the proper state function of a system being a linear superposition of eigenstates.

We may well ask if this is the only acceptable way to describe what we think of as a free particle, if this is the unique and only way to write a state function for a free particle. The answer is "no." We might well write other state functions of the same $\langle\mathbf{r}\rangle$, $\langle\mathbf{p}\rangle$, and $\Delta\mathbf{r}$, for instance, a rectangular probability density such as is drawn in the upper part of Fig. 7.1 or Fig. 7.2. This state function would embody our knowledge of the particle $\langle\mathbf{r}\rangle$, $\langle\mathbf{p}\rangle$, and $\Delta\mathbf{r}$, just as does the minimum uncertainty-packet of Eq. (7.58). The rectangular wave packet would, however, have a substantially greater $\Delta\mathbf{p}$ than would the gaussian packet. We would be introducing an unnecessary increment in uncertainty in our state function, and into our knowledge of the particle position at all subsequent times, simply because we chose a nonoptimum wave packet to describe the initial state. The minimum uncertainty state function of Eq. (7.58), also called a *Kennard packet*, is therefore the optimum state function for describing a particle, and is almost universally used to describe a particle.

We may make the particle arbitrarily well localized in space by making $\Delta\mathbf{r}$ as small as we wish (pass the particle through a very small hole), but we pay for the privilege by introducing an increased spread in the momentum eigenfunctions required to build the more localized particle. The spread in momentum eigenfunctions in the "wave packet" causes the packet to change its shape as time progresses. We may think, by analogy, of a group of runners who have a spread in the speeds at which they can run. Although the runners may be bunched at the start of the race, the fast runners will soon pull ahead and the slow ones fall behind, causing the bunch to spread out.

We can calculate the motion and spreading of the minimum wave packet with time. The superposition state (the wave packet), while not an eigenstate of the system, is still a solution of the time-dependent Schrödinger equation,

$$H\Psi = -\frac{\hbar}{i}\frac{\partial \Psi}{\partial t} \tag{7.59}$$

If we know Ψ at some time t_0, we can obtain its evolution with time by integrating Eq. (7.59) with respect to time. We will get a formal solution

$$\Psi(\mathbf{r},t) = \Psi(\mathbf{r},t_0)e^{-(i/\hbar)H(t-t_0)} \tag{7.60}$$

The expression of Eq. (7.60) contains an operator in the exponent, a situation we have not yet learned to handle. However, we can quickly learn all we need to know to handle this special case. To do this, let us return again to the subject of the momentum representation. We have observed repeatedly that there exists a function $\varphi(\mathbf{p})$ of momentum which is the transform into momentum space of the Schrödinger wave function $\psi(\mathbf{r})$ in coordinate space. We now observe that the operators of Eq. (3.12), which we used to form Schrödinger's equation, all have transforms into momentum representation, some of which are as follows:

Dynamical variable	Coordinate space operator		Momentum space operator
x	x	$\leftrightarrow$	$-\dfrac{\hbar}{i}\dfrac{\partial}{\partial p_x}$
p_x	$\dfrac{\hbar}{i}\dfrac{\partial}{\partial x}$	$\leftrightarrow$	p_x
$F(x)$	$F(x)$	$\leftrightarrow$	$F\left(-\dfrac{\hbar}{i}\dfrac{\partial}{\partial p_x}\right)$
$F(p_x)$	$F\left(\dfrac{\hbar}{i}\dfrac{\partial}{\partial x}\right)$	$\leftrightarrow$	$F(p_x)$
$\mathbf{p}$	$\dfrac{\hbar}{i}\nabla$	$\leftrightarrow$	$\mathbf{p}$
$\mathbf{p}^2$	$-\hbar^2\nabla^2$	$\leftrightarrow$	$\mathbf{p}^2$

$$(7.61)$$

The momentum space operators are Hermitian and obey the commutation rules of Eq. (3.11). We therefore now assert that the momentum space operators represent a completely satisfactory set of operators for association with dynamical variables, and that the Schrödinger equation in momentum representation will be

$$H_{op}\Phi(\mathbf{p},t) = -\frac{\hbar}{i}\frac{\partial}{\partial t}\Phi(\mathbf{p},t) \qquad (7.62)$$

where H_{op} is formed by the literal substitution of the momentum space operators of Eq. (7.61) into the classical Hamiltonian for the system. The entire Eq. (7.62) is the Fourier transform into momentum space of

$$H_{op}\Psi(\mathbf{r},t) = -\frac{\hbar}{i}\frac{\partial}{\partial t}\Psi(\mathbf{r},t) \qquad (7.63)$$

where H_{op} was formed using the operator associations of Eq. (3.12). It also follows from these statements that $\Psi(\mathbf{r},t)$ and $\Phi(\mathbf{p},t)$ are the Fourier transforms of each other, as well as $\psi(\mathbf{r})$ and $\varphi(\mathbf{p})$.

Using the momentum representation, we can quickly ascertain the time variation of the minimum uncertainty free-particle wave packet. The transform of Eq. (7.60) into momentum space is

$$\Phi(\mathbf{p},t) = \Phi(\mathbf{p},t_0) \exp\left[-\frac{i}{\hbar}H(t - t_0)\right] \qquad (7.64)$$

Now the Hamiltonian operator in momentum representation is simply $p^2/2m$, so we have

$$\Phi(\mathbf{p},t) = \Phi(\mathbf{p},0) \exp\left(-\frac{i}{\hbar}\frac{p^2}{2m}t\right) \qquad (7.65)$$

where we have taken $t_0 = 0$ for convenience. It follows from Eq. (7.65) that

$$\Phi^*(\mathbf{p},t)\Phi(\mathbf{p},t) = \Phi^*(\mathbf{p},0)\Phi(\mathbf{p},0) \qquad (7.66)$$

and the free-particle probability density *in the momentum representation* is invariant with time. We can now find $\Psi(\mathbf{r},t)$ by simply transforming $\Phi(\mathbf{p},t)$ into coordinate space.

$$\Psi(\mathbf{r},t) = \frac{c'}{(2\pi\hbar)^{3/2}}\int_0^\infty \exp\left[-\frac{(\mathbf{p} - \langle\mathbf{p}\rangle)^2}{4(\Delta p)^2} - \frac{i}{\hbar}(\mathbf{p} - \langle\mathbf{p}\rangle)\cdot\langle\mathbf{r}\rangle\right]$$
$$\times \exp\left(-\frac{i}{\hbar}\frac{p^2}{2m}t\right)\exp\left(\frac{i}{\hbar}\mathbf{p}\cdot\mathbf{r}\right)d\mathbf{p} \qquad (7.67)$$

To simplify a little the already cumbersome mathematics, we will take $\langle\mathbf{r}\rangle = 0$ at $t = 0$. This assumption is simply equivalent to taking the origin of coordinates at the center of the particle at $t = 0$, and we do not lose by such an assumption any features of the particle's subsequent behavior which are of physical interest. Taking $\langle \mathbf{r} \rangle = 0$ causes one substantial term in the first exponential to drop out. Making also the temporary notational simplification $\Delta \mathbf{p} = \mathbf{a}$, we rewrite the integral of Eq. (7.67), collecting like powers of $\mathbf{p}$:

$$\Psi(\mathbf{r},t) = \frac{c'}{(2\pi\hbar)^{3/2}} \int_0^\infty \exp\left[-\left(\frac{1}{4a^2} + \frac{i}{\hbar}\frac{t}{2m}\right)p^2\right]$$

$$\times \exp\left[\left(\frac{\langle\mathbf{p}\rangle}{2a^2} + \frac{i}{\hbar}\mathbf{r}\right)\cdot\mathbf{p}\right] \exp\left(-\frac{\langle\mathbf{p}\rangle^2}{4a^2}\right) d\mathbf{p} \quad (7.68)$$

The last term in the integrand is independent of $\mathbf{p}$ and may be brought outside the integral. We can complete the square in $\mathbf{p}$ in the integrand by multiplying the integrand by the $\mathbf{p}$-independent term $e^{-\beta^2}$ (and the whole integral by $e^{+\beta^2}$ to cancel this alteration), obtaining

$$\Psi(\mathbf{r},t) = \frac{c'\exp(-\langle\mathbf{p}\rangle^2/4a^2)e^{+\beta^2}}{(2\pi\hbar)^{3/2}} \int_0^\infty \exp\left[-(\alpha\mathbf{p} + \beta)^2\right] d\mathbf{p} \quad (7.69)$$

where
$$\alpha = \left(\frac{1}{4a^2} + \frac{i}{\hbar}\frac{t}{2m}\right)^{1/2}$$

$$\beta = -\frac{\left(\dfrac{\langle\mathbf{p}\rangle}{2a^2} + \dfrac{i}{\hbar}\mathbf{r}\right)}{2\alpha} \quad\quad (7.70)$$

If we denote $\lambda = \alpha\mathbf{p} + \beta$, we can reduce the integral to tabulated form:

$$\Psi(\mathbf{r},t) = \frac{c'}{(2\pi\hbar)^{3/2}} \exp\left(-\frac{\langle\mathbf{p}\rangle^2}{4a^2} + \beta^2\right)\frac{1}{\alpha} \int_0^\infty e^{-\lambda^2} d\lambda \quad (7.71)$$

The definite integral is equal to $(\pi/2)^{3/2}$, so

$$\Psi(\mathbf{r},t) = \binom{\text{normalizing}}{\text{consts.}} \alpha^{-1} \exp\left(-\frac{\langle\mathbf{p}\rangle^2}{4a^2} + \beta^2\right) \quad (7.72)$$

We can see that β^2 will contain terms in $\langle\mathbf{p}\rangle^2$, $\mathbf{r}^2$, and $i(\langle\mathbf{p}\rangle\cdot\mathbf{r})/\hbar$. If we make the substitutions of β and α back into Eq. (7.72) and carry out the rather substantial algebra of the collection and condensation of terms, we obtain ultimately

$$\Psi(\mathbf{r},t) = \frac{c''}{\hbar^3\left(\dfrac{1}{4a^2} + \dfrac{i}{\hbar}\dfrac{t}{2m}\right)^{3/2}} \exp\left[-\frac{\left(\mathbf{r} - \dfrac{\langle\mathbf{p}\rangle}{m}t\right)^2}{4\hbar^2\left(\dfrac{1}{4a^2} + \dfrac{i}{2\hbar}\dfrac{t}{m}\right)}\right]$$

$$\times \exp\left[\frac{i}{\hbar}\langle\mathbf{p}\rangle\cdot\left(\mathbf{r} - \frac{\langle\mathbf{p}\rangle}{2m}t\right)\right] \quad (7.73)$$

with the associated probability density

$$\Psi^*\Psi = \frac{(c'')^2}{\hbar^6\left[\left(\frac{1}{4a^2}\right)^2 + \left(\frac{t}{2\hbar m}\right)^2\right]^{3/2}} \exp\left\{-\frac{\left(\mathbf{r} - \frac{\langle \mathbf{p}\rangle}{m}t\right)^2}{8\hbar^2 a^2\left[\left(\frac{1}{4a^2}\right)^2 + \left(\frac{t}{2\hbar m}\right)^2\right]}\right\}$$

(7.74)

Recalling at this point that $a^2 = (\Delta \mathbf{q})^2$ and that $(\Delta \mathbf{r})^2 = \hbar^2/4a^2$ (since this is a minimum uncertainty-product wave function), we rewrite the probability density in configuration space for the free particle as

$$\Psi^*\Psi = \frac{(c'')}{\left[(\Delta \mathbf{r})^4 + \left(\frac{\hbar t}{2m}\right)^2\right]^{3/2}} \exp\left\{-\frac{\left(\mathbf{r} - \frac{\langle \mathbf{p}\rangle}{m}t\right)}{2\left[(\Delta \mathbf{r})^2 + \left(\frac{\hbar t}{2m(\Delta \mathbf{r})}\right)^2\right]}\right\}$$ (7.75)

These expressions look enormously cumbersome, but actually we can extract a great deal of information from a simple inspection of them. First, the packet remains gaussian in shape, as can be seen from Eq. (7.75), with a width which increases linearly with the time. We can write an effective width for a one-dimensional packet of

$$(\Delta x)_{\text{eff}} = \Delta x\left[1 + \left(\frac{\hbar t}{2m(\Delta x)^2}\right)^2\right]^{1/2}$$ (7.76)

Inasmuch as the distribution is broadening, the normalization constant must also contain a time-dependent term to lower the peak amplitude as the probability distribution spreads, preserving unity normalization. From either Eq. (7.73) or Eq. (7.75), we can see that the center of the wave packet moves with a velocity $\langle \mathbf{p}\rangle/m$, equal to the classical expression for **v**. This is the group velocity of the packet. The phase velocity may be obtained from the last periodic term in Eq. (7.73); and the phase velocity is seen to be $\langle \mathbf{p}\rangle/2m$, or one-half the group velocity.

It is well to remind ourselves that it is our knowledge of the particle's exact whereabouts which is degrading and spreading out, not the particle itself. If we make a subsequent (in time) measurement of the particle's position with a measuring apparatus having a very small $\langle \Delta x\rangle$, we will either catch a whole particle or none at all with our slit; we will not find that the particle has literally gotten fat and cannot "fit" through a small slit.

It is interesting to put some numbers into Eq. (7.76) for $(\Delta x)_{\text{eff}}$. The wave packet will be doubled in width when

$$\frac{\hbar}{m}\frac{t}{(\Delta x)^2} = 2\sqrt{3} \tag{7.77}$$

Now $\hbar$ and m for an electron are both approximately equal to 10^{-27} cgs units, so the time required for an electron to double its spread is given by

$$t(\text{sec}) \approx 3 \times (\Delta x \text{ in cm})^2 \tag{7.78}$$

An electron wave packet passed through a 10^{-3}-cm slit will double its spread in approximately 10^{-6} sec. An electron wave packet confined to a region of atomic dimensions, 10^{-8} cm, will double its Δx in some 10^{-16} sec. We can see immediately why the notion of an electron in planetary orbit cannot be carried over literally to the atomic case; the electron will spread out by an amount commensurate with the orbit length in the time required to complete one orbital revolution. The spreading formula of Eq. (7.76) cannot be applied literally to bound atomic cases for two reasons: Eq. (7.76) was derived for free particles only, and the expression is not correct in the relativistic limit. The order of magnitude of the answers obtained from Eq. (7.76) are, however, essentially correct, so the heuristic arguments about electron wave packets spreading out over an orbit in one cycle are valid. The construction of a wave packet and the computation of its properties are in general meaningful operations only for the free or nearly free particle.

Summary

Important points to remember from Chap. 7:

For any two observables p and q there exists a minimum uncertainty product $\Delta p \Delta q$ given by

$$(\Delta p)^2 (\Delta q)^2 \geq \tfrac{1}{4} |\langle [Q,P] \rangle|^2$$

The uncertainty product restricts the precision with which the expectation values $\langle p \rangle$ and $\langle q \rangle$ can simultaneously be measured or specified. If P and Q commute, the statistical variation of $\langle p \rangle$ and $\langle q \rangle$ may both be reduced to arbitrarily small quantities. If P and Q fail to commute, there is a lower limit on the product of uncertainties. If the statistical spread Δp is reduced, Δq is necessarily increased, and vice versa.

Any state function $\Psi(\mathbf{r},t)$ in configuration space has a completely equivalent state function $\Phi(\mathbf{p},t)$ which is its transform into momentum space. $\Phi(\mathbf{p},t)$ obeys a Schrödinger equation in momentum representation:

$$H_{op}\Phi(\mathbf{p},t) = -\frac{\hbar}{i}\frac{\partial}{\partial t}\Phi(\mathbf{p},t)$$

where H_{op} is constructed by the use of the appropriate operators in the momentum representation.

The uncertainty $\Delta\mathbf{r}$ associated with $\Psi(\mathbf{r},t)$ transforms unambiguously into the $\Delta\mathbf{p}$ associated with $\Phi(\mathbf{p},t)$ in momentum space, thus specifying entirely the uncertainty product associated with the state without reference to measuring equipment.

The minimum uncertainty-product state function has a gaussian distribution of probability density both in configuration space and in momentum space.

The minimum uncertainty-product wave function corresponding to a free particle moves with group velocity $\langle\mathbf{p}\rangle/m$ and phase velocity $\langle\mathbf{p}\rangle/2m$, spreading out with time as it proceeds. It is our knowledge of the particle's position which degrades with time (corresponding to a spreading of the probability density) not the particle itself. The particle will still pass through a small hole after an arbitrarily long time has elapsed.

Problems

7.1 Consider some general (superposition) state $\Psi(x,t)$ of a single particle in a one-dimensional square well of infinite depth and of width $2a$. Prove that Δp, the statistical uncertainty in momentum, is a constant independent of time for such a state.

7.2 As the result of a set of simultaneous measurements upon a number of one-dimensional simple harmonic oscillators of identical preparation and history, we know the expectation values $\langle x\rangle$ and $\langle p\rangle$, and the statistical spread in x, Δx, for the state characterizing the system. What is the minimum value that ΔE, the statistical spread in energy, may assume compatible with the $\langle x\rangle$, $\langle p\rangle$, and Δx already determined?

7.3 a Write Schrödinger's equation (including time) for the one-dimensional harmonic oscillator in the momentum representation, and separate this equation into the equation containing time and the time-independent Schrödinger equation.

b Write down a typical eigenfunction of the time-independent equation in the momentum representation. (You should be able to do this almost immediately from comparison with the x-representation case.)

c Write the matrix for H in the basis provided by the eigenfunctions obtained in part **b** above.

d Write the matrix for X in the basis provided by the eigenfunctions obtained in part **b** above.

7.4 Compute the expectation value $\langle f \rangle$ of the operator

$$F = \tfrac{1}{2}(QP + PQ) - \langle q \rangle P - \langle p \rangle Q + \langle p \rangle \langle q \rangle$$

for an eigenstate of the Hamiltonian of the one-dimensional harmonic oscillator.

7.5 A one-dimensional harmonic oscillator is known to be in its ground state when the spring suddenly snaps. Discuss the subsequent development with time of the state function, of $\langle x \rangle$, $\langle p \rangle$, Δx, and Δp.

7.6 Prove that a minimum uncertainty wave packet of the simple harmonic oscillator eigenstates moves in an oscillatory fashion about the zero-displacement position without change in width with time. This property is peculiar to the simple harmonic oscillator.

Bibliography

A useful reference on the Fourier transform, used extensively in this chapter is:

Bracewell, R.: "The Fourier Transform and Its Applications," McGraw-Hill Book Company, New York, 1965.

The uncertainty principle is discussed at great length in many books. Undoubtedly the most thorough discussion of measurement, the uncertainty principle, and the interpretation of quantum mechanics is:

Bohm, D.: "Quantum Theory," part 1, pp. 59–140, Prentice-Hall, Inc., Englewood Cliffs, N.J., 1951.

Good discussions occur also in:

Messiah, A.: "Quantum Mechanics," vol. 1, chap. 4, Interscience Publishers, Inc., New York, 1961.
Dicke, R. H., and J. P. Wittke: "Introduction to Quantum Mechanics," chap. 8, Addison-Wesley Publishing Company, Inc., Reading, Mass., 1960.
Merzbacher, E.: "Quantum Mechanics," chap. 8, John Wiley & Sons, Inc., New York, 1961.

CHAPTER 8

The Particle at a Potential Barrier or in a Potential Well

8.1 THE PARTICLE AT A RECTANGULAR POTENTIAL BARRIER To understand the quantum-mechanical behavior of real particles in real physical situations, it is useful to examine some simplified prototype situations. A real configuration can often be roughly approximated by some such simplified prototype model, and the general character of the solution quickly grasped through an understanding of the prototype case.

In particular, a number of situations of physical interest can be approximated by a model in which a particle moves from one region of constant potential into another region (or a succession of other regions) of different but still constant potential. We will therefore study in this chapter several prototype problems involving potential steps between regions of constant potential. The simplest such problem is that of a particle incident upon a rectangular potential barrier or step.

We will use the Schrödinger wave-mechanical formalism throughout this discussion since it lends itself so well to the visualization of the concepts involved. Let us start by refreshing our memory on what the wave functions look like for a free particle. We will find that these wave functions can be easily extrapolated to the particle in a constant potential region.

The free-particle Hamiltonian is

$$\frac{\hbar^2}{2m} \nabla^2 \Psi(\mathbf{r},t) = \frac{\hbar}{i} \frac{\partial}{\partial t} \Psi(\mathbf{r},t) \tag{8.1}$$

which has the eigenfunctions

$$\Psi(\mathbf{r},t) = e^{+(i/\hbar)\mathbf{p}\cdot\mathbf{r}} e^{-(i/\hbar)Et} \tag{8.2}$$

where

$$E = \frac{p^2}{2m} \tag{8.3}$$

We observed in the preceding chapter that these wave functions were not normalizable without tricks, and represented a probability distribution which was constant throughout space. In fact, these are plane-wave solutions, as can be readily seen by the substitutions

$$\mathbf{k} = \frac{\mathbf{p}}{\hbar} \tag{8.4}$$

and
$$\omega = \frac{E}{\hbar} \tag{8.5}$$

which throw the eigenfunctions into the form

$$\Psi^{\circ}(\mathbf{r},t) = e^{i(\mathbf{k}\cdot\mathbf{r}-\omega t)} \tag{8.6}$$

the classical plane-wave expression.

We further saw, however, that a gaussian packet of these plane waves of the form

$$\Psi^{\circ}(\mathbf{r},\, t = 0) = (2\pi\, \Delta\mathbf{r})^{-\frac{1}{4}} \exp\left[-\frac{(\mathbf{r} - \langle\mathbf{r}\rangle)^2}{4(\Delta\mathbf{r})^2}\right] \exp\left[\frac{i}{\hbar}(\langle\mathbf{p}\rangle\cdot\mathbf{r})\right] \tag{8.7}$$

with its momentum transform

$$\Phi(\mathbf{p},\, t = 0) = (2\pi\, \Delta\mathbf{p})^{-\frac{1}{4}} \exp\left[-\frac{(\mathbf{p} - \langle\mathbf{p}\rangle)^2}{4(\Delta\mathbf{p})^2}\right] \exp\left[-\frac{i}{\hbar}(\mathbf{p} - \langle\mathbf{p}\rangle)\cdot\mathbf{r}\right]$$
$$\tag{8.8}$$

gave at $t = 0$ a state function which had all the proper characteristics to represent a particle as we know it in the classical correspondence limit.

To calculate the behavior of a particle with time, we should, in principle, calculate the behavior of the whole packet as the time evolves. We did so for the free particle, and found that the momentum space distribution was constant with time but that the particle "spreads out" in real coordinate space. We can describe the behavior of a particle in a region of constant potential [$V(\mathbf{r}) = V$, for instance] by a very simple extension of our previous treatment. The Hamiltonian of the system is now

$$\left(\frac{\hbar^2}{2m}\nabla^2 - V\right)\Psi^{\circ}(\mathbf{r},t) = \frac{\hbar}{i}\frac{\partial}{\partial t}\Psi^{\circ}(\mathbf{r},t) \tag{8.9}$$

This Hamiltonian is also separable, and has solutions formally identical with Eq. (8.2) or (8.6), except that now

$$E - V = \frac{p^2}{2m} \tag{8.10}$$

and
$$|k| = \left|\left[\frac{2m}{\hbar^2}(E - V)\right]^{\frac{1}{2}}\right| \tag{8.11}$$

As long as the kinetic energy is greater than the potential energy $[(E - V) > 0]$, **k** and **p** will remain real, and the wave packet formalism of the free particle can be taken over intact. We find, in fact, that the packet moves as before with group velocity **p**/m and without change in distribution in momentum space but with

$$|p| = |[2m(E - V)]^{\frac{1}{2}}|$$ (8.12)

When the total energy is less than the potential energy $[(E - V) < 0]$, **k** and **p** become purely imaginary, and the eigenfunctions look like

$$\Psi(\mathbf{r},t) = e^{\pm \boldsymbol{\alpha} \cdot \mathbf{r}} e^{-(i/\hbar)Et}$$ (8.13)

where $\boldsymbol{\alpha}$ is real. Ψ has, in such a region, the form of an exponentially growing or exponentially decaying probability amplitude. For unbounded regions, only the decaying component is physically allowed, or Ψ would go to infinity at infinity. The exponentially decaying wave function for $V > E$ also reflects the fact that the particle is classically forbidden from entering such a region. In some cases, however, such as for potential barriers of finite thickness, both the positive and negative exponents are physically acceptable solutions, since Ψ develops no infinities in the bounded region. We will then find particles in a region from which classical mechanics would exclude them.

Returning our attention to the wavelike cases, we see that for both the free particle and the particle in a constant potential, the wave packet remains grouped in momentum space about the central eigenfunction. In order to calculate the dynamic properties of a particle, then, it is necessary only to keep track of the behavior of the central eigenfunction, that belonging to $\langle \mathbf{p} \rangle$, to keep track of the whole particle. If the packet is narrow in **p** space, it is even sufficient to calculate the properties of any typical eigenfunction contained in the packet. The computational problem is immensely reduced from that of keeping track of a whole bundle of **k** states to that of keeping track of one representative **k** state. For the spatial region where **k** is imaginary, we cannot build time-stable wave packets in the same sense that we can for the wavelike solutions. It remains true, however, that for a narrow range of $|p|$ or $|k|$ the behavior of the particle can be followed by examining the properties of the central (or of a typical) $|k|$. This is stated without proof, but the hypothesis is deemed plausible enough to be accepted without proof at this point. By the end of this chapter we will have considered the situation sufficiently that the reader will have available the mathematical machinery to satisfy himself on the validity of this assumption.

Let us examine now our first prototype configuration, a one-dimensional problem in which a particle moves from a region I of potential V_1 into a region *II* of potential V_2 (Fig. 8.1). We shall call the wave function in region *I*, Ψ_I and that in region *II*, Ψ_{II}. At the interface we require

$$\Psi_I(x = x_0) = \Psi_{II}(x = x_0) \qquad (8.14)$$

and

$$\left. \frac{\partial \Psi_I}{dx} \right|_{x=x_0} = \left. \frac{\partial \Psi_{II}}{dx} \right|_{x=x_0} \qquad (8.15)$$

These equations represent, respectively, the conditions of continuity of Ψ and of its first derivative as required in our original restrictions on Ψ.

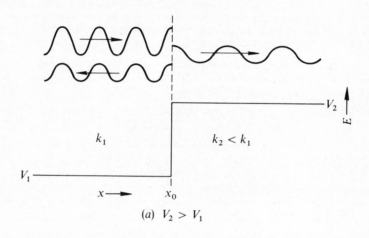

(a) $V_2 > V_1$

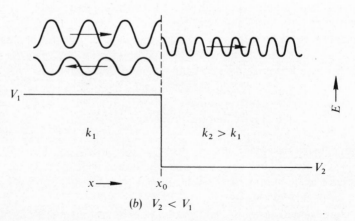

(b) $V_2 < V_1$

Fig. 8.1 *The particle incident upon a potential step with $E > V_1$ or V_2.*

Normalization will be attempted or accomplished only after we build a packet of k states; we carry this fact along in the back of our minds while we solve for typical plane-wave solutions to the problem.

Let us consider a particle incident from the left (from negative x) with energy E, where E is greater than V_1 or V_2. In region I, Ψ_I will have a component representing the incident wave,

$$\Psi_I(\text{incident}) = Ae^{i(k_1 x - \omega t)} \qquad (8.16)$$

and a component representing the reflected wave,

$$\Psi_I(\text{reflected}) = Be^{i(-k_1 x - \omega t)} \qquad (8.17)$$

where, in both instances,

$$k_1 = \left[\frac{2m(E - V_1)}{\hbar^2}\right]^{\frac{1}{2}} \qquad (8.18)$$

In region II there will be a transmitted wave moving toward $+x$, but no reflected wave since we consider that region II extends to $x = +\infty$ and contains no reflecting discontinuities.

$$\Psi_{II}(\text{transmitted}) = Ce^{i(k_2 x - \omega t)} \qquad (8.19)$$

where

$$k_2 = \left[\frac{2m(E - V_2)}{\hbar^2}\right]^{\frac{1}{2}} \qquad (8.20)$$

From the condition of Eq. (8.14) on the continuity of Ψ, we obtain

$$Ae^{ik_1 x_0} + Be^{-ik_1 x_0} = Ce^{ik_2 x_0} \qquad (8.21)$$

(the time-dependent part cancels out). From the condition of Eq. (8.15) on the continuity of the derivative of Ψ, we obtain

$$ik_1 Ae^{ik_1 x_0} - ik_1 Be^{-ik_1 x_0} = ik_2 Ce^{ik_2 x_0} \qquad (8.22)$$

We have now two equations in three unknowns, so we can solve for B and C in terms of A, giving the reflection and transmission coefficients. By solving for the ratios B/A and C/A instead of for A, B, and C absolutely, we again sidestep the normalization problem. The required ratios are

$$\frac{B}{A} = \frac{k_1 - k_2}{k_1 + k_2} e^{2ik_1 x_0} \quad \text{and} \quad \frac{C}{A} = \frac{2k_1}{k_1 + k_2} e^{i(k_1 - k_2)x_0} \qquad (8.23)$$

which lead to probability densities in the reflected and transmitted waves of

$$\left|\frac{B}{A}\right|^2 = \left(\frac{k_1 - k_2}{k_1 + k_2}\right)^2 \quad \text{and} \quad \left|\frac{C}{A}\right|^2 = \left(\frac{2k_1}{k_1 + k_2}\right)^2 \qquad (8.24)$$

To convert these probability densities into reflection and transmission coefficients, we must multiply them by the appropriate group velocities of the particle in regions *I* and *II*. From the discussion of the free-particle case, we know that

$$v_I = \frac{p_1}{m} = \frac{k_1 \hbar}{m} \quad \text{and} \quad v_{II} = \frac{p_2}{m} = \frac{k_2 \hbar}{m} \tag{8.25}$$

We have then the reflection and transmission coefficients

$$R = \frac{v_I}{v_I} \left| \frac{B}{A} \right|^2 = \left| \frac{B}{A} \right|^2 = \frac{(k_1 - k_2)^2}{(k_1 + k_2)^2}$$

$$T = \frac{v_{II}}{v_I} \left| \frac{C}{A} \right|^2 = \frac{k_2}{k_1} \left| \frac{C}{A} \right|^2 = \frac{4k_1 k_2}{(k_1 + k_2)^2} \tag{8.26}$$

We note that $R + T = 1$, as must be the case.

Quantum-mechanically there is a partial reflection at the potential step, whether the step be upward ($V_2 > V_1$) or downward ($V_2 < V_1$). Both cases are illustrated in Fig. 8.1. For the upward step, B/A is positive and the reflected wave is not shifted in phase upon reflection at the interface; for the downward step, B/A is negative and the reflected wave suffers a 180° phase reversal upon reflection. The situation is quite analogous to that which occurs when light (an electromagnetic wave) passes from one medium to another that has a different refractive index. There is a reflection from the interface regardless of whether the light is passing from a medium of lesser density to one of greater density or vice versa, and there is either no phase shift or a 180° phase shift upon reflection, depending on the sign of the change in index. The particle behaves rather as we would expect waves to behave on a purely classical picture. The particle does not behave as we would expect a classical particle to, however. The possibility of reflection is totally absent in the equivalent classical dynamical theory of particle motion. For E greater than V_1 or V_2, the particle will (classically) climb the barrier (with a loss in velocity) or fall off the step (with a gain in velocity) every time. We see in the behavior of a particle incident upon a barrier some of the features which are summed up in the grossly oversimplified statement that "quantum-mechanically, particles behave like waves," which we sometimes hear.

It is also instructive to examine the case (Fig. 8.2) where $V_1 < E < V_2$. The classical equivalent is the particle incident on a potential step with insufficient kinetic energy to climb the step. In region *I*, plane-wave solutions still obtain, and we can still speak of a reflection coefficient. In region *II*, we will have an imaginary k giving a real component

$$\Psi_{II} = Ce^{-\alpha x - i\omega t} \tag{8.27}$$

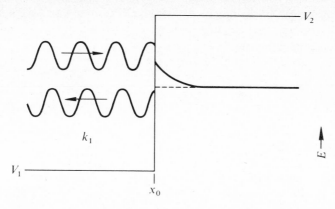

Fig. 8.2   *The particle incident on a barrier with $V_1 < E < V_2$.*

where
$$\alpha = \left[\frac{2m(V_2 - E)}{\hbar^2}\right]^{\frac{1}{2}} \tag{8.28}$$

We have retained only the negative exponent in region *II* since the positive exponent $+\alpha x$ would give a term diverging at infinity. Writing equations analogous to Eqs. (8.21) and (8.22) and solving, we obtain

$$\frac{B}{A} = -\frac{\alpha + ik_1}{\alpha - ik_1} e^{2ik_1 x_0} \tag{8.29}$$

with the reflection coefficient

$$R = \left|\frac{B}{A}\right|^2 = 1 \tag{8.30}$$

Just as in the classical case, all the incident particles are reflected. On the other hand, C/A has the nonzero value

$$C/A = \frac{2ik_1}{ik_1 - \alpha} e^{ik_1 x_0} e^{\alpha x_0} \tag{8.31}$$

and Ψ_{II} will be of the form

$$\Psi_{II} = \frac{2ik_1 A}{ik_1 - \alpha} e^{-\alpha(x - x_0)} \tag{8.32}$$

where the phase factor $\exp{(ik_1 x_0)}$ has been shifted to ψ_I to make its argument of the form $\exp{[ik_1(x - x_0)]}$. The particle does, then, penetrate into the reflecting wall by an amount that depends on the magnitude of $V_2 - E$. No particles are stored in the barrier, and no net flux to the right of the barrier exists, so the reflection coefficient is still unity in the sense that one particle is reflected for every particle incident. The penetration of the barrier can be thought of as giving rise to a dwell time on the barrier, which shows up in the complex nature of the B/A ratio (phase shift on reflection neither zero nor 180°).

If the barrier is not infinitely thick, the penetration of the incident wave has important consequences. Suppose the barrier is only δ thick (Fig. 8.3). Then the wave function will have decayed to only $e^{-\alpha\delta}$ times its value at the first interface when it strikes a second interface, from which it can

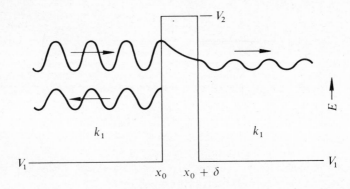

Fig. 8.3   *The particle incident on a barrier of $V_2 > E$ but of finite width.*

emerge as a propagating wave again. The situation is shown graphically in Fig. 8.3. The accurate solution will have reflection and transmission at both interfaces, with Ψ and its derivatives matched at both boundaries. We will not work out the algebra of the problem here, but the transmission through the barrier is given by

$$T = \left[1 + \frac{(V_2 - V_1)^2 \sinh^2 \alpha\delta}{4(E - V_1)(V_2 - E)}\right]^{-1} \tag{8.33}$$

where
$$\alpha = \left[\frac{2m(V_2 - E)}{\hbar^2}\right]^{\frac{1}{2}} \tag{8.34}$$

for $E < V_2$, and by

$$T = \left[1 + \frac{(V_2 - V_1)^2 \sin^2 k_2\delta}{4(E - V_1)(E - V_2)}\right]^{-1} \tag{8.35}$$

where
$$k_2 = \left[\frac{2m(E - V_2)}{\hbar^2}\right]^{\frac{1}{2}} \tag{8.36}$$

for $E > V_2$. The transmission coefficient through such a barrier is shown in Fig. 8.4.

The transmission curve has several important features. First, there is transmission through the barrier even for $E < V_2$, under circumstances where classical dynamics would predict complete reflection. The existence of this quantum-mechanical tunneling is very important to many phenomena in both physics and electronics. Perhaps the best known instance of quantum-mechanical tunneling is in the Esaki, or tunnel, diode, where tunneling through a potential barrier produces an unusual current vs. voltage curve, displaying negative-resistance characteristics. The same

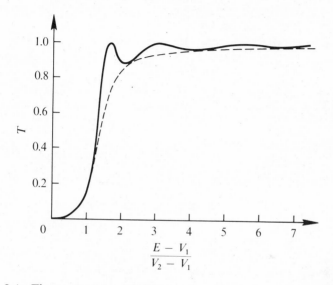

Fig. 8.4 *The transmission coefficient of a particle passing through a rectangular barrier plotted as a function of particle energy.*

tunnel effect has been used to measure the "superconducting gap" in superconductors, and is involved in electron emission through thin insulating films.

A second important feature of the transmission curve is the oscillatory nature of the transmission coefficient for incident energies greater than the barrier height. There exist certain energies for which the transmission is total, though the transmission drops off for incident energies slightly greater or slightly less. The transmission coefficient maximizes whenever $k_2\delta = n\pi$; whenever the barrier contains an integral number of half wavelengths. This same constructive interference effect is well known in optics, and is the physical basis for the thin-film optical filters. Once again the dynamics describing the particle's trajectory has wavelike characteristics.

8.2 THE PARTICLE IN A ONE-DIMENSIONAL SQUARE WELL A second prototype configuration worthy of serious consideration is the particle in a square potential well. We consider first the one-dimensional case as shown in Fig. 8.5. The zero of energy has been taken for convenience to be the bottom of the well, and we will discuss here primarily the bound states for which E is less than V, the depth of the potential well.

Following a procedure similar to that of the previous section, we divide the one-dimensional space into regions *I*, *II*, and *III*, corresponding to $x < -a$, $-a < x < a$, and $x > a$, respectively. For these regions the wave functions will be of the form

$$\psi_I = Ae^{\alpha x}$$
$$\psi_{II} = Be^{ikx} + Ce^{-ikx} \tag{8.37}$$
$$\psi_{III} = De^{-\alpha x}$$

where
$$k = \left(\frac{2mE}{\hbar^2}\right)^{\frac{1}{2}} \qquad \alpha = \left[\frac{(2m(V - E)}{\hbar^2}\right]^{\frac{1}{2}} \tag{8.38}$$

Continuity of ψ at $-a$ and $+a$ gives the relations

$$Ae^{-\alpha a} = Be^{-ika} + Ce^{ika} \tag{8.39a}$$
$$Be^{ika} + Ce^{-ika} = De^{-\alpha a} \tag{8.39b}$$

and matching $d\psi/dx$ at $-a$ and $+a$ yields

$$\alpha Ae^{-\alpha a} = ikBe^{-ika} - ikCe^{ika} \tag{8.40a}$$
$$ikBe^{ika} - ikCe^{-ika} = -\alpha De^{-\alpha a} \tag{8.40b}$$

Eliminating the term in $Ae^{-\alpha a}$ between Eqs. (8.39a) and (8.40a) gives

$$0 = (\alpha - ik)Be^{-ika} + (\alpha + ik)Ce^{ika} \tag{8.41a}$$

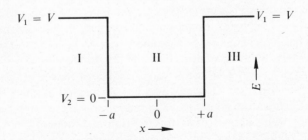

Fig. 8.5 *One-dimensional square-well potential.*

and eliminating the term in $De^{-\alpha a}$ between Eqs. (8.39b) and (8.40b) yields

$$(\alpha + ik)Be^{ika} + (\alpha - ik)Ce^{-ika} = 0 \qquad (8.42a)$$

These two equations may also be rewritten as

$$(\alpha - ik)Be^{-ika} = -(\alpha + ik)Ce^{ika} \qquad (8.41b)$$

$$(\alpha + ik)Be^{ika} = -(\alpha - ik)Ce^{-ika} \qquad (8.42b)$$

Multiplying the left side of Eq. (8.41b) by the left side of Eq. (8.42b) and the right side of Eq. (8.41b) by the right side of Eq. (8.42b) we have

$$(\alpha^2 + k^2)B^2 = (\alpha^2 + k^2)C^2 \qquad (8.43)$$

from which we conclude that $B^2 = C^2$, or

$$B = \pm C \qquad (8.44)$$

The solutions inside the potential well are then either of the form

$$e^{ikx} + e^{-ikx} = 2\cos kx \qquad (8.45)$$

or of the form

$$e^{ikx} - e^{-ikx} = 2i\sin kx \qquad (8.46)$$

The cosine solutions are even solutions unchanged upon reflection in the origin [$\cos kx = \cos(-kx)$], and the sine solutions are odd solutions which change sign upon reflection in the origin [$\sin kx = -\sin(-kx)$].

The cosine and sine solutions appropriate to the interior of the well must be matched at the well boundaries onto exponentially decaying functions. Such a matching is shown graphically in Fig. 8.6 for various sizes of α. The larger α is (the larger V) the more nearly is an integral number of cycles of the sine or cosine function confined to the well region. The condition for matching at the boundaries can be obtained analytically as follows:

From either Eq. (8.41b) or (8.42b) and the knowledge that $B = \pm C$, we obtain

$$\frac{\alpha - ik}{\alpha + ik} = \pm e^{2ika} \qquad (8.47)$$

Rationalizing the denominator of Eq. (8.47), we obtain an equation containing real and imaginary parts on both sides of the equation. Equating the real parts and the imaginary parts separately, we have

$$\frac{\alpha^2 - k^2}{\alpha^2 + k^2} = \pm\cos 2ka \qquad (8.48a)$$

and

$$-\frac{2\alpha k}{\alpha^2 + k^2} = \pm\sin 2ka \qquad (8.48b)$$

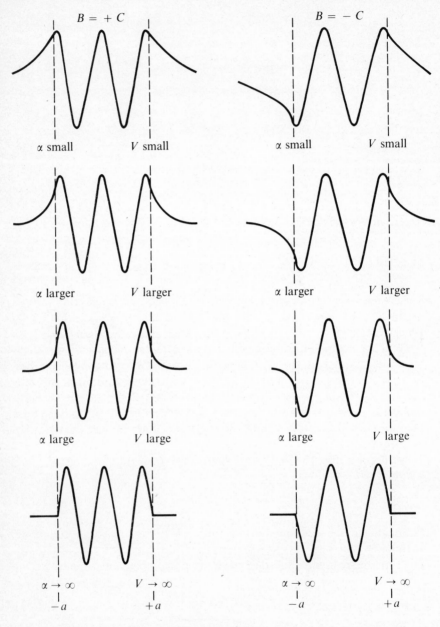

Fig. 8.6 *Wave functions, even and odd, for one-dimensional square well.*

Dividing Eq. (8.48*b*) by Eq. (8.48*a*), we obtain the matching condition

$$\tan 2ka = -\frac{2\alpha k}{\alpha^2 - k^2} \tag{8.49}$$

Equation (8.49) will be satisfied for only certain discrete values of the energy E. These values may be determined graphically as shown in Fig. 8.7. Both sides of Eq. (8.49) can be plotted as functions of ka since both α and k are related to E and V through Eq. (8.38). Referring to Fig. 8.7, the left side of Eq. (8.49) gives rise to the family of tangent curves and the right side to the dashed curve. The intersections of the two curves give the allowed k's, hence the allowed E's, the eigenenergies of the system. (The apparent root at $k = 0$ is spurious, since the resultant eigenfunction has also $A = B = C = D = 0$.) There are only a finite number of solutions, since E must remain less than V for the state to be bound.

The general character of the eigenenergies can be seen if we consider the limiting case in which $V \to \infty$. The boundary condition of Eq. (8.49) then becomes

$$\tan 2ka \to 0 \quad \text{as} \quad V \to \infty \tag{8.50}$$

which has the solutions

$$ka = \frac{n\pi}{2} \tag{8.51}$$

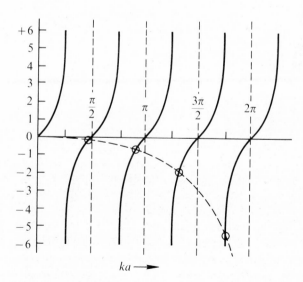

Fig. 8.7 *Graphical solution of boundary-value problem for square-well potential (see text).*

Letting $V \to \infty$ can be seen to be equivalent to requiring that ψ vanish at the well's edges. Since k is related to E through Eq. (8.38), we have

$$E = \frac{\hbar^2 k^2}{2m} = \frac{\hbar^2}{2m}\left(\frac{n\pi}{2a}\right)^2 = \frac{\hbar^2 \pi^2}{8ma^2} n^2 \qquad (8.52)$$

where n is a nonzero integer, even or odd. The even-integer solutions correspond to $\sin ka$ solutions within the well, and the odd-integer solutions correspond to $\cos ka$ wave functions within the well. Positive and negative n's correspond to the same eigenstate, so we will consider only the positive integers for n.

The eigenenergies corresponding to a finite potential are all slightly less than those for $V = \infty$. If we refer to Fig. 8.6, we can see that the

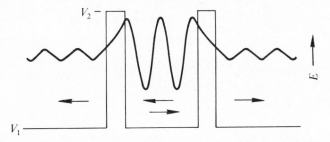

Fig. 8.8 *Schematic of the wave function of a particle in a potential well with walls of finite thickness. Escape by tunneling is shown.*

wave function must have more curvature inside the well for $V = \infty$ than for finite V in order to fit the full sinusoidal period into the well. The increased curvature implies greater $d^2\Psi/dx^2$ for $V = \infty$, which by correspondence implies greater p^2 and greater energy. The sequence of eigenvalues is never changed, nor are new types of solutions introduced, by reducing V from infinity to some finite value. The infinitely deep well is therefore a useful artifice for identifying and labeling our solutions.

Before passing on to the three-dimensional square well, we might pause to comment on a variation of the square-well problem, the one shown schematically in Fig. 8.8. If the walls of the well are of finite height and thickness, there is a finite probability of the particle escaping from the well by a tunneling process. Just such a tunneling process is responsible for the spontaneous α decay of radioactive nuclei. We can compute a transmission probability through the well wall just as we can for any barrier. We can also, from a knowledge of the energy of the α particle within the nucleus, estimate the number of times per second the particle will traverse the nucleus and impinge on the barrier. The lifetime of the nucleus is then determined by the rate of incidence times the probability of escape per incidence upon the barrier. Such a simple calculation gives substantial agreement with the experimental facts and has proved useful in understanding α decay and in formulating quantitative estimates of the depth and shape of the potential well holding nucleons within a nucleus.

8.3 THE THREE-DIMENSIONAL SQUARE WELL The principal features of the eigenfunctions and eigenvalues for the three-dimensional square-well potential can be obtained by a direct extension of the conclusions for the one-dimensional case just considered. The Hamiltonian for the three-dimensional case is

$$-\frac{\hbar^2}{2m}\nabla^2\Psi(\mathbf{r},t) + V(\mathbf{r})\Psi(\mathbf{r},t) = -\frac{\hbar}{i}\frac{\partial}{\partial t}\Psi(\mathbf{r},t) \tag{8.53}$$

where
$$V(\mathbf{r}) = 0 \quad \text{for} \begin{cases} -a < x < +a \\ -b < y < +b \\ -c < z < +c \end{cases}$$

$$\tag{8.54}$$

$$V(\mathbf{r}) = V \quad \text{for} \begin{cases} x < -a \text{ and } x > +a \\ y < -b \text{ and } y > +b \\ z < -c \text{ and } z > +c \end{cases}$$

The Hamiltonian is separable in x, y, z, and t, giving three equivalent spatial equations

$$\left[\frac{\hbar^2}{2m}\frac{d^2}{dx_i^2} + (E_i - V)\right]\psi(x_i) = 0 \tag{8.55}$$

and one time equation

$$-\frac{\hbar}{i}\frac{d}{dt}\varphi(t) = E\varphi(t) \tag{8.56}$$

where x_i is successively x, y, and z and where

$$E = E_x + E_y + E_z \tag{8.57}$$

The eigenfunctions will be of the form

$$\Psi(\mathbf{r},t) = \psi_1(x)\psi_2(y)\psi_3(z)e^{-(i/\hbar)Et} \tag{8.58}$$

with each of the factor eigenfunctions being of the form $\sin k_i x_i$ or $\cos k_i x_i$ within the well and exponentially decaying outside the well. The quantizing conditions on the E_i are obtained separately from the boundary-matching equations

$$\tan 2k_i a_i = -\frac{2\alpha_i k_i}{\alpha_i^2 - k_i^2} \tag{8.59}$$

with $\quad k_i = \left(\frac{2mE_i}{\hbar^2}\right)^{\frac{1}{2}} \quad$ and $\quad \alpha_i = \left[\frac{2m(V - E_i)}{\hbar^2}\right]^{\frac{1}{2}} \tag{8.60}$

Passing immediately to the limiting case where all the $V \to \infty$, we obtain the boundary-condition equations

$$\tan 2k_i a_i = 0 \tag{8.61}$$

with the separate solutions

$$k_x = \frac{n_x \pi}{2a} \qquad k_y = \frac{n_y \pi}{2b} \qquad k_z = \frac{n_z \pi}{2c} \tag{8.62}$$

The n_x, n_y, and n_z are *all* required to be *nonzero* integers. If any one were zero its corresponding $\psi(x_i)$ would be zero and the product wave function $\Psi(\mathbf{r},t)$ would also be identically zero.

The total energy of the particle is

$$E = \frac{\pi^2 \hbar^2}{8m}\left(\frac{n_x^2}{a^2} + \frac{n_y^2}{b^2} + \frac{n_z^2}{c^2}\right) \tag{8.63}$$

If $a \neq b \neq c$, the eigenvalues will be in general nondegenerate, i.e., only one eigenfunction per eigenvalue. Let us consider, however, the special case where $a = b = c$, a cubical potential well. Calling the cube edge $2l$, we have

$$E = \frac{\pi^2 \hbar^2}{8ml^2}(n_x^2 + n_y^2 + n_z^2) \tag{8.64}$$

The solutions are now in general degenerate, with more than one eigenfunction belonging to any given eigenenergy. We may check this quickly with a few low-lying states. The ground state is nondegenerate, since $n^2 = n_x^2 + n_y^2 + n_z^2 = 1 + 1 + 1 = 3$ can be accomplished in only one way. The next eigenvalue of E, corresponding to $n^2 = 6$, can be made up in either of three ways, since either n_x, n_y, or n_z can be 2 while the others remain unity. There are then three distinct eigenfunctions for $n^2 = 6$. There are six distinct eigenfunctions for $n^2 = 1 + 4 + 9 = 14$, corresponding to the different assignments to n_x, n_y, and n_z which can be made of the "quantum numbers" 1, 2, and 3. The degree of degeneracy increases with n^2 and becomes very high for large n. The problem of counting these states if n is very large occurs regularly in a number of physical problems (for instance, in semiconductor physics) and will be the subject of the next section.

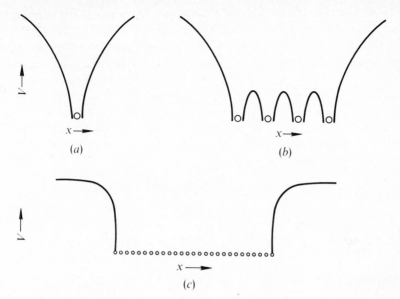

Fig. 8.9 *Schematic of the development of a square-well potential by a crystal.*

Before proceeding to the counting of states in a cubical potential well, we will pause briefly to indicate the relevance of such a simplified prototype configuration to a real physical situation. The three-dimensional rectangular well is in fact a useful approximation to the potential acting upon an electron in a solid. That this is the case can be seen by reference to Fig. 8.9. The potential due to a single positively charged nucleus is seen in Fig. 8.9a, that due to a few nuclei in a row shown in Fig. 8.9b, and that due to a large number of closely spaced positive nuclei shown in Fig. 8.9c. We can readily see that the actual potential has real similarity to the square well of our prototype.

8.4 THE DENSITY OF STATES IN A THREE-DIMENSIONAL SQUARE WELL

The problem of counting the available eigenstates in a three-dimensional square potential well comes up with some regularity in problems related to gaseous electronics and to solid-state physics and engineering. One frequently knows from the chemistry of a solid how many "free" electrons per cubic centimeter will be supplied to the solid by the elemental constituents. The gross electrical characteristics of the solid, i.e., whether it will have the conductivity of a metal, a semiconductor or an insulator, will all be determined by the number and disposition of the available energy states.

The quantity most frequently desired is the density of energy states available per unit volume as a function of energy. We therefore define $N(E)\,dE$ as the number of energy eigenstates per unit volume with energies between E and $E + dE$. We will evaluate this number by counting the density of states in a cubical, infinitely deep square well with edges $2a = 2b = 2c = 2l$. The final result, valid in the limit of large n (wavelength of the wave function very small), will turn out to be independent of the well length $2l$, as it must. The number of eigenstates per unit volume (in the same limit of large n) must also be independent of the exact shape of the well, so we choose the cubical well for computational convenience.

The eigenenergies of the cubical box are given by

$$E = \frac{\pi^2 \hbar^2}{8ml^2}\,(n_x^2 + n_y^2 + n_z^2) \qquad (8.64)$$

and there is a distinct eigenstate associated with each distinct assignment of positive nonzero integers to n_x, n_y, and n_z. The restriction to positive integers is purely to preserve the one-to-one correspondence between eigenstates and the assignment of n_x, n_y, n_z. If we allow positive *and* negative n_i values, there are then eight combinations of $\pm n_x$, $\pm n_y$, and $\pm n_z$ corresponding to the same eigenfunction. Such redundance of specification would exist over and above any degeneracy arising from the fact that several combinations of $\sum_i n_i^2$ may give the same energy.

Though it is not directly obvious how to count the number of eigenstates per unit increment in energy, it is relatively easy to count the eigenstates in what we will call *n space*. Imagine a three-dimensional space whose coordinates axes are n_x, n_y, and n_z. We completely specify the location of a point in n space by giving its n_x, n_y, and n_z coordinates. For every point in n space whose coordinates are integers, there corresponds an eigenstate of the square potential well. The density of eigenstates in n space is, then, one per unit volume.

Let us ask the question "How many eigenstates are there of energy E or less in the square well?" Looking at Eq. (8.64), we can see that all such states will be contained in a sphere of radius n, where

$$n = (n_x^2 + n_y^2 + n_z^2)^{1/2} = \left(\frac{8ml^2}{\pi^2 \hbar^2}\, E\right)^{1/2} \qquad (8.65)$$

How many distinct eigenstates are there in this sphere? We will restrict our count to distinct states if we confine our attention to positive n_x, n_y, and n_z only, that is, to one octant of the sphere of radius n. Since the density of states in n space is unity, the number of states in this octant is equal to the volume of the octant, so

$$\int_0^E N(E)\,dE = \frac{1}{8}\frac{4}{3}\pi n^3 \tag{8.66}$$

where n is given by Eq. (8.65). We will incur some error in our count by treating the distribution of eigenstates in n space as continuous rather than discrete, which is the actual case. However, for large n, usually the case of interest, the fractional error incurred by this assumption is negligible, and the continuous model is more than sufficiently accurate. From Eq. (8.66) it follows that

$$N(E)\,dE = \frac{1}{8}4\pi n^2\,dn \tag{8.67}$$

We may obtain Eq. (8.67) by direct differentiation of Eq. (8.66) or by observing that $4\pi n^2\,dn$ is the volume of the spherical shell in n space between the radii of n and $n + dn$. The right side of Eq. (8.67) can be readily expressed in terms of E and the particle and well parameters using the relation of Eq. (8.65):

$$n^2 = \frac{8ml^2}{\pi^2\hbar^2}\,E \tag{8.68a}$$

and

$$dn = \frac{1}{2}\left(\frac{8ml^2}{\pi^2\hbar^2}\right)^{1/2}E^{-1/2}\,dE \tag{8.68b}$$

Direct substitution into Eq. (8.67) gives

$$
\begin{aligned}
N(E)\,dE &= \frac{\pi}{2}\,n^2\,dn \\
&= \frac{\pi}{2}\left(\frac{8ml^2}{\pi^2\hbar^2}\,E\right)\frac{1}{2}\left(\frac{8ml^2}{\pi^2\hbar^2}\right)^{1/2}E^{-1/2}\,dE \\
&= \frac{\pi}{4}\left[\frac{2m(2l)^2}{\pi^2\hbar^2}\right]^{3/2}E^{1/2}\,dE
\end{aligned}
\tag{8.69}
$$

Dividing by $(2l)^3$, the volume of the well, in order to obtain the state density per unit volume, we have

$$N(E)\,dE = \frac{\sqrt{2}\,m^{3/2}}{2\pi^2\hbar^3}\,E^{1/2}\,dE \tag{8.70}$$

which is the desired expression.

Our density of states is calculated for particles which themselves have no "internal" degrees of freedom. We have assumed that specifying the spatial (square well) eigenstate of the particle describes the particle completely. In actuality, most particles also have a "spin," and to specify the particle completely, we need to know not only the quantum numbers

n_x, n_y, and n_z associated with its spatial state but also two more, s and s_z, specifying the spin state. We will delay any detailed discussion of this situation until we take up angular momentum, and simply assert here that $2s + 1$ distinct spin states (for a particle of fixed s) will be associated with each of the spatial states we have so carefully counted. The density of state functions for a spin-bearing particle will then be $(2s + 1)$ times that of Eq. (8.70), or in general

$$N(E) = \frac{\sqrt{2}\,m^{3/2}}{2\pi^2\hbar^3}\, E^{1/2}(2s + 1) \tag{8.71}$$

for particles of spin s in a rectangular potential well.

Summary

Important points to remember from Chap. 8:

A particle in a region of constant potential moves, if the potential is less than the total energy of the particle, very much like a particle in a field-free region, except that its propagation vector (velocity) is altered.

The propagation vector is imaginary for a particle in a region of constant potential where the potential energy exceeds the total particle kinetic energy. The wave function is not identically zero in such a region, so quantum mechanics predicts that particles will be found in spatial regions forbidden to them by classical dynamics and that particles will penetrate (tunnel through) potential barriers which would, classically, block the particles entirely.

A particle incident upon a potential discontinuity, whatever the sign of the discontinuity, always will be at least partially reflected, that is, have some finite probability of being reflected from the discontinuity.

A particle in a square potential well has a discrete set of eigenstates whose energy increases quadratically with the quantum number specifying the number of nodes in the wave function. For a one-dimensional well of width $2a$ and of infinite depth, the eigenenergies are

$$E_n = \frac{\hbar^2\pi^2}{8ma^2}\, n^2$$

where n is the quantum number specifying the state.

The density of energy states per unit volume (in the limit of large n) for a three-dimensional potential well is

$$N(E) = \frac{\sqrt{2}m^{3/2}}{2\pi^2\hbar^3}\, E^{1/2}(2s + 1)$$

Problems

8.1 Consider a one-dimensional rectangular potential well such that (Fig. P8.1).

$V = V_1$ for $x < -a$
$V = 0$ for $-a < x < 0$
$V = V_1/2$ for $0 < x < a$
$V = V_1$ for $x > a$

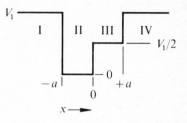

Write the wave functions in regions I through IV and the equations describing boundary conditions on these wave functions for

  a $E > V_1$
  b $V_1 > E > V_1/2$
  c $E < V_1/2$

Fig. P8.1

  d   Solve for the eigenenergies of the system lying between $V_1/2$ and V_1 (corresponding to part **b** above).

8.2 A particle of energy E is incident upon a potential barrier of height V_0 and width d (Fig. P8.2). Calculate the transmission of the particle through the barrier as a function of E. Locate maxima and minima in the transmission for $E > V_0$.

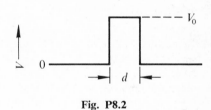

Fig. P8.2

8.3 A particle of potential E is incident on a potential well of depth V_0 and width a (Fig. P8.3). Calculate the transmission of the particle past the well. Locate maxima and minima in the transmission (a) for $\beta = 10$; (b) for $\beta = 250$, where

$$\beta = \sqrt{\frac{2m V_0 a^2}{\hbar^2}} = k_0 a$$

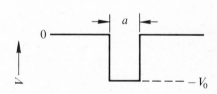

Fig. P8.3

8.4 Consider the one-dimensional potential of Fig. P8.4.

		Region
$V = \infty$	$x < 0$	I
$V = -V_0$	$0 < x < a$	II
$V = 0$	$a < x$	III

a Obtain, for the potential of Fig. P8.4, the equation whose solution gives the eigenenergies of the bound states ($E < 0$).

b Sketch the three eigenfunctions of lowest energy.

c A flux of particles ($E > 0$) is incident upon the potential of Fig. P8.4 from the right. The particles are reflected at two potential discontinuities, at $x = a$ and at $x = 0$. We seek the relative effectiveness of these two discontinuities in reflecting the particles. Call the wave function in regions II and III $A\psi_{II}^+(x) + B\psi_{II}^-$ and $C\psi_{III}^+(x) + D\psi_{III}^-(x)$, respectively, where ($+$) and ($-$) denote waves moving toward $+x$ and toward $-x$, respectively. Calculate $|B/D|^2$ as a function of E/V_0, and sketch a graphical presentation of the result.

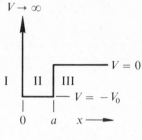

Fig. P8.4

d From part **c** above, we see that the discontinuity at $x = a$ can, under appropriate conditions, reflect very effectively particles incident upon it from the right. If it can reflect effectively particles incident from the left, we may have "virtual" or "metastable" states of $E > 0$. For such a state, $|A/C|^2 \gg 1$, and a particle created in region II will remain there for a considerable time. Determine if any such metastable states exist, and if so, calculate the energy of the lowest such state.

8.5 A particle of mass m is contained in the one-dimensional potential well of Fig. P8.5. We wish to know if the probability of finding the particle between $-b$ and $+b$ is greater or less when V_0 is finite than when $V_0 = 0$. One might argue on one hand that the particle will seek a low-energy region and tend to dwell in the region $-b < x < +b$, or one might argue, on the other hand, that the propagation constant of the particle is greater in this region so the particle tends to hurry past the well.

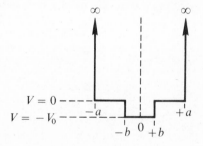

Fig. P8.5

Answer the question by solving for the relative size of the coefficients of the eigenfunctions in region $-b < x < +b$ as compared with region $-a < x < -b$ or $b < x < a$ for $E > 0$.

Sketch the behavior of one eigenstate (for example, that corresponding to $n = 5$ in the $V_0 \to 0$ limit) as V_0 increases.

8.6 A stream of particles is directed at an angle α upon the plane interface between two regions of constant potential V_1 and V_2. Take the potential discontinuity to be the $z = 0$ plane. The particle energy E is greater than both V_1 and V_2.

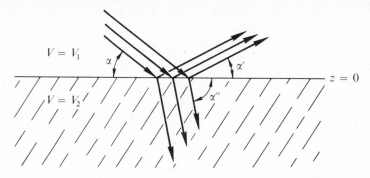

Fig. P8.6

a Write the wave functions in region I ($V = V_1$) and in region II ($V = V_2$).
b Calculate the angle of reflection α' and the angle of refraction α''.
c Calculate the coefficients of reflection and transmission. Take the flux through a plane perpendicular to the reflected or transmitted beams in computing these coefficients.

8.7 A spherical particle of mass m and isotropic moment of inertia I is contained in a smooth-walled, perfectly elastic cubical box of cube edge $2l$.
a Write the Hamiltonian of the system.
b Write Schrödinger's equation for the system.
c Obtain the eigenenergies of the system.
d Will the density-of-states function equation (8.71) apply to this system? If not, outline how a correct density-of-states function could be obtained.

Bibliography

The particle at a potential barrier or in a potential well is treated in:

Messiah, A.: "Quantum Mechanics," vol. 1, chap. 3, Interscience Publishers, Inc., New York, 1961.

Dicke, R. H., and J. P. Wittke: "Introduction to Quantum Mechanics," chap. 3, Addison-Wesley Publishing Company, Inc., Reading, Mass., 1960.

Merzbacher, E.: "Quantum Mechanics," chap. 6, John Wiley & Sons, Inc., New York, 1961.

Eisberg, R. M.: "Fundamentals of Modern Physics," chap. 8, John Wiley & Sons, Inc., New York, 1961.

CHAPTER 9

The Hydrogen Atom:
Central Forces and
Angular Momentum

**9.1 THE HAMILTONIAN FOR HYDROGEN AND CENTRAL-FORCE PROB-
LEMS** There are only three problems which can be "truly" solved by
quantum mechanics in the sense that the relevant equations can be solved
in closed form and the eigenfunctions specified in terms of "elementary
functions." The first is the harmonic oscillator; the second is the particle
in a region of uniform potential or at rectangular potential steps (including
the square well); the third is the particle in a central-force field of simple
form. Actual physical systems are usually reduced by one approximation
or another to one of these models, or at least treated using the eigenfunctions and eigenvalues of these prototype models as a point of departure. As was remarked earlier, the oscillations of any electric, magnetic,
or acoustic system about its equilibrium configuration can frequently be
treated through a harmonic-oscillator approximation. The transport
properties of particles, including electrons in solids, start out from the
free particle or particle-in-a-well picture. The calculation of the properties
of atomic systems starts out with the hydrogenic wave functions or at
least the angular-momentum eigenfunctions as a point of departure. We
will discuss in this chapter that third prototype, the particle in a central
force, and in particular the hydrogen atom.

The first problem to which Schrödinger applied his wave mechanics
was that of calculating the energy levels of the hydrogen atom, and his
success in this endeavor underscored heavily the validity of his wave
mechanics. The hydrogen atom is a sufficiently simple system that few
and relatively minor approximations are necessary; the quantitative
results of the calculation may be compared directly with the experimental
data, and all agreements and discrepancies taken quite seriously. The

170

hydrogen atom is also an important quantum-mechanical problem from a pedagogical point of view because it is an example of a larger class of problems, the central-force problems. By a "central force" we mean a force which is always directed radially inward or outward from the origin and whose magnitude is a function of radial distance from the origin only, not of any azimuthal angle.

The Hamiltonian for a particle in a central-force field is

$$H = \frac{p^2}{2m} + V(r) \tag{9.1}$$

where we have also assumed that $V(r)$ is independent of time. The Schrödinger equation for the particle whose Hamiltonian is given by Eq. (9.1) will be separable in spatial and temporal coordinates, giving

$$\frac{\hbar^2}{2m} \nabla^2 \psi(\mathbf{r}) + [E - V(r)]\psi(\mathbf{r}) = 0 \tag{9.2}$$

$$-\frac{\hbar}{i} \frac{\partial}{\partial t} \varphi(t) = E\varphi(t) \tag{9.3}$$

with the usual $e^{-(i/\hbar)Et}$ solutions for the time equation.

The time-independent Schödinger equation (9.2) is also further separable in spherical coordinates (as well as the less convenient parabolic coordinates). We may write Eq. (9.2) in spherical coordinates in its properly invariant form.

$$\frac{\hbar^2}{2m} \left[\frac{1}{r^2} \frac{\partial}{\partial r}\left(r^2 \frac{\partial}{\partial r}\right) + \frac{1}{r^2 \sin\theta} \frac{\partial}{\partial \theta}\left(\sin\theta \frac{\partial}{\partial \theta}\right) + \frac{1}{r^2 \sin^2\theta} \frac{\partial^2}{\partial \varphi^2} \right] \psi(r,\theta,\varphi)$$
$$+ [E - V(r)]\psi(r,\theta,\varphi) = 0 \tag{9.4}$$

The angular and radial coordinate equations may be separated by writing

$$\psi(r,\theta,\varphi) = R(r)Y(\theta,\varphi) \tag{9.5}$$

and working the usual separation manipulations upon Eq. (9.4). We then obtain

$$\frac{1}{r^2} \frac{d}{dr}\left(r^2 \frac{d}{dr}\right) R(r) + \frac{2m}{\hbar^2}[E - V(r)]R(r) - \frac{\lambda}{r^2} R(r) = 0 \tag{9.6}$$

and

$$\frac{1}{\sin\theta} \frac{\partial}{\partial \theta}\left(\sin\theta \frac{\partial}{\partial \theta}\right) Y(\theta,\varphi) + \frac{1}{\sin^2\theta} \frac{\partial^2}{\partial \varphi^2} Y(\theta,\varphi) + \lambda Y(\theta,\varphi) = 0 \tag{9.7}$$

where λ is our separation constant. Finally, putting

$$Y(\theta,\varphi) = \Theta(\theta)\Phi(\varphi) \tag{9.8}$$

we can separate the angular equation (9.7) into two ordinary differential equations

$$\frac{1}{\sin\theta}\frac{d}{d\theta}\left(\sin\theta\,\frac{d}{d\theta}\right)\Theta(\theta) + \left(\lambda - \frac{\beta}{\sin^2\theta}\right)\Theta(\theta) = 0 \tag{9.9}$$

and
$$\frac{d^2}{d\varphi^2}\,\Phi(\varphi) + \beta\Phi(\varphi) = 0 \tag{9.10}$$

where β is the last separation constant.

If we look now at the separated Eqs. (9.6), (9.9), and (9.10) in r, θ, and φ, respectively, we note that in order to solve the radial equation (9.6), we need to specify $V(r)$, but that the θ and φ equations may be solved without reference to the radial potential $V(r)$. The angular eigenfunctions for the central-force potential are then independent of the precise form of $V(r)$, and will be the same for the coulombic attractive potential, the isotropic three-dimensional harmonic oscillator, the particle in a spherical well, planetary motion in a gravitational field—or for any other potential which is a function of the radial coordinate only. The separation constants β and λ must correspond to constants of the motion which are independent of the specific form of the central-force field. What might these constants of the motion be? To find our answer we need only look at the corresponding classical dynamical problem. If we solve the classical problem of a particle in a central-force field we find that both the total angular momentum $\mathbf{L} = \mathbf{r} \times \mathbf{p}$ and any component of angular momentum (for instance, the z component) are constants of the motion for the central-force potential. We suspect, then, that the angular equations (9.7), (9.9), and (9.10) must yield the quantum-mechanical description of angular momentum. Let us pursue this hypothesis by deriving the operators to be associated with angular-momentum observables and comparing these operators with the above angular portions of the Schrödinger equation.

The definition of angular momentum is

$$\mathbf{L} = \mathbf{r} \times \mathbf{p} \tag{9.11}$$

which has the equivalent cartesian component equations

$$L_x = yp_z - zp_y$$
$$L_y = zp_x - xp_z \tag{9.12}$$
$$L_z = xp_y - yp_x$$

We can write the operators to be associated with **L** and its components easily in cartesian coordinates using the operator associates of Eq. (3.12)

$$(L_x)_{\text{op}} = \frac{\hbar}{i}\left(y\frac{\partial}{\partial z} - z\frac{\partial}{\partial y}\right)$$

$$(L_y)_{\text{op}} = \frac{\hbar}{i}\left(z\frac{\partial}{\partial x} - x\frac{\partial}{\partial z}\right) \qquad (9.13)$$

$$(L_z)_{\text{op}} = \frac{\hbar}{i}\left(x\frac{\partial}{\partial y} - y\frac{\partial}{\partial x}\right)$$

These operators obey a very interesting set of commutation rules, as may be verified by direct calculation.

$$[L_x, L_y] = i\hbar L_z$$
$$[L_y, L_z] = i\hbar L_x \qquad (9.14)$$
$$[L_z, L_x] = i\hbar L_y$$

Further, defining

$$(L^2)_{\text{op}} \equiv (L_x)^2_{\text{op}} + (L_y)^2_{\text{op}} + (L_z)^2_{\text{op}} \qquad (9.15)$$

we have that

$$[L^2, L_x] = [L^2, L_y] = [L^2, L_z] = 0 \qquad (9.16)$$

If we are to see the relation between these operators and our central-force Schrödinger equation, we will have to convert the operators into spherical coordinates. This can, of course, be done by writing the relations

$$x = r\sin\theta\cos\varphi$$
$$y = r\sin\theta\sin\varphi \qquad (9.17)$$
$$z = r\cos\theta$$

and taking appropriate derivatives. For instance,

$$\frac{\partial}{\partial\varphi} = \frac{\partial x}{\partial\varphi}\frac{\partial}{\partial x} + \frac{\partial y}{\partial\varphi}\frac{\partial}{\partial y} + \frac{\partial z}{\partial\varphi}\frac{\partial}{\partial z}$$

$$= -r\sin\theta\sin\varphi\frac{\partial}{\partial x} + r\sin\theta\cos\varphi\frac{\partial}{\partial y} + 0\frac{\partial}{\partial z}$$

$$= -y\frac{\partial}{\partial x} + x\frac{\partial}{\partial y} \qquad (9.18)$$

Comparing this result with the third of Eq. (9.13), we see that

$$(L_z)_{\text{op}} = \frac{\hbar}{i}\frac{\partial}{\partial\varphi} \qquad (9.19)$$

Equation (9.10) is, then, precisely the eigenvalue equation for the operator L_z^2.

$$(L_z)_{op}^2 \, u(\mathbf{r}) = \left(\frac{\hbar}{i}\frac{\partial}{\partial\varphi}\right)^2 u(\mathbf{r}) = l_z^2 u(\mathbf{r}) \qquad (9.20)$$

or, equivalently,

$$\frac{\partial^2}{\partial\varphi^2}\, u(\mathbf{r}) + \frac{l_z^2}{\hbar^2}\, u(\mathbf{r}) = 0 \qquad (9.21)$$

where the separability of $u(\mathbf{r})$ has not yet been assumed. We may therefore expect to associate $(l_z/\hbar)^2$ with the separation constant β of Eq. (9.10) and assign to β the physical significance of the square of the z component of angular momentum.

Following the same line of development, we may write in spherical coordinates the operators associated with L_x and L_y:

$$L_x = -\frac{\hbar}{i}\left(\sin\varphi\,\frac{\partial}{\partial\theta} + \cot\theta\cos\varphi\,\frac{\partial}{\partial\varphi}\right)$$
$$L_y = \frac{\hbar}{i}\left(\cos\varphi\,\frac{\partial}{\partial\theta} - \cot\theta\sin\varphi\,\frac{\partial}{\partial\varphi}\right) \qquad (9.22)$$

The operators L_x and L_y do not themselves resemble any part of our Schrödinger equation, but if we form the operator associated with $L^2 = L_x^2 + L_y^2 + L_z^2$, we obtain

$$(L^2)_{op} = -\hbar^2\left(\frac{1}{\sin\theta}\frac{\partial}{\partial\theta}\sin\theta\,\frac{\partial}{\partial\theta} + \frac{1}{\sin^2\theta}\frac{\partial^2}{\partial\varphi^2}\right) \qquad (9.23)$$

Referring back to the separated central-force Schrödinger equation, we see that Eq. (9.7) is precisely the eigenvalue equation for the operator L^2, and we will expect to associate with the separation constant λ the square of the total angular momentum of the system.

We have, then, established that the angular portions of the central-force Schrödinger equation do in fact describe the angular momentum of the particle moving in a central-force field.

9.2 SOLUTION OF THE θ AND φ PORTIONS OF THE CENTRAL-FORCE SCHRÖDINGER EQUATION In the preceding section we assigned a physical interpretation to the angular portions of the central-force Schrödinger equation, Eqs. (9.7), (9.8), and (9.10). Let us proceed with the solution of these equations to obtain the quantum-mechanical description of angular momentum.

The φ equation may be integrated directly to give

$$\Phi(\varphi) = Ce^{i\beta^{1/2}\varphi} \qquad (9.24)$$

where C is a normalization constant. We note that $\beta^{1/2}$, hence also β, must be dimensionless (a pure number) for the exponent to be a pure number. Checking back through the separations of the Schrödinger equation, we find that β and λ have the same dimensions as each other, and the same dimensions as $(2mr^2/\hbar^2)E$. E has, of course, the dimensions of energy, and indeed $(2mr^2/\hbar^2)E$ does prove to be a dimensionless quantity. Our separation constants λ and β are then pure numbers, and not energies, as has proved to be the case in the separations treated earlier in this book.

Returning to Eq. (9.24), we recall that the domain of φ is from 0 to 2π, so it is necessary that

$$\Phi(\varphi) = \Phi(\varphi + 2\pi) \tag{9.25}$$

if the state function Ψ is to be a single-valued function of position. Such single-valuedness, as well as the continuity of Ψ and its first derivative with respect to φ, is guaranteed if $\beta^{1/2}$ is an integer, positive or negative. Our φ eigenfunction is therefore

$$\Phi(\varphi) = C_m e^{\pm im\varphi} \tag{9.26}$$

where

$$m = 0, 1, 2, 3, \ldots \tag{9.27}$$

and the normalization requirement

$$\int_0^{2\pi} |C_m|^2 \, \Phi^*(\varphi)\Phi(\varphi) \, d\varphi = 1 \tag{9.28}$$

gives

$$C_m = \frac{1}{\sqrt{2\pi}} \tag{9.29}$$

The solution of the θ equation does not proceed quite so expeditiously. We make first the variable change

$$z = \cos\theta \tag{9.30}$$

and the identification of our new eigenfunction $P(z)$ with $\Theta(\theta)$

$$P(z) = \Theta(\theta) \tag{9.31}$$

whereupon our equation in θ, Eq. (9.9), becomes

$$\frac{d}{dz}(1 - z^2)\frac{d}{dz}P(z) + \left(\lambda - \frac{m^2}{1 - z^2}\right)P(z) = 0 \tag{9.32}$$

The domain of z is from -1 to $+1$, since the domain of θ is from 0 to π, and we seek solutions which are single valued, continuous, and square integrable throughout this domain.

Equation (9.32) is a well-known equation of mathematical physics arising in many boundary-value problems having spherical symmetry. It therefore received extensive attention by the mathematicians of the eighteenth and nineteenth centuries, notably by Legendre. Its solution is complicated by the singularities in the equation itself at $z = \pm 1$. We shall proceed with the solution of this equation by the same power-series polynomial technique which we used in solving Schrödinger's equation for the linear harmonic oscillator. This is by no means the most elegant or powerful technique for the solution of such equations, but it does display quite explicitly the manner in which discrete eigenvalues are associated with physically acceptable solutions to the time-independent Schrödinger equation. It happens that for Eq. (9.32) formal solutions exist which cannot be expressed as power series of finite degree in a real argument, and hence will evade our solution technique. These solutions can all be shown not to be square integrable, however, so cannot represent physically acceptable solutions to the equation. The reader interested in pursuing the formal mathematics of these solutions further will find them treated in texts on Legendre functions, especially in the chapter bearing that name in Whittaker and Watson's "Modern Analysis."

To solve Eq. (9.32) by the power-series technique, we solve first for the special case of $m = 0$. Our differential equation is then

$$\frac{d}{dz}(1 - z^2)\frac{d}{dz}P(z) + \lambda P(z) = 0 \tag{9.33}$$

and we have eliminated one of the sources of mathematical embarrassment, the term $m^2/(1 - z^2)$. Equation (9.33) also occurs frequently in the literature of boundary-value problems and of mathematical physics and is known as *Legendre's equation*. We propose a trial function of the form

$$P(z) = \sum_n a_n z^n \tag{9.34}$$

and substitute this trial function into Legendre's equation (9.33). We obtain therefrom, by procedures entirely analogous to those used for the simple harmonic oscillator, a recursion relation for the coefficients which proves to be

$$a_{l+2} = \frac{l(l + 1) - \lambda}{(l + 1)(l + 2)} a_l \tag{9.35}$$

We note that the ratio of coefficients approaches unity as l becomes large:

$$\frac{a_{l+2}}{a_l} \to 1 \quad \text{as} \quad l \to \infty \tag{9.36}$$

so the polynomial $P(z)$ will clearly diverge for $z = 1$ unless the polynomial is terminated after a finite number of terms. The termination condition is seen to be

$$\lambda = l(l + 1) \qquad (9.37)$$

where l is zero or a positive integer. The polynomial in z of order l so defined is known as the *Legendre polynomial of the first kind* and is notated by $P_l(z)$. $P_l(z)$, properly normalized, is a physically acceptable eigenfunction of the θ equation [Eq. (9.9)] for the special case of $m = 0$. There is a second set of solutions, conventionally called $Q_l(z)$, which are polynomials of order l in $(1/z)$. These solutions all have an infinity at $z = 0$, and do not represent physically acceptable solutions to Schrödinger's equation.

So far we have solved Eq. (9.9) only for the special case of $m = 0$. We may verify by direct substitution, however, that if $P_l(z)$ is a solution to Eq. (9.33) ($m = 0$ case) then

$$P_l^m (z) = (1 - z^2)^{m/2} \frac{d^m P_l(z)}{dz^m} \qquad (9.38)$$

is a solution of the more general equation for arbitrary m, Eq. (9.32). The "quantum number" m is, of course, constrained to be an integer by the conditions on the solution of the φ equation. If $P_l(z)$ is a polynomial in z^n, so also will $d^m/dz^m[P_l(z)]$ be a power-series polynomial in z. The recursion relation for the coefficients of this polynomial is, by direct calculation

$$a_{k+2} = \frac{(k + m)(k + m + 1) - \lambda}{(k + 1)(k + 2)} a_k \qquad (9.39)$$

and the polynomial will terminate after $(l - m)$ terms (as must the mth derivative of a polynomial of order l) if

$$[(l - m) + m][(l - m) + m + 1] - \lambda = 0 \qquad (9.40)$$

which is equivalent to

$$\lambda = l(l + 1) \qquad (9.41)$$

just as was true for the special case $m = 0$. We see further from the definition of $P_l^m(z)$, that l must be greater than or equal to m if $P_l^m(z)$ is not to be trivially equal to zero. The separation constants for the two angular equations are then summarized as

$$m = 0, 1, 2, \ldots, n$$
$$\lambda = l(l + 1) \qquad (9.42)$$
$$l \geq m$$

The $P_l^m(z)$ are known as the *associated Legendre functions* (they are no longer simple polynomials, because of the multiplicative $(1 - z^2)^{1/2}$ factor), and a few·of them, including the $P_l^0(z) = P_l(z)$, are given in Table 9.1.

TABLE 9.1

Some of the Associated Legendre Functions $P_l^m(z)$

l	m			
	0	1	2	3
0	1	0	0	0
1	z	$(1 - z^2)^{\frac{1}{2}}$	0	0
2	$\frac{1}{2}(3z^2 - 1)$	$3z(1 - z^2)^{\frac{1}{2}}$	$3(1 - z^2)$	0
3	$\frac{1}{2}(5z^3 - 3z)$	$\frac{3}{2}(5z^2 - 1)(1 - z^2)^{\frac{1}{2}}$	$15z(1 - z^2)$	$15(1 - z^2)^{\frac{3}{2}}$

We have now established the eigenfunctions of the angular portion of the central-force Schrödinger equation, Eq. (9.7). The eigenfunctions are

$$Y_l^{\pm m}(\theta,\varphi) = N_l^{\pm m} P_l^m(\cos \theta) e^{\pm im\varphi} \qquad (9.43)$$

where $N_l^{\pm m}$ is a normalization constant arising from the condition

$$\int_{\varphi=0}^{2\pi} \int_{\theta=0}^{\pi} Y_l^{\pm m*}(\theta,\varphi) Y_l^{\pm m}(\theta,\varphi) \sin \theta \, d\theta \, d\varphi = 1 \qquad (9.44)$$

and equal to

$$N_l^{\pm m} = \left[\frac{(2l + 1)(l - m)!}{4\pi(l + m)!}\right]^{\frac{1}{2}} \qquad (9.45)$$

The $Y_l^{\pm m}(\theta,\varphi)$ functions are fully orthogonal in that

$$\iint Y_{l'}^{m'}(\theta,\varphi)^* Y_l^m(\theta,\varphi) \sin \theta \, d\theta \, d\varphi = \delta_{ll'} \, \delta_{mm'} \qquad (9.46)$$

We have established earlier the connection between our angular eigen-value equations and the angular momentum of the system, so we may now place a physical interpretation upon the separation constants λ and m. From Eqs. (9.7), (9.23), and (9.42), we may establish the correlations

$$\left(\frac{1}{\sin \theta} \frac{\partial}{\partial \theta} \sin \theta \frac{\partial}{\partial \theta} + \frac{1}{\sin^2 \theta} \frac{\partial^2}{\partial \varphi^2}\right) Y_l^{\pm m}(\theta,\varphi) = -\lambda Y_l^{\pm m}(\theta,\varphi)$$

$$-\frac{1}{\hbar^2} L^2 Y_l^{\pm m}(\theta,\varphi) = -l(l + 1) Y_l^{\pm m}(\theta,\varphi) \qquad (9.47)$$

and finally

$$L^2 Y_l^{\pm m}(\theta,\varphi) = l(l + 1)\hbar^2 Y_l^{\pm m}(\theta,\varphi) \qquad (9.48)$$

Equation (9.48) tells us that the eigenvalues of orbital angular momentum squared are $l(l + 1)\hbar^2$—a celebrated result. The integer l is called the *angular momentum quantum number*, or, especially in the older literature on atomic structure, the *azimuthal quantum number*. Note that the magnitude of the total orbital angular momentum $|L \cdot L|^{\frac{1}{2}}$ is not equal to $l\hbar$ but to $\sqrt{l(l + 1)}\,\hbar$. Concerning the component of **L** along some arbitrary direction, we have from Eqs. (9.10), (9.19), and (9.42) that

$$L_z Y_l^{\pm m}(\theta,\varphi) = \frac{\hbar}{i}\frac{\partial}{\partial\varphi}\,Y_l^{\pm m}(\theta,\varphi) = \frac{\hbar}{i}\,(\pm im)\,Y_l^{\pm m}(\theta,\varphi) \qquad (9.49)$$

or
$$L_z Y_l^{\pm m}(\theta,\varphi) = \pm m\hbar\, Y_l^{\pm m}(\theta,\varphi) \qquad (9.50)$$

Equation (9.50) tells us that the z component of the orbital angular momentum is equal to $\pm m\hbar$. The requirement that l be greater than or equal to m, imposed by the θ equations, is seen to be physically equivalent to the requirement that the z component of angular momentum cannot exceed the magnitude of the angular momentum. In fact, the z component of angular momentum cannot (except for $l = m = 0$) quite equal the magnitude of the angular momentum, since

$$|L| = [l(l + 1)]^{\frac{1}{2}}\hbar \qquad (9.51)$$
while
$$|L_z|_{\max} = l\hbar \qquad (9.52)$$

The relations of Eqs. (9.51) and (9.52) represent again a manifestation of the minimum uncertainty-product characteristic of noncommuting observables. Since L_x, L_y, and L_z do not commute (except for the trivial and uninteresting case of $l = 0$), we cannot know them exactly simultaneously. If $|L_z|_{\max}$ were permitted to be equal to $|L|$, then we would know for this state that $L_x = L_y \equiv 0$, and would simultaneously know exactly L_x, L_y, and L_z, in violation of the commutation requirements.

The physical significance of l and m makes the rules concerning them [given in Eq. (9.42)] easy to remember. The quantum number l specifies the magnitude of the orbital angular-momentum vector [$= \sqrt{l(l + 1)}\hbar$], and, since it deals with a magnitude, takes on only positive (integral) values. The quantum number m (sometimes called the *magnetic quantum number*) specifies the vector component of **L** in some particular direction. Since a component of a vector cannot exceed the magnitude of the vector, m is restricted to values equal to or less than l. Since a vector component carries with it a positive or negative sense with respect to the chosen axis, we find m preceded by $\pm$ signs in our various equations.

We have chosen the z axis for our problem quite arbitrarily. The central-force potential is characterized by having no unique axis. Our conclusion that the z component of angular momentum must equal $\pm m\hbar$ must, then, apply to any arbitrary axis. We will discuss the mechanics of switching from one coordinate frame to another very shortly in matrix notation where the transformations are most conveniently formulated. For the present we should remember that if we measure the component of orbital angular momentum along any arbitrary axis, we will obtain one of the eigenvalues $\pm m\hbar$, independent of the details of the system, as long as a central-force potential is involved.

**9.3 SOLUTION OF THE RADIAL EQUATION FOR A COULOMBIC POTEN-
TIAL** The radial equation of Schrödinger's separated time-independent equation for the central-force potential is given by

$$\frac{1}{r^2}\frac{d}{dr}\left(r^2\frac{d}{dr}\right)R(r) + \frac{2m}{\hbar^2}[E - V(r)]R(r) - \frac{l(l+1)}{r^2}R(r) = 0 \qquad (9.53)$$

where we have substituted the now-known value of λ $[l(l + 1)]$ into Eq. (9.6). For the hydrogenic atom, $V(r)$ is a simple coulombic potential

$$V(r) = -\frac{Ze^2}{r} \qquad (9.54)$$

where Ze is the nuclear charge. We have taken the zero of our potential energy to be that of the system when the electron is removed to infinity. We first make some notational changes which simplify Eq. (9.53) somewhat and, more importantly, reduce it to a form comparable with a similar equation considered by the ubiquitous eighteenth- and nineteenth-century mathematicians. We first define two parameters α and n such that

$$\alpha^2 = -\frac{8mE}{\hbar^2} \qquad n = \frac{2mZe^2}{\alpha\hbar^2} \qquad (9.55)$$

Inserting these into our radial equation places it in the form

$$\frac{1}{r^2}\frac{d}{dr}\left(r^2\frac{d}{dr}\right)R(r) + \left[\frac{\alpha n}{r} - \frac{\alpha^2}{4} - \frac{l(l+1)}{r^2}\right]R(r) = 0 \qquad (9.56)$$

Converting finally to a dimensionless parameter ρ, where

$$\rho = \alpha r \qquad (9.57)$$

the radial equation becomes

$$\frac{1}{\rho^2}\frac{d}{d\rho}\left(\rho^2\frac{d}{d\rho}\right)S(\rho) + \left[\frac{n}{\rho} - \frac{l(l+1)}{\rho^2} - \frac{1}{4}\right]S(\rho) = 0 \qquad (9.58)$$

where
$$S(\rho) = R(r) \qquad (9.59)$$

and we again seek a solution which is physically acceptable in the sense that $S(\rho)$ and $R(r)$ vanish sufficiently rapidly as $r \to \infty$ that the radial eigenfunction converges and is square integrable. We again employ a solution technique which is a modification of the polynomial approach used earlier. The arguments leading to an appropriate trial function to satisfy Eq. (9.58) are involved and not of paramount interest here. An acceptable function turns out to be a polynomial in ρ times an exponential function in ρ:

$$S(\rho) = e^{-\rho/2} \rho^l \sum_\nu a_\nu \rho^\nu \qquad (9.60)$$

The requirement that $S(\rho)$ converge as $\rho \to \infty$ and that $S(\rho)$ be square integrable again turns out to be equivalent to requiring that the power series in ρ terminate after a finite number of terms. Substituting $S(\rho)$ of Eq. (9.60) into Eq. (9.58) gives the recursion relation

$$a_{\nu+1} = \frac{n - (l + \nu + 1)}{2(\nu + 1)(l + 1) + \nu(\nu + 1)} a_\nu \qquad (9.61)$$

The polynomial will then terminate after ν terms, and $S(\rho)$ will be a physically acceptable eigenfunction if

$$n = l + \nu + 1 \qquad (9.62)$$

where l and ν are zero or positive integers, and where n is therefore a positive integer equal to or greater than unity. The quantum number n is called the *total quantum number* of the state. The quantum number ν is called the *radial quantum number* and is usually designated by n'. Note that the radial quantum number is redundant for specifying the state if we know n and l, so it is frequently omitted in the state description.

We will shortly plot the probability amplitudes and probability densities associated with the radial eigenfunction $S(\rho)$. However, we first direct our attention to the eigenvalues associated with these eigenfunctions. We note that the eigenfunction $S(\rho)$ contains both n and l (but not overtly m) in its specification, so we now identify a particular eigenfunction by the designation $S_{nl}(\rho)$, where both n and l are integers. The eigenenergies of the hydrogenic atom are related to the quantum number n through the parameter definitions of Eq. (9.55):

$$E = -\frac{\alpha^2 \hbar^2}{8m} \qquad (9.63)$$

and

$$\alpha = \frac{2mZe^2}{n\hbar^2} \qquad (9.64)$$

whence

$$E = -\left(\frac{2mZe^2}{n\hbar^2}\right)^2 \frac{\hbar^2}{8m} = -\frac{mZ^2e^4}{2\hbar^2 n^2} \qquad (9.65)$$

The eigenenergies, sketched in Fig. 9.1, are negative since we have taken the zero of energy as corresponding to the electron removed to infinity and are considering bound states. There is an infinity of such bound states, becoming very closely spaced for large n. The energy depends only on n and not explicitly on l or m (E depends implicitly on l or m in the sense that $n > l \geq m$). If we examine the solutions of Schrödinger's equation for the hydrogenic atom for solutions corresponding to $E > 0$, we find a continuum of states which correspond to electrons not bound to the nucleus but simply modified in their behavior as they pass near the nucleus. Such states are of no particular interest to us and will not be discussed further.

The eigenfunctions of the hydrogenic atom are multiply degenerate. For the slightly simplified model of the hydrogenic atom used, the energy depends only on the principal quantum number n, yet the specification of the full eigenfunction $S_{nl}(\rho) Y_l^{\pm m}(\theta, \varphi)$ requires the specification of three

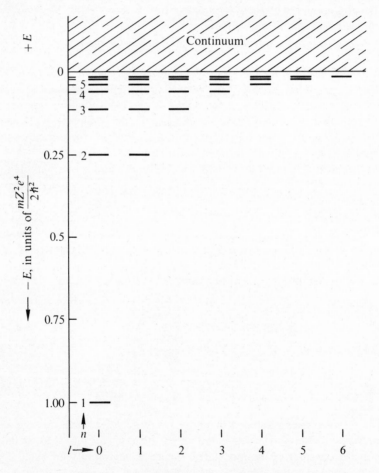

Fig. 9.1   *Energy levels of hydrogenic atom.*

quantum numbers n, l, and m. For every value of n there are a number of possible values of l. There are in fact n possible values of l: the integers $0, 1, 2, \ldots, (n-1)$. Further, for every value of l there are a number of acceptable values of m: the integers $0, 1, 2, \ldots, l$. Since the $\pm m$ states are physically distinguishable, there are $2l+1$ eigenstates of the same l but different l_z $[l, (l-1), (l-2), \ldots, 0, \ldots, -(l-2), -(l-1), -l]$. The total degeneracy of a state of given n will be, therefore,

$$N(n) = \sum_{l=0}^{l=n-1} (2l+1) = n^2 \tag{9.66}$$

As we shall see, some of these degeneracies will in actuality be removed by effects not considered in this nonrelativistic spin-free model of the atom.

We return now to the eigenfunctions $S_{nl}(\rho)$ of the radial equation, and plot out some of the associated probability distributions. Our task is made easier by the fact that the polynomials $\sum_{v} a_v \rho^v$ occurring in $S_{nl}(\rho)$ are closely related to a set of polynomials known as the *associated Laguerre polynomials*, and in fact the functions $S_{nl}(\rho)$ are, apart from normalization conventions, the same as the *associated Laguerre functions* of classical mathematics. In particular, the associated Laguerre polynomial satisfying Eq. (9.58) and terminating after $n' = n - l - 1$ terms is noted conventionally as L_{n+l}^{2l+1} in the classical texts on associated Laguerre functions. We may therefore write our radial wave functions as

$$R_{nl}(r) = S_{nl}(\rho) = A_{nl}e^{-\rho/2}\rho^l L_{n+l}^{2l+1}(\rho) \tag{9.67}$$

A_{nl} is again a normalization constant determined from the requirement that

$$\int_0^\infty S_{nl}^*(\rho)S_{nl}(\rho)r^2\,dr = 1 \tag{9.68}$$

Consulting tables of integrals of the Laguerre polynomials, we find that

$$
\begin{aligned}
A_{nl} &= \left\{\alpha^3 \frac{(n-l-1)!}{2n[(n+l)!]^3}\right\}^{\frac{1}{2}} \\
&= \left\{\left(\frac{2mZe^2}{n\hbar^2}\right)^3 \frac{(n-l-1)!}{2n[(n+l)!]^3}\right\}^{\frac{1}{2}}
\end{aligned}
\tag{9.69}
$$

The first few $R_{nl}(r)$ are listed in Table 9.2. In this table, and for the $R_{nl}(r)$ generally, it is convenient to introduce the unit

$$a_0 = \frac{\hbar^2}{me^2} \tag{9.70}$$

a unit known as the *Bohr radius* because it is the most probable value of r for the ground state ($n = 1$) of the hydrogen atom. A few of the $R_{nl}(r)$

TABLE 9.2

Some Normalized Radial Wave Functions $R_{nl}(r)$

$$R_{10}(r) = \left(\frac{Z}{a_0}\right)^{3/2} 2e^{-Zr/a_0}$$

$$R_{20}(r) = \left(\frac{Z}{2a_0}\right)^{3/2} 2\left(1 - \frac{Zr}{2a_0}\right)e^{-Zr/2a_0}$$

$$R_{21}(r) = \left(\frac{Z}{2a_0}\right)^{3/2} \frac{1}{\sqrt{3}} \frac{Zr}{a_0} e^{-Zr/2a_0}$$

$$R_{30}(r) = \left(\frac{Z}{3a_0}\right)^{3/2} 2\left[1 - \frac{2}{3}\frac{Zr}{a_0} + \frac{2}{27}\left(\frac{Zr}{a_0}\right)^2\right]e^{-Zr/3a_0}$$

$$R_{31}(r) = \left(\frac{Z}{3a_0}\right)^{3/2} \frac{4\sqrt{2}}{3} \frac{Zr}{a_0}\left(1 - \frac{1}{6}\frac{Zr}{a_0}\right)e^{-Zr/3a_0}$$

$$R_{32}(r) = \left(\frac{Z}{3a_0}\right)^{3/2} \frac{2\sqrt{2}}{27\sqrt{5}}\left(\frac{Zr}{a_0}\right)^2 e^{-Zr/3a_0}$$

$$a_0 = \frac{\hbar^2}{me^2}$$

are drawn in Fig. 9.2. Since the $R_{nl}(r)$ all contain a factor r^l, they all are zero at the origin, except the states for which $l = 0$ (known as *s states* in the code of spectroscopists). An important corollary of this fact is that *s* states interact with the nuclear moments more strongly than do other states. Note also that each $R(r)$ has $n' = n - (l + 1)$ nodes.

The probability density for finding the electron at radius r is given by $r^2|R(r)|^2$, where the multiplicative factor r^2 adjusts for the greater volume of spherical shells at larger radii. The radial probability density $r^2|R(r)|^2$ is plotted in Fig. 9.3 for a few of the lower $R_{nl}(r)$.

The full three-dimensional probability density $\psi^*(r\theta\varphi)\psi(r\theta\varphi)$ is difficult to draw in a two-dimensional figure. A very interesting set of photographs of mechanical models constructed to simulate the charge cloud in the hydrogen atom appears in H. E. White's "Introduction to Atomic Spectra." The reader will find it instructive to examine these photographs.

9.4 RELATIVISTIC AND SPIN EFFECTS IN THE HYDROGEN ATOM
The Hamiltonian solved in Secs. 9.1 through 9.3 is a nonrelativistic Hamiltonian, so it cannot be truly accurate in representing the actual situation. It is possible to add correction terms to the nonrelativistic

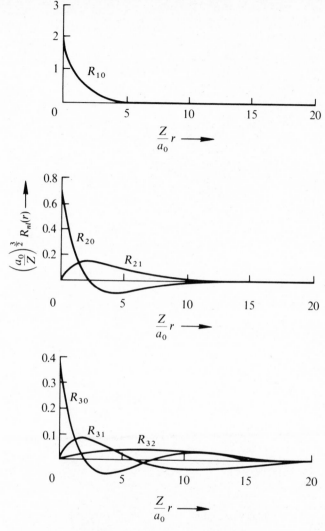

Fig.9.2 $R_{nl}(r)$ *vs.* r *for a few states.*

Hamiltonian to account for the major relativistic effects. However, since it is also possible to solve exactly the full relativistic Hamiltonian for the hydrogen atom, there is not great merit in approaching the problem by a succession of approximations. The relativistic case is beyond the scope of this book, so we will describe only some of the features of the relativistic solution.

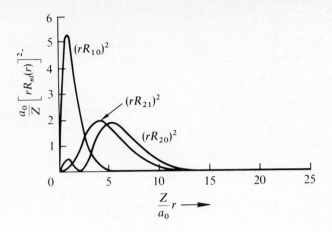

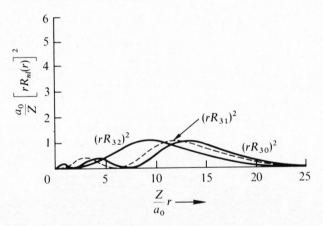

Fig. 9.3 *Radial probability density vs. r.*

The relativistic solution has two principal features not appearing in the nonrelativistic case:

1. States of the same n but different l are no longer degenerate.
2. An additional observable having the dimensions of angular momentum enters the description of the atomic state. This observable we interpret as the *spin* of the electron, and the energy associated with it as a spin-orbit interaction.

Effect 1, the lifting of the degeneracy between states of the same n but different l, can be understood in a qualitative way by thinking of the n and l together as giving a measure of the ellipticity of the electron path involved. For any fixed n, l will range from 0 to $(n - 1)$. For $l = 0$, the electron orbit has no angular momentum associated with it, and may be thought of as a linear orbit (extremely elongated ellipse) passing through the origin. For $l = n - 1$, the electron generates maximum angular momentum and must be in a more nearly circular orbit. Certainly the velocity distributions associated with the two kinds of orbits will differ, the relativistic energy will differ, and the degeneracy of states with the same n but different l will be lifted. The reader is, of course, cautioned not to take the orbital concept too literally; the arguments presented above are intended to be heuristic rather than quantitative. It is perhaps amazing that a calculation (by Sommerfeld) which took the elliptical orbits quite seriously led to a fairly accurate relativistic correction to the non-relativistic Hamiltonian.

The second relativistic effect, the introduction of electron spin and its interaction with its environment, has far-reaching consequences in atomic theory. The angular momentum of Secs. 9.1 and 9.2 was all *orbital* angular momentum. The relativistic theory endows the electron with one more "internal" variable, which behaves for all the world like an angular momentum of magnitude $s = \sqrt{\tfrac{1}{2}(\tfrac{1}{2} + 1)}\,\hbar$, with a z component of angular momentum $m_s = \pm\tfrac{1}{2}\hbar$. This internal variable is regularly identified with spin angular momentum. Spin angular momentum eludes completely the nonrelativistic Schrödinger equation. If we make a model of the electron as a spinning sphere of charge and compute its angular momentum—forming the Schrödinger equation from a classical Hamiltonian by operator substitution as before—we again obtain only integral values for the angular-momentum quantum number. The matrix formulation of the angular-momentum problem, on the other hand, yields half-integral angular momenta and their properties quite naturally, as we shall see in the section immediately following.

The complete specification of the eigenstates of the hydrogenic atom then requires the description of two kinds of angular momentum: orbital angular momentum, whose quantum description involves l and m_l (we add now the subscript l to m), and spin angular momentum, specified by s and m_s. A rigorous treatment of their joint properties and interaction requires mathematical tools—in particular, group theory—not now at our disposal. We can obtain a generally useful understanding of their interrelation on a vector model. We think of **L** and **S** as two vectors which add to form a total vector **J**.

$$\mathbf{L} + \mathbf{S} = \mathbf{J} \tag{9.71}$$

The vector addition can take place in any of several ways, depending on the relative orientations of **L** and **S**, so we may expect j to range from $|l + s|$ to $|l - s|$. The magnitude of **J** will be given, as for all quantum-mechanical angular momenta, by

$$|J| = \sqrt{j(j+1)}\,\hbar \tag{9.72}$$

For the electron $s = \frac{1}{2}$, so each l state of the hydrogen atom will give rise to two j states,

$$j = l + \tfrac{1}{2} \qquad j = l - \tfrac{1}{2} \tag{9.73}$$

except for $l = 0$, where we have only $j = \frac{1}{2}$ possible. If the interaction between **L** and **S** is small or nonexistent, the wave equation is still separable in the φ variable, and m_l and m_s remain "good" quantum numbers. The z component of the total angular momentum **J** will then be

$$\pm m_j = \pm |m_l \pm m_s| \tag{9.74}$$

The maximum possible value of m_j is

$$
\begin{aligned}
(m_j)_{\text{max}} &= (m_l)_{\text{max}} + (m_s)_{\text{max}} \\
&= l + s \\
&= j
\end{aligned} \tag{9.75}
$$

just as was the case for the orbital angular momentum.

There is a magnetic interaction between the magnetic moment associated with the electron's orbital moment and the magnetic moment associated with the electron's spin. This interaction has the form

$$W = A\mathbf{L} \cdot \mathbf{S} \tag{9.76}$$

and causes the state of $\mathbf{J} = \mathbf{L} + \mathbf{S}$ to have somewhat different energy from the state with $\mathbf{J} = \mathbf{L} - \mathbf{S}$. This interaction gives rise to the "multiplet separation" and shows up as a splitting of the absorption or emission lines in the atomic spectra known as "fine structure." A drawing of the hydrogen energy levels, including the relativistic effects 1 and 2, is given in Fig. 9.4.

For multielectron atoms, the potential $V(\mathbf{r})$ in which each electron moves is not simply the coulomb field of the nucleus but rather the nuclear potential plus that due to all the other electrons. The problem of solving for the exact orbit of each electron then becomes very complicated, in fact borders on the hopeless. Whatever the complexities of the individual electron wave functions, the square of the total angular momentum of the electron J^2 and any of its components (J_z, for instance) will remain constants of the motion and may be used to label unambiguously the energy levels of the atom. As long as the problem remains a central-force problem, the angular-momentum eigenfunctions will play a useful role in analyzing the eigenstates of the system.

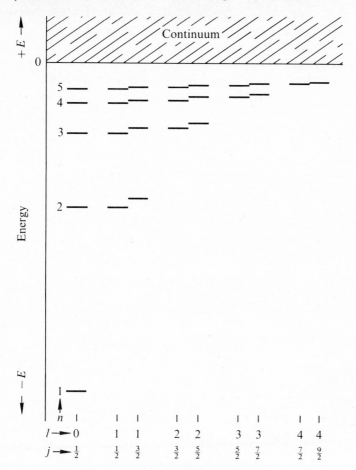

Fig. 9.4 *Hydrogenic energy levels including relativistic and spin effects. (Fine splittings are exaggerated.)*

9.5 THE MATRICES FOR ANGULAR MOMENTUM In Sec. 9.2 we solved the angular portions of the central-force Schrödinger equation, obtaining a set of eigenfunctions which we will now use as basis functions for representing the angular-momentum operators. The angular-momentum operators L^2, L_x, L_y, and L_z are given in Eqs. (9.23), (9.22), and (9.19), respectively. We may obtain the elements of the matrices representing these operators by direct computation:

$$(L_i)_{l,m;\,l',m'} = \langle lm | L_i | l'm' \rangle$$
$$= \int_0^{2\pi} \int_0^{\pi} Y_l^m(\theta,\varphi)^* L_i Y_{l'}^{m'}(\theta,\varphi) \sin\theta \, d\theta \, d\varphi \qquad (9.77)$$

The matrices of $l = 0$ are all trivially equal to zero. The first interesting case is that of $l = 1$. There are three eigenfunctions having $l = 1$: $Y_1^1(\theta,\varphi)$, $Y_1^0(\theta,\varphi)$, and $Y_1^{-1}(\theta,\varphi)$. The matrices generated by these three eigenfunctions will be 3×3 matrices, and we shall choose the convention connecting Schrödinger eigenfunctions and basis vectors to be

$$Y_1^1(\theta,\varphi) = \begin{bmatrix} 1 \\ 0 \\ 0 \end{bmatrix} \qquad Y_1^0(\theta,\varphi) = \begin{bmatrix} 0 \\ 1 \\ 0 \end{bmatrix} \qquad Y_1^{-1}(\theta,\varphi) = \begin{bmatrix} 0 \\ 0 \\ 1 \end{bmatrix} \qquad (9.78)$$

Choosing a different set of correspondences would change only the order of rows and columns in the resultant matrices and not the value of any entry or of any expectation value. The matrices for L^2 and L_z are particularly simple to compute, since the basis functions are eigenfunctions of these operators and the resultant matrices are diagonal.

$$\mathbf{L}^2 = \hbar^2 \begin{bmatrix} 2 & 0 & 0 \\ 0 & 2 & 0 \\ 0 & 0 & 2 \end{bmatrix}$$

$$\mathbf{L}_z = \hbar \begin{bmatrix} 1 & 0 & 0 \\ 0 & 0 & 0 \\ 0 & 0 & -1 \end{bmatrix} \qquad (9.79)$$

The matrices for L_x and L_y require somewhat more computational labor, but using the operators of Eq. (9.22), the eigenfunctions of Eq. (9.43), and the orthogonality relations of Eq. (9.46), we arrive at

$$\mathbf{L}_x = \hbar \begin{bmatrix} 0 & \dfrac{1}{\sqrt{2}} & 0 \\[2mm] \dfrac{1}{\sqrt{2}} & 0 & \dfrac{1}{\sqrt{2}} \\[2mm] 0 & \dfrac{1}{\sqrt{2}} & 0 \end{bmatrix}$$

$$ \qquad (9.80)$$

$$\mathbf{L}_y = \hbar \begin{bmatrix} 0 & -\dfrac{i}{\sqrt{2}} & 0 \\[2mm] \dfrac{i}{\sqrt{2}} & 0 & -\dfrac{i}{\sqrt{2}} \\[2mm] 0 & \dfrac{i}{\sqrt{2}} & 0 \end{bmatrix}$$

Note that although L^2 and L_z are diagonal, the vector operator $L_x\mathbf{i} + L_y\mathbf{j} + L_z\mathbf{k} = \mathbf{L}$ is not. The matrices of Eqs. (9.79) and (9.80) obey the commutation relations peculiar to angular momentum, as we may readily verify by direct matrix multiplication:

$$
L_xL_y - L_yL_x = \hbar
\begin{bmatrix}
0 & \dfrac{1}{\sqrt{2}} & 0 \\[2mm]
\dfrac{1}{\sqrt{2}} & 0 & \dfrac{1}{\sqrt{2}} \\[2mm]
0 & \dfrac{1}{\sqrt{2}} & 0
\end{bmatrix}
\hbar
\begin{bmatrix}
0 & -\dfrac{i}{\sqrt{2}} & 0 \\[2mm]
\dfrac{i}{\sqrt{2}} & 0 & -\dfrac{i}{\sqrt{2}} \\[2mm]
0 & \dfrac{i}{\sqrt{2}} & 0
\end{bmatrix}
$$

$$
- \hbar
\begin{bmatrix}
0 & -\dfrac{i}{\sqrt{2}} & 0 \\[2mm]
\dfrac{i}{\sqrt{2}} & 0 & -\dfrac{i}{\sqrt{2}} \\[2mm]
0 & \dfrac{i}{\sqrt{2}} & 0
\end{bmatrix}
\hbar
\begin{bmatrix}
0 & \dfrac{1}{\sqrt{2}} & 0 \\[2mm]
\dfrac{1}{\sqrt{2}} & 0 & \dfrac{1}{\sqrt{2}} \\[2mm]
0 & \dfrac{1}{\sqrt{2}} & 0
\end{bmatrix}
$$

$$
= \hbar^2
\begin{bmatrix}
\dfrac{i}{2} & 0 & -\dfrac{i}{2} \\[2mm]
0 & 0 & 0 \\[2mm]
\dfrac{i}{2} & 0 & -\dfrac{i}{2}
\end{bmatrix}
- \hbar^2
\begin{bmatrix}
-\dfrac{i}{2} & 0 & -\dfrac{i}{2} \\[2mm]
0 & 0 & 0 \\[2mm]
\dfrac{i}{2} & 0 & \dfrac{i}{2}
\end{bmatrix}
= i\hbar^2
\begin{bmatrix}
1 & 0 & 0 \\
0 & 0 & 0 \\
0 & 0 & -1
\end{bmatrix}
= i\hbar L_z \quad (9.81)
$$

We can verify by direct multiplication that these matrices satisfy the relation

$$
L^2 = L_x^2 + L_y + L_z^2 = \hbar^2
\begin{bmatrix}
0 & \dfrac{1}{\sqrt{2}} & 0 \\[2mm]
\dfrac{1}{\sqrt{2}} & 0 & \dfrac{1}{\sqrt{2}} \\[2mm]
0 & \dfrac{1}{\sqrt{2}} & 0
\end{bmatrix}
\begin{bmatrix}
0 & \dfrac{1}{\sqrt{2}} & 0 \\[2mm]
\dfrac{1}{\sqrt{2}} & 0 & \dfrac{1}{\sqrt{2}} \\[2mm]
0 & \dfrac{1}{\sqrt{2}} & 0
\end{bmatrix}
$$

$$
+ \hbar^2
\begin{bmatrix}
0 & -\dfrac{i}{\sqrt{2}} & 0 \\[2mm]
\dfrac{i}{\sqrt{2}} & 0 & -\dfrac{i}{\sqrt{2}} \\[2mm]
0 & \dfrac{i}{\sqrt{2}} & 0
\end{bmatrix}
\begin{bmatrix}
0 & -\dfrac{i}{\sqrt{2}} & 0 \\[2mm]
\dfrac{i}{\sqrt{2}} & 0 & -\dfrac{i}{\sqrt{2}} \\[2mm]
0 & \dfrac{i}{\sqrt{2}} & 0
\end{bmatrix}
$$

$$
+ \hbar^2
\begin{bmatrix}
1 & 0 & 0 \\
0 & 0 & 0 \\
0 & 0 & -1
\end{bmatrix}
\begin{bmatrix}
1 & 0 & 0 \\
0 & 0 & 0 \\
0 & 0 & -1
\end{bmatrix}
$$

$$
= \hbar^2
\begin{bmatrix}
\tfrac{1}{2} & 0 & \tfrac{1}{2} \\
0 & 1 & 0 \\
\tfrac{1}{2} & 0 & \tfrac{1}{2}
\end{bmatrix}
+ \hbar^2
\begin{bmatrix}
+\tfrac{1}{2} & 0 & -\tfrac{1}{2} \\
0 & 1 & 0 \\
-\tfrac{1}{2} & 0 & +\tfrac{1}{2}
\end{bmatrix}
+ \hbar^2
\begin{bmatrix}
1 & 0 & 0 \\
0 & 0 & 0 \\
0 & 0 & 1
\end{bmatrix}
$$

$$
= \hbar^2
\begin{bmatrix}
2 & 0 & 0 \\
0 & 2 & 0 \\
0 & 0 & 2
\end{bmatrix}
= L^2 \qquad (9.82)
$$

We can also calculate the angular-momentum matrices for the case of $l = 2$. There are five eigenfunctions spanning the space of $l = 2$: $Y_2^2(\theta,\varphi)$, $Y_2^1(\theta,\varphi)$, $Y_2^0(\theta,\varphi)$, $Y_2^{-1}(\theta,\varphi)$, and $Y_2^{-2}(\theta,\varphi)$. These five functions will generate 5×5 matrices for L^2, L_z, L_x, and L_y, just as did the $Y_1^{\pm m}$ for the $l = 1$ case, and these matrices are given at the end of this chapter. We can also verify by direct calculation that there are no matrix elements of $\mathbf{L}$ or $\mathbf{L}^2$ between states of different l, that is,

$$\langle lm| \, \mathbf{L} \, |l'm' \rangle = \delta_{ll'} f(l, mm') \tag{9.83}$$

The seven eigenfunctions belonging to $l = 3$ will generate a set of 7×7 matrices for angular momentum; the nine eigenfunctions belonging to $l = 4$ will generate a set of 9×9 matrices, and so on. All the matrices we generate in this fashion are of odd rank, that is, are of dimension $(2l + 1)$ by $(2l + 1)$. We might well wonder if there are not matrices of even rank, (for instance, 2×2 or 4×4) which will satisfy the commutation relations typical of angular momentum. Consider, for instance, the set of 2×2 matrices

$$L^2 = \hbar^2 \begin{bmatrix} \tfrac{3}{4} & 0 \\ 0 & \tfrac{3}{4} \end{bmatrix} \qquad L_z = \hbar \begin{bmatrix} \tfrac{1}{2} & 0 \\ 0 & -\tfrac{1}{2} \end{bmatrix}$$

$$L_x = \hbar \begin{bmatrix} 0 & \tfrac{1}{2} \\ \tfrac{1}{2} & 0 \end{bmatrix} \qquad L_y = \hbar \begin{bmatrix} 0 & -\dfrac{i}{2} \\ \dfrac{i}{2} & 0 \end{bmatrix} \tag{9.84}$$

As we may quickly verify by direct matrix multiplication, these matrices satisfy the angular-momentum commutation relations and the condition $L^2 = L_x^2 + L_y^2 + L_z^2$. Are they not valid representations of angular momentum, and if so, what is their physical interpretation? They are, of course, the Pauli spin matrices, and represent the angular momentum of a system (particle) having an angular momentum whose maximum projection on any axis is $\hbar/2$, half the value of our $l = 1$ states. These are the matrices representing spin angular momentum, such as is possessed by the electron, proton, or neutron. There may also be constructed matrices of larger even rank, 4×4, 6×6, etc., which obey the angular momentum commutation rules and which are satisfactory representations for the angular momentum of states of larger half-integral angular momentum, $\tfrac{3}{2}$, $\tfrac{5}{2}$, etc. Let us designate the more general angular momentum by $\mathbf{J}$, with components J_x, J_y, and J_z, and include angular momenta of both integral and half-integral value in this definition. Orbital angular momentum, with only integral eigenvalues of L_z, is then a special case of the general angular momentum.

We have written 2×2 matrices for angular momentum without specifying explicitly the eigenfunctions generating the representations. We produced the matrices, verified that they obeyed the same algebra as angular-momentum matrices of more carefully documented pedigree, and then argued that these were physically significant matrices. Can we now produce some explicit eigenfunction, analogous to the $Y_l^{\pm m}(\theta,\varphi)$ eigenfunctions, which will, by direct Schrödinger computation, produce our matrix elements? Surprisingly enough the answer is "No, we cannot." There do not exist analytic functions of θ and φ which will generate the 2×2 angular-momentum matrices, nor in fact generate any of the angular-momentum matrices of even rank. Our wave-equation approach— obtaining Schrödinger's equation by direct operator substitution into a classical non-relativistic Hamiltonian—simply fails to produce any description of half-integral angular momentum. The matrix formulation of quantum mechanics is somewhat more general and more powerful than the wave-equation approach precisely because the matrix formulation does not require explicit eigenfunctions satisfying differential equations in real coordinate space. In particular, a pure matrix treatment of angular momentum, which we develop in the next section, yields correctly the operator matrices of all rank, including those matrices corresponding to half-integral angular momentum.

9.6 PURE MATRIX TREATMENT OF ANGULAR MOMENTUM The matrix treatment of angular momentum resembles in many ways the matrix treatment of the harmonic oscillator (Sec. 6.4). We first establish a relation between successive eigenvalues of the operator involved, allowing us to generate a full set of eigenvalues, given any one; then we introduce some physical argument serving to fix one eigenvalue.

We will designate our angular momentum by **J** rather than **L** to indicate its more general nature, and start with the commutation relations for the angular-momentum matrices.

$$[J_x, J_y] = i\hbar J_z$$
$$[J_y, J_z] = i\hbar J_x \qquad (9.85)$$
$$[J_z, J_x] = i\hbar J_y$$

and $\qquad [J^2, J_x] = [J^2, J_y] = [J^2, J_z] = 0 \qquad (9.86)$

From these commutation relations, we know that we can simultaneously diagonalize J^2 and *one only* of its projections. Let us choose J^2 and J_z to be simultaneously diagonalized. If J^2 and J_z are simultaneously diagonalized, then it will be characteristic of an eigenstate that it will produce one eigenvalue when operated on by J^2 and another, probably different, eigenvalue when operated on by J_z. Each eigenfunction needs, then, two labels, one specifying the J^2 eigenvalue and the other specifying the J_z eigenvalue. Let us call these two labels j and m_j, and designate our typical eigenfunction by $|j,m_j\rangle$. This eigenfunction has the property

$$J^2|j,m_j\rangle = f(j)\hbar^2|j,m_j\rangle$$
$$J_z|j,m_j\rangle = g(m_j)\hbar|j,m_j\rangle$$

(9.87)

We have included the $\hbar^2$ and $\hbar$ in our eigenvalue equations because we know that J^2 and J_z will have the dimensions of $\hbar^2$ and $\hbar$, respectively, and $f(j)$ and $g(m_j)$ will therefore have the dimensions of pure numbers (a convenience in later manipulation). At this point we do not know the functional form of $f(j)$ and $g(m_j)$. Let us set $g(m_j) = m_j$. This does not represent an assumption about our spectrum of eigenvalues, only an agreement to write in the second position of our eigenfunction $|j,m_j\rangle$ whatever numeric value the eigenvalue of J_z assumes for that state, an agreement on the convention to be used in labeling the eigenstate. We have then

$$J_z|j,m_j\rangle = m_j\hbar|j,m_j\rangle$$

(9.88)

It will turn out that this is a convenient convention for J_z but not for J^2; we will accordingly leave the eigenvalue of J^2 as $f(j)$. We label the eigenfunction of J^2 not by the eigenvalue of J^2 but by the argument of some function which gives the eigenvalue of J^2. Consider now the operators

$$J_+ = J_x + iJ_y$$
$$J_- = J_x - iJ_y = J_+^\dagger$$

(9.89)

These operators are the Hermitian adjoints of one another, but are not themselves Hermitian. Using the commutation relations of Eq. (9.85), we can show that

$$J_zJ_\pm = J_\pm(J_z \pm \hbar)$$

(9.90)

from which it follows that

$$J_zJ_\pm|j,m_j\rangle = J_\pm(J_z \pm \hbar)|j,m_j\rangle$$
$$= J_\pm(m_j\hbar \pm \hbar)|j,m_j\rangle$$
$$= (m_j \pm 1)\hbar J_\pm|j,m_j\rangle$$

(9.91)

Equation (9.91) tells us that if $|j,m_j\rangle$ is an eigenfunction of J_z belonging to the eigenvalue $m_j\hbar$, then $J_+|j,m_j\rangle$ is an eigenfunction of J_z belonging to the eigenvalue $(m_j + 1)\hbar$ and that $J_-\,|\,j,m_j\rangle$ is an eigenfunction of J_z belonging to the eigenvalue $(m_j - 1)\hbar$.

$$J_z(J_+\,|\,j,m_j\rangle) = (m_j + 1)\hbar(J_+\,|\,j,m_j\rangle)$$
$$J_z(J_-\,|\,j,m_j\rangle) = (m_j - 1)\hbar(J_-\,|\,j,m_j\rangle)$$
(9.92)

J_+ is called the *promotion operator* and J_- is called the *demotion operator*. They are both called *ladder operators*, because between them they generate, given one eigenstate m_j, a ladder of equally spaced (by $\hbar$) eigenstates of J_z.

$$J_\pm\,|\,j,m_j\rangle = N_\pm\,|\,j,m_j \pm 1\rangle$$
(9.93)

$N_\pm$ is a scalar (perhaps complex) required to specify the effect of $J_\pm$ on the normalization of the eigenstate as it is promoted or demoted.

We know from physical arguments, however, that the ladder of J_z eigenvalues cannot extend indefinitely in both directions, because $J^2 = J_x^2 + J_y^2 + J_z^2$, and the magnitude of the z component of J cannot exceed $|\mathbf{J}| = (J \cdot J)^{\frac{1}{2}}$. For every value of $|\mathbf{J}|$, specified somehow by the label j, there exist a maximum m_j and a minimum m_j, such that their squares are less than $|J^2|$. Let us call these values m_j^g (greatest m_j) and m_j^l (least m_j), respectively. For these states

$$J_+\,|\,j,m_j^g\rangle = 0$$
(9.94)

and
$$J_-\,|\,j,m_j^l\rangle = 0$$
(9.95)

The state of greatest m_j can be promoted no further and the state of least m_j can be demoted (toward large negative values) no further. Operating on Eq. (9.94) with J_-, we have

$$J_-J_+\,|\,j,m_j^g\rangle = 0$$
$$(J_x - iJ_y)(J_x + iJ_y)\,|\,j,m_j^g\rangle = 0$$
$$[J_x^2 + J_y^2 + i(J_xJ_y - J_yJ_x)]\,|\,j,m_j^g\rangle = 0$$
$$(J^2 - J_z^2 - \hbar J_z)\,|\,j,m_j^g\rangle = 0$$
$$[f(j)\hbar^2 - m_j^{g2}\hbar^2 - m_j^g\hbar^2]\,|\,j,m_j^g\rangle = 0$$
(9.96)

Since
$$\langle j,m_j^g\,|\,j,m_j^g\rangle = 1$$
(9.97)

the expansion in brackets must be equal to zero:

$$f(j) = m_j^g(m_j^g + 1)$$
(9.98)

On the other hand, if we operate on Eq. (9.95) with J_+, we obtain

$$J_+J_-\,|\,j,m_j^l\rangle = 0$$
$$(J_x + iJ_y)(J_x - iJ_y)\,|\,j, m_j^l\rangle = 0$$
$$[J_x^2 + J_y^2 - i(J_xJ_y - J_yJ_x)]\,|\,j,m_j^l\rangle = 0$$
$$(J^2 - J_z^2 + \hbar J_z)\,|\,j,m_j^l\rangle = 0$$
$$[f(j)\hbar^2 - m_j^{l2}\hbar^2 + m_j^l\hbar^2]\,|\,j,m_j^l\rangle = 0$$
(9.99)

Again, since

$$\langle j, m_j^l \mid j, m_j^l \rangle = 1 \tag{9.100}$$

the expression in brackets must be equal to zero:

$$f(j) = +m_j^l(m_j^l - 1) \tag{9.101}$$

For Eqs. (9.98) and (9.101) both to be true it is necessary that

$$m_j^l = -m_j^g \tag{9.102}$$

The least allowed value of m_j is exactly the negative of the greatest allowed value. The ladder of equally spaced (by $\hbar$) eigenvalues must be symmetrically disposed about zero. If the ladder has an odd number of rungs, the J_z eigenvalues will be disposed as follows:

$$m_j^g, m_j^g - 1, \ldots, +2, +1, 0, -1, -2, \ldots, (m_j^g - 1), -m_j^g \tag{9.103}$$

and the largest value m_j^g will be an integer.

If there is an even number of rungs on the ladder, the J_z eigenvalues will be disposed as follows:

$$m_j^g, m_j^g - 1, \ldots, +\tfrac{3}{2}, +\tfrac{1}{2}, -\tfrac{1}{2}, -\tfrac{3}{2}, \ldots, -(m_j^g - 1), -m_j^g \tag{9.104}$$

and the maximum value m_j^g will be half integral. Furthermore, we have established through Eq. (9.98) or (9.101) the value of $f(j)$ needed to specify the eigenvalues of J^2. We simply give to m_j^g the name of j,

$$j = m_j^g = |m_j^l| \tag{9.105}$$

and use this maximum value of the z component of angular momentum as the label for our eigenfunctions of J^2. We have then

$$J^2 | j, m_j \rangle = j(j+1)\hbar^2 | j, m_j \rangle \tag{9.106}$$

The states with integral m_j^g correspond to the states of integral angular momentum, representable by the $Y_l^m(\theta, \varphi)$; the states with half integral m_j^g correspond to the states of half-integral angular momentum, absent in the Schrödinger treatment.

We now know all we need to know to write the (diagonal) matrices for J^2 and J_z. These matrices are given in Tables 9.3 and 9.4. We see that there are $2j + 1$ values of m_j associated with each j value, and the correspondence to the earlier treatment of angular momentum is apparent.

We are also now in a position to determine the matrices for J_x and J_y. We do so by first determining the matrices for J_+ and J_-, whose entries are, in fact, the scalars $N_{\pm}$ of Eq. (9.93).

$$\langle j', m_j' | J_+ | j, m_j \rangle = N_+(j,m_j)\langle j', m_j' \mid j, m_j + 1 \rangle$$
$$= N_+(j,m_j)\, \delta_{j'j}\, \delta_{m_j',m_j+1} \tag{9.107}$$

and
$$\langle j', m_j' | J_- | j, m_j \rangle = N_-(j,m_j)\langle j', m_j' \mid j, m_j - 1 \rangle$$
$$= N_-(j,m_j)\, \delta_{j'j}\, \delta_{m_j',m_j-1} \tag{9.108}$$

The Hydrogen Atom: Central Forces and Angular Momentum

TABLE 9.3

Matrix of J^2. States Are Labeled along the Top of the Matrix

j	½	½	1	1	1	3/2	3/2	3/2	3/2	2	2	2	$\cdots$
m_j	+½	−½	+1	0	−1	+3/2	+½	−½	−3/2	+2	+1	0	$\cdots$

$$J^2 = \hbar^2$$

3/4	0		0				0				0	
0	3/4											
		2	0	0								
0		0	2	0			0				0	
		0	0	2								
					15/4	0	0	0				
0		0			0	15/4	0	0			0	
					0	0	15/4	0				
					0	0	0	15/4				
									6	0	0	$\cdots$
0		0					0		0	6	0	$\cdots$
									0	0	6	$\cdots$

where we have further labeled the N_+ and N_- with j and m_j to indicate the state upon which $J_\pm$ is operating. The matrices for J_+ and J_- will be "diagonal in j," that is, the matrices will have nonzero elements only between states of the same j, and "off diagonal by one in m_j," that is, they will have nonzero elements only between states differing by one in

TABLE 9.4

Matrix of J_z. States Are Labeled along the Top of the Matrix

	½	½	1	1	1	3/2	3/2	3/2	3/2	2	2	2	2	2
m_j	+½	−½	+1	0	−1	+3/2	+½	−½	−3/2	+2	+1	0	−1	−2

$$J_z = \hbar$$

+½	0		0				0				0		
0	−½												
		+1	0	0									
0		0	0	0			0				0		
		0	0	−1									
					+3/2	0	0	0					
0		0			0	+½	0	0			0		
					0	0	−½	0					
					0	0	0	−3/2					
									+2	0	0	0	0
									0	+1	0	0	0
0		0					0		0	0	0	0	0
									0	0	0	−1	0
									0	0	0	0	−2

TABLE 9.5

Matrix of J_+. States Are Labeled at the Top of the Matrix

j	½	½	1	1	1	3/2	3/2	3/2	3/2	2	2	2	2	⋯
m_j	+½	−½	+1	0	−1	+3/2	+½	−½	−3/2	+2	+1	0	−1	⋯
	0	1	0	0	0	0	0	0	0	0	0	0	0	
	0	0	0	0	0	0	0	0	0	0	0	0	0	
	0	0	0	$\sqrt{2}$	0	0	0	0	0	0	0	0	0	
	0	0	0	0	$\sqrt{2}$	0	0	0	0	0	0	0	0	
	0	0	0	0	0	0	0	0	0	0	0	0	0	
$J_+ = \hbar$	0	0	0	0	0	0	$\sqrt{3}$	0	0	0	0	0	0	
	0	0	0	0	0	0	0	2	0	0	0	0	0	
	0	0	0	0	0	0	0	0	$\sqrt{3}$	0	0	0	0	
	0	0	0	0	0	0	0	0	0	0	0	0	0	
	0	0	0	0	0	0	0	0	0	0	2	0	0	⋯
	0	0	0	0	0	0	0	0	0	0	0	$\sqrt{6}$	0	⋯
	0	0	0	0	0	0	0	0	0	0	0	0	$\sqrt{6}$	⋯
	0	0	0	0	0	0	0	0	0	0	0	0	0	⋯

TABLE 9.6

Matrix of J_-. States Are Labeled at the Top of the Matrix

j	½	½	1	1	1	3/2	3/2	3/2	3/2	2	2	2	2	⋯
m_j	+½	−½	+1	0	−1	+3/2	+½	−½	−3/2	+2	+1	0	−1	⋯
	0	0	0	0	0	0	0	0	0	0	0	0	0	
	1	0	0	0	0	0	0	0	0	0	0	0	0	
	0	0	0	0	0	0	0	0	0	0	0	0	0	
	0	0	$\sqrt{2}$	0	0	0	0	0	0	0	0	0	0	
	0	0	0	$\sqrt{2}$	0	0	0	0	0	0	0	0	0	
$J_- = \hbar$	0	0	0	0	0	0	0	0	0	0	0	0	0	
	0	0	0	0	0	$\sqrt{3}$	0	0	0	0	0	0	0	
	0	0	0	0	0	0	2	0	0	0	0	0	0	
	0	0	0	0	0	0	0	$\sqrt{3}$	0	0	0	0	0	
	0	0	0	0	0	0	0	0	0	0	0	0	0	⋯
	0	0	0	0	0	0	0	0	0	2	0	0	0	⋯
	0	0	0	0	0	0	0	0	0	0	$\sqrt{6}$	0	0	⋯
	0	0	0	0	0	0	0	0	0	0	0	$\sqrt{6}$	0	⋯

m_j. Further, since J_+ and J_- are Hermitian adjoints of each other, their matrix elements will be related by

$$\langle j, m_j + 1| J_+ | j, m_j \rangle = \langle j, m_j| J_- | j, m_j + 1 \rangle^*$$
$$\langle j, m_j - 1| J_- | j, m_j \rangle = \langle j, m_j| J_+ | j, m_j - 1 \rangle^* \qquad (9.109)$$

Suppose we operate successively on some state $|j,m_j\rangle$ with J_+ and J_-:

$$\begin{aligned}
J_- J_+ |j,m_j\rangle &= J_- N_+(j,m_j) |j, m_j + 1\rangle \\
&= J_- \langle j, m_j + 1| J_+ | j, m_j \rangle |j, m_j + 1\rangle \\
&= \langle j, m_j + 1| J_+ | j, m_j \rangle J_- |j, m_j + 1\rangle \\
&= \langle j, m_j + 1| J_+ | j, m_j \rangle N_-(j, m_j + 1) |j, m_j\rangle \\
&= \langle j, m_j + 1| J_+ | j, m_j \rangle \langle j, m_j| J_- | j, m_j + 1\rangle |j, m_j\rangle \\
&= |\langle j, m_j + 1| J_+ | j, m_j \rangle|^2 |j, m_j\rangle \\
&= |\langle j, m_j| J_- | j, m_j + 1\rangle|^2 |j, m_j\rangle \qquad (9.110)
\end{aligned}$$

where the last two steps follow from Eq. (9.109). We know also from Eqs. (9.96) and (9.106) that

$$\begin{aligned}
J_- J_+ |j, m_j\rangle &= (J^2 - J_z^2 - \hbar J_z) |j, m_j\rangle \\
&= \hbar^2 [j(j+1) - m_j(m_j + 1)] |j, m_j\rangle \qquad (9.111)
\end{aligned}$$

Equating $\langle j,m_j| J_- J_+ |j,m_j\rangle$ calculated from Eq. (9.110) with the same quantity evaluated using Eq. (9.111), we have

$$|\langle j, m_j + 1| J_+ | j, m_j \rangle|^2 \langle j, m_j | j, m_j\rangle$$
$$= \hbar^2 [j(j+1) - m_j(m_j + 1)] \langle j, m_j | j, m_j\rangle \quad (9.112)$$

$$|\langle j, m_j + 1| J_+ | j, m_j \rangle|^2 = \hbar^2 [j(j+1) - m_j(m_j + 1)]$$

or
$$\langle j, m_j + 1| J_+ | j, m_j \rangle = \hbar\sqrt{j(j+1) - m_j(m_j + 1)} \qquad (9.113)$$

where we have assumed that the scalars $N_\pm$ and the matrix elements of $J_\pm$ are real. Making this assumption is equivalent to assuming a particular convention concerning the phases of states of successive m_j values. Fortunately, choosing these elements real is not only convenient here but also corresponds to the same convention implicitly assumed when we use the $Y_l^{\pm m}(\theta,\varphi)$ as the basis functions for representing the angular momenta of integral magnitude. Using Eq. (9.113) and the Hermitian adjoint relation between J_+ and J_-, we may now write these two matrices, as is done in Tables 9.5 and 9.6.

Finally, from the definitions of J_+ and J_-, we know that

$$J_x = \tfrac{1}{2}(J_+ + J_-) \qquad J_y = \frac{1}{2i}(J_+ - J_-) \qquad (9.114)$$

TABLE 9.7

Matrix of J_x. States Are Labeled at the Top of the Matrix

j	½	½	1	1	1	3/2	3/2	3/2	3/2	2	2	2	2	$\cdots$
m_j	$+\frac12$	$-\frac12$	$+1$	0	-1	$+\frac32$	$+\frac12$	$-\frac12$	$-\frac32$	$+2$	$+1$	0	-1	$\cdots$

$J_x = \hbar$

0	$\frac12$												
$\frac12$	0												
		0	$\frac{1}{\sqrt2}$	0									
		$\frac{1}{\sqrt2}$	0	$\frac{1}{\sqrt2}$									
		0	$\frac{1}{\sqrt2}$	0									
					0	$\frac{\sqrt3}{2}$	0	0					
					$\frac{\sqrt3}{2}$	0	1	0					
					0	1	0	$\frac{\sqrt3}{2}$					
					0	0	$\frac{\sqrt3}{2}$	0					
									0	1	0	0	$\cdots$
									1	0	$\frac{\sqrt6}{2}$	0	$\cdots$
									0	$\frac{\sqrt6}{2}$	0	$\frac{\sqrt6}{2}$	$\cdots$

TABLE 9.8

Matrix of J_y. States Are Labeled at the Top of the Matrix

j	½	½	1	1	1	3/2	3/2	3/2	3/2	2	2	2	2	$\cdots$
m_j	$+\frac12$	$-\frac12$	$+1$	0	-1	$+\frac32$	$+\frac12$	$-\frac12$	$-\frac32$	$+2$	$+1$	0	-1	$\cdots$

$J_y = \hbar$

0	$-\frac{i}{2}$												
$\frac{i}{2}$	0												
		0	$\frac{-i}{\sqrt2}$	0									
		$\frac{i}{\sqrt2}$	0	$\frac{-i}{\sqrt2}$									
		0	$\frac{i}{\sqrt2}$	0									
					0	$\frac{-i\sqrt3}{2}$	0	0					
					$\frac{i\sqrt3}{2}$	0	$-i$	0					
					0	i	0	$\frac{-i\sqrt3}{2}$					
					0	0	$\frac{i\sqrt3}{2}$	0					
									0	$-i$	0	0	$\cdots$
									i	0	$\frac{-i\sqrt6}{2}$	0	$\cdots$
									0	$\frac{i\sqrt6}{2}$	0	$\frac{-i\sqrt6}{2}$	$\cdots$

200

so we can construct the matrices for J_x and J_y directly from those of J_+ and J_-. The matrices for J_x and J_y are given in Tables 9.7 and 9.8.

We have now therefore derived the matrices for J^2 and for any component of **J**, for any allowed j or m_j, integral or half integral, by purely matrix techniques and without ever solving explicitly for an eigenfunction

9.7 THE SACRED z DIRECTION AND CHANGE OF COORDINATE AXES

From the commutation relations of Eqs. (9.85) and (9.86), we know that we may construct a set of eigenfunctions of the angular-momentum operators which are simultaneously eigenfunctions of J^2 and of any one component of **J**, or, equivalently, that the matrices of J^2 and of any one component of **J** may be simultaneously diagonal. The component of **J** chosen to share eigenfunctions with J^2 seems inevitably to be the z component J_z, and the reader may well have begun to suspect that there is more to this uniform practice than meets the eye. So we shall take a moment to discuss the selection of coordinate frames, as applied to angular momentum.

For a system displaying spherical symmetry (e.g., the hydrogen atom), all directions are equivalent. Let us suppose that the system (an atom, for instance) has nonzero angular momentum, and let us choose its angular momentum (for purposes of concrete illustration) to correspond to $j = \frac{3}{2}$. The magnitude of the angular momentum is then $|\mathbf{J}| = \sqrt{j(j+1)}\,\hbar = \sqrt{15/4}\,\hbar$. If we measure the projection of this angular momentum upon any direction in space, we will obtain the value $\pm\frac{3}{2}\hbar$ or $\pm\frac{1}{2}\hbar$. If we measure the projection of this angular momentum upon some other axis in space, tilted 5, 15, or 90° away from the first, we will still obtain the values $\pm\frac{3}{2}\hbar$ or $\pm\frac{1}{2}\hbar$. The relative probability with which we obtain the various allowed values will depend upon the previous preparation of the system and upon the choice of axes, but the eigenvalues of the projection of angular momentum upon any axis are the same.

In the preceding section we derived matrices for J_z, J_x, and J_y in a representation which caused J_z to be diagonal. Consider now the J_x matrix. There exists some unitary transformation S_1 which will diagonalize the J_x matrix.

$$S_1 J_x S_1^{-1} = J_x' \tag{9.115}$$

where J_x' is diagonal. The diagonalized matrix J_x' will be identical with the J_z matrix of Table 9.4. The matrix for J_z in the new representation

$$S_1 J_z S_1^{-1} = J_z' \tag{9.116}$$

will no longer be diagonal, and the S_1 transformation will also convert J_y from one nondiagonal matrix to J_y', another nondiagonal matrix. The new set of matrices J'_x, J'_y, and J'_z is in every way as good a representation of the angular-momentum operators as was the original set. The two sets differ only in that the primed set has J'_x diagonal while the unprimed set had J_z diagonal. Similarly, we could produce a different unitary transformation S_2 which will generate J''_x, J''_y, and J''_z, where J''_y is diagonal and looks entirely like the J_z matrix of Table 9.4. The choice of representation for the spherically symmetric case is purely a matter of taste and convenience.

If we remove the spherical symmetry of the system by the application of an electric or magnetic field, all directions in space are no longer physically equivalent. One direction is unique, and it is only reasonable to choose a coordinate frame reflecting the physical situation. If we were faced with solving an electromagnetic boundary-value problem involving a cylindrical conductor, we would certainly choose a coordinate frame with one axis along the cylinder axis. The charge distribution will not depend upon the coordinate frame chosen for its description, but the description will certainly be easier in an appropriate coordinate scheme than in an inappropriate one. Similarly, if we can simultaneously diagonalize J^2 and only one component of $\mathbf{J}$, it is reasonable to choose the component of $\mathbf{J}$ along the physically unique axis to be diagonalized, rather than some arbitrary oblique component. The unique axis is almost invariably called the z *axis* (by analogy with the unique axis in spherical and cylindrical coordinate schemes). Hence, the diagonalized component of $\mathbf{J}$ is usually called J_z, a usage which is generally carried over even to the spherically symmetric case where there is indeed no unique axis.

In short, if the physical situation we wish to describe quantum-mechanically has some unique axis, we generally call this axis the z axis and choose J_z as the component of angular momentum to share eigenfunctions with J^2. If there is no unique axis to the problem, we may choose any arbitrary direction in space as our mathematically (but not physically) unique z axis. By choosing this axis for our z coordinate, we in no way render the direction physically unique.

Summary

Angular momentum, introduced in this chapter, plays a very important role in the quantum mechanics of atomic systems. Some of the important points to remember from Chap. 9 are:

Schrödinger's equation for a nonrelativistic central-force problem is always separable in radial and angular coordinates, no matter what the specific form of $V(r)$.

The angular portions of the separated Schrödinger equation involve a differential operator in θ and φ. This operator is in fact the operator to be associated with L^2, the square of the orbital angular momentum of the state. The resultant eigenvalue equation is

$$L^2_{\text{op}} Y^m_l(\theta,\varphi) = l(l+1)\hbar^2 Y^m_l(\theta,\varphi)$$

A satisfactory set of eigenfunctions of the L^2 operator are the spherical harmonics $Y^m_l(\theta,\varphi)$, and the eigenvalue associated with any $Y^m_l(\theta,\varphi)$ is $l(l+1)\hbar^2$, where l is an integer.

If the angular portion of the Schrödinger equation is further separated in θ and φ, the operator involved in the φ equation is in fact the operator to be associated with L_z, and the resultant eigenvalue equation is

$$(L_z)_{\text{op}} e^{\pm im\varphi} = \pm m\hbar e^{\pm im\varphi}$$

The eigenfunctions of L_z are the functions $e^{\pm im\varphi}$, and the eigenvalues of L_z are $\pm m\hbar$, where m is an integer equal to or less than l.

The commutation relations for angular momentum, of which orbital angular momentum (**L**) is a special case, are

$$[J_x, J_y] = i\hbar J_z$$
$$[J_y, J_z] = i\hbar J_x$$
$$[J_z, J_x] = i\hbar J_y$$

and $$[J^2, J_x] = [J^2, J_y] = [J^2, J_z] = 0$$

The former set can be written in brief as $\mathbf{J} \times \mathbf{J} = i\hbar\mathbf{J}$.

The eigenvalues of J^2 are $j(j+1)\hbar^2$, where j is integral or half integral. These eigenvalues may be obtained by pure matrix techniques. Angular momentum, generally considered, contains orbital angular momentum as a special case, that for which the angular-momentum quantum number is integral. There does not exist a set of analytic functions of θ and φ which constitute (in the Schrödinger sense) a set of eigenfunctions for the half-integral angular-momentum states.

The eigenvalues of J_z are $m_j\hbar$, where m_j takes on the integral or half-integral values $j, j-1, j-2, \ldots, -(j-2), -(j-1), -j$. Again L_z is a special case of J_z, the case where the eigenvalues are all integral.

Two very useful operators in problems pertaining to angular momentum are the promotion and demotion operators J_+ and J_-, defined by

$$J_+ = J_x + iJ_y \qquad J_- = J_x - iJ_y$$

which have the properties

$$J_+ |j, m_j\rangle = \hbar\sqrt{j(j+1) - m_j(m_j+1)} \, |j, m_j+1\rangle$$
$$J_- |j, m_j\rangle = \hbar\sqrt{j(j+1) - m_j(m_j-1)} \, |j, m_j-1\rangle$$

The angular-momentum eigenvalues may be used to classify the eigenfunctions of any central-force Hamiltonian, independent of the specific form of the potential $V(r)$.

If $V(r)$ is the coulombic potential

$$V(r) = -\frac{Ze^2}{r}$$

the eigenvalues of the Hamiltonian are

$$E_n = -\frac{mZ^2e^4}{2\hbar^2 n^2}$$

where n is a nonzero integer.

The eigenfunctions of the radial portion of Schrödinger's equation are related to Laguerre's associated polynomials, and are plotted in most textbooks on quantum mechanics.

Problems

9.1 An "unpolarized" beam of particles is one for which $\langle J_x \rangle = \langle J_y \rangle = \langle J_z \rangle = 0$. Write the angular-momentum state function for an unpolarized particle of $J = 1$.

9.2 An important experiment in the history of quantum physics was the Stern-Gerlach experiment, which measured the z component of angular momentum of atoms of silver. The experiment involves observing the translational motion imparted to the atoms by the interaction of the magnetic dipole moment of the atom with a nonhomogeneous magnetic field. Prove, for an atom with a magnetic moment $\boldsymbol{\mu} = g\mathbf{J}$ placed in a magnetic field oriented in the z direction but with nonvanishing derivatives $\partial H/\partial x$, $\partial H/\partial y$, and $\partial H/\partial z$, that the translational force upon the atom is

$$\mathbf{F} = gJ_z \frac{\partial H}{\partial z} \mathbf{z_0}$$

where $\mathbf{z_0}$ is a unit vector in the z direction.

9.3 An unpolarized beam of atoms of angular-momentum quantum number $J = 1$ passes through a z-oriented nonhomogeneous magnetic field, as in Fig. P9.3.

What would you expect classically to be the beam shape and distribution of atoms at the target?

Into how many beams does quantum mechanics predict that the incident beam will be split by the deflecting magnet?

What will be the relative intensities of the emergent component beams?

Write the state function for the particles in the uppermost emergent beam.

Imagine that the uppermost beam has been deflected to such an extent that it is physically separated from the other beams. This uppermost beam is then passed through a second deflecting magnet identical with the first except that it has been rotated an angle θ about the y axis. Into how many beams is the upper beam now split? What are the relative intensities of the beams into which it is split?

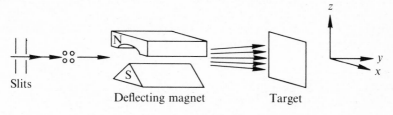

Fig. P9.3

9.4 A beam of ammonia molecules is sent through a focusing structure which spatially separates states having different values of L_z. [The ammonia molecule is a symmetric rotor (see Prob. 4.2).] The beam is unpolarized before passing through the focusing structure and is composed of states of rotational quantum number 0, 1, and 2 in relative abundance 10, 6, and 1, respectively.

    a What is the expectation value of the rotational energy of the incident beam?

    b Into how many emergent beams is the incident beam split?

    c What are the relative intensities of the emergent beams?

    d What is the expectation value of the rotational energy in each of the emergent beams?

If the incident beam is in thermal equilibrium with its environment, any of the emergent beams having an expectation value of rotational energy greater than that of the incident will try to get rid of the excess energy by spontaneous or induced emission, i.e., are potential maser beams.

    e Are any of the emergent beams of the above apparatus potential maser beams, and if so, which ones?

9.5 An important interaction in atoms is the $\mathbf{L} \cdot \mathbf{S}$ interaction. Express the operator $\mathbf{L} \cdot \mathbf{S}$ in terms of L_z and S_z and in terms of the promotion and demotion operators $L_\pm$ and $S_\pm$.

Bibliograpy

Perhaps the most complete Schrödinger treatment of the hydrogenic atom is given in:

Pauling, L., and E. B. Wilson: "Introduction to Quantum Mechanics," chap. 5, McGraw-Hill Book Company, New York, 1935.

Other complete Schrödinger treatments are:

Eisberg, R. M.: "Fundamentals of Modern Physics," chap. 10, John Wiley & Sons, Inc., New York, 1961.

Leighton, R. B.: "Principles of Modern Physics," chap. 5, McGraw-Hill Book Company, New York, 1959.

Merzbacher, E.: "Quantum Mechanics," chap. 9, John Wiley & Sons, Inc., New York, 1961.

Schiff, L. I.: "Quantum Mechanics," 2d ed., chap. 4, McGraw-Hill Book Company, New York, 1955.

The matrix representation of angular momentum is presented in:

Schiff, L. I.: "Quantum Mechanics," 2d ed., chap. 6, McGraw-Hill Book Company, New York, 1955.

Dicke, R. H., and J. P. Wittke: "Introduction to Quantum Mechanics," chap. 12, Addison-Wesley Publishing Company, Inc., Reading, Mass., 1960.

Messiah, A.: "Quantum Mechanics," vol. 2, chap. 13, Interscience Publishers, Inc., New York, 1962.

Bohm, D.: "Quantum Theory," chap. 17, Prentice-Hall, Inc., Englewood Cliffs, N.J., 1951.

CHAPTER 10

Time-Independent
Perturbation Theory

10.1 PERTURBATION THEORY FOR NONDEGENERATE SYSTEMS The great majority of problems for which quantum mechanics has proved valuable cannot be solved exactly. The experimental evidence we collect concerning atomic, gaseous, and solid-state systems usually involves the interaction of the subject system with an electric or magnetic field—static, radio-frequency, or optical. The presence of the measuring fields themselves may well render impossible the exact solution of the system properties. Add an externally generated electric or magnetic field to even such a simple dynamical system as the hydrogen atom, and the associated quantum-mechanical eigenvalue problem cannot be solved exactly.

It is, on the other hand, often possible to solve exactly for the properties of a system closely resembling the actual system and to correct for the differences by using some form of perturbation theory. To find the properties of the hydrogen atom in the presence of an electric field, for instance, we would solve for the properties of the free hydrogen atom and then calculate how these properties would be altered as an electric field is added. If a convergent scheme of calculating these "perturbation effects" is available, the actual problem can, in principle, be solved to any desired degree of accuracy. We will now develop the foundations of perturbation theory, starting with the time-independent case.

Suppose we have a time-independent Hamiltonian H, in operator form, for which we seek the eigenfunction and eigenvalues.

$$H\psi_k = E_k\psi_k \tag{10.1}$$

Suppose further that H can be divided into a dominant part H^0, which is solvable exactly and for which we know the eigenfunctions and eigenvalues, and a smaller part H', which we will regard as a perturbation on the original system described by H^0.

$$H = H^0 + H' \tag{10.2}$$

For such an approach to be valid it is necessary that the energy associated with H^0 be substantially greater than that associated with H'. It is a useful artifice to write

$$H = H^0 + \lambda H' \tag{10.3}$$

where λ is a variable parameter which we ultimately set equal to 1. If $\lambda \to 0$, the perturbed Hamiltonian reduces to the simpler Hamiltonian H^0, and by letting λ grow from 0 to 1, we introduce an artifice which enables us to trace the development of our perturbed solutions from the unperturbed solutions. Let us write these known unperturbed eigenfunctions and eigenvalues as

$$H^0 u_n = E_n^0 u_n \tag{10.4}$$

where the u_n and E_n^0 represent the known eigenfunctions and the known eigenvalues, respectively. We assume for the present developments that E_n^0 is nondegenerate, i.e., that one distinct u_n is associated with each E_n^0. We next make a formal expansion of our desired eigenfunctions and eigenvalues, the solutions of Eq. (10.1), as power series in the perturbation parameter λ.

$$\psi_k = \psi_{0k} + \lambda \psi_{1k} + \lambda^2 \psi_{2k} + \lambda^3 \psi_{3k} + \cdots$$
$$E_k = E_{0k} + \lambda E_{1k} + \lambda^2 E_{2k} + \lambda^3 E_{3k} + \cdots \tag{10.5}$$

The subscripts $0k$, $1k$, $2k$, etc., refer to successively smaller corrections to the unperturbed wave functions and eigenvalues, as we shall see below. In the limit $\lambda \to 0$, the perturbation vanishes, and we know that the perturbed ψ_k and E_k reduce to the unperturbed solutions.

$$\psi_k \to \psi_{0k} \equiv u_k \qquad \text{as } \lambda \to 0$$
$$E_k \to E_{0k} \equiv E_k^0 \qquad \text{as } \lambda \to 0 \tag{10.6}$$

We therefore have immediately the leading, or zeroth-order, terms of the perturbation solution. Again we see that our perturbation approach will have validity only if there is some u_k which is very similar to the actual ψ_k, and some E_k^0 not very different from the actual E_k.

The important part of our perturbation theory deals, of course, with those terms in Eq. (10.5) which depend on λ and cannot be estimated from the $\lambda = 0$ case. To solve for those terms, we substitute the expansions of Eq. (10.5) into the Hamiltonian eigenvalue equation (10.3):

$$(H^0 + \lambda H')(\psi_{0k} + \lambda \psi_{1k} + \lambda^2 \psi_{2k} + \cdots)$$
$$= (E_{0k} + \lambda E_{1k} + \lambda^2 E_{2k} + \cdots)(\psi_{0k} + \lambda \psi_{1k} + \lambda^2 \psi_{2k} + \cdots) \tag{10.7}$$

Both sides of Eq. (10.7) can be rewritten as polynomials in λ:

$$H^0\psi_{0k} + \lambda(H^0\psi_{1k} + H'\psi_{0k}) + \lambda^2(H^0\psi_{2k} + H'\psi_{1k}) + \cdots$$
$$= E_{0k}\psi_{0k} + \lambda(E_{0k}\psi_{1k} + E_{1k}\psi_{0k}) + \lambda^2(E_{0k}\psi_{2k} + E_{1k}\psi_{1k} + E_{2k}\psi_{0k}) + \cdots$$
$$(10.8)$$

These equations remain valid as λ is varied, so the coefficients of the various powers of λ must be separately equal.

$$H^0\psi_{0k} = E_{0k}\psi_{0k}$$
$$H^0\psi_{1k} + H'\psi_{0k} = E_{0k}\psi_{1k} + E_{1k}\psi_{0k} \qquad (10.9)$$
$$H^0\psi_{2k} + H'\psi_{1k} = E_{0k}\psi_{2k} + E_{1k}\psi_{1k} + E_{2k}\psi_{0k}$$
$$\cdots \cdots \cdots = \cdots \cdots \cdots \cdots$$

The first of Eqs. (10.9) tells us nothing new, since it represents a re-statement of our unperturbed starting point, and we see again

$$\psi_{0k} = u_k \qquad E_{0k} = E_k^0 \qquad (10.10)$$

From the second of Eqs. (10.9), we commence to obtain new information. First we expand ψ_{1k} in the unperturbed eigenfunctions u_k:

$$\psi_{1k} = \sum_n c_{nk}^{(1)} u_n \qquad (10.11)$$

Substituting the ψ_{1k} into the second of Eqs. (10.9), and remembering that $\psi_{0k} = u_k$, we have

$$H^0 \sum_n c_{nk}^{(1)} u_n + H'u_k = E_k^0 \sum_n c_{nk}^{(1)} u_n + E_{1k}u_k \qquad (10.12)$$

Since the u_n are eigenfunctions of H^0 with the eigenvalues E_n^0,

$$\sum_n E_n^0 c_{nk}^{(1)} u_n + H'u_k = E_k^0 \sum_n c_{nk}^{(1)} u_n + E_{1k}u_k \qquad (10.13)$$

Multiplying from the left by u_k^* and integrating over the relevant volume, we have

$$E_k^0 c_{kk}^{(1)} + (H')_{kk} = E_k^0 c_{kk}^{(1)} + E_{1k} \qquad (10.14)$$

The terms in E_k^0 cancel and we have the important result

$$E_{1k} = (H')_{kk} \qquad (10.15)$$

The first-order perturbation of the eigenenergy E_k from its unperturbed value $(= H_{kk}^0)$ is given by the diagonal element of the perturbing Hamiltonian H', evaluated using the unperturbed wave function u_k. We obtain the first-order correction to the energy by using the zeroth-order approximation to the wave functions.

If we multiply Eq. (10.13) on the left by some u_l^*, where $l \neq k$, and again integrate, we obtain

$$E_l^0 c_{lk}^{(1)} + (H')_{lk} = E_k^0 c_{lk}^{(1)} + 0 \qquad (10.16)$$

From this equation we can solve for the $c_{lk}^{(1)}$, the expansion coefficients of the first-order corrections to the unperturbed wave function ψ_{0k}.

$$c_{kl}^{(1)} = \frac{(H')_{lk}}{E_k^0 - E_l^0} \quad l \neq k \qquad (10.17)$$

The relevance of the assumption that the unperturbed system was non-degenerate becomes apparent here. If u_l and u_k were associated with the same energy, $E_k^0 - E_l^0 = 0$, and the expansion coefficient becomes infinite. The present formal treatment is applicable, therefore, only to nondegenerate systems, and the formalism for degenerate systems will be developed below.

Equation (10.17) gives all the $c_{lk}^{(1)}$ except $c_{kk}^{(1)}$. We note that $c_{kk}^{(1)}$ is a measure of the amount of u_k which must be added to (or subtracted from) ψ_{0k}, which is itself equal to u_k. We can obtain $c_{kk}^{(1)}$ from the conditions of orthonormality of the perturbed ψ_k. We find after so doing that

$$c_{kk}^{(1)} = 0 \qquad (10.18)$$

that is, by taking $\psi_{0k} = u_k$ (which might be thought of as taking $c_{kk}^0 = 1$, all other $c_{mk}^0 = 0$) we have included the proper amount of u_k in our wave-function to first order in the perturbation H'.

Inserting the proper values of $c_{kl}^{(1)}$, we have, to first order,

$$\psi_k = u_k + \sum_{l \neq k} \frac{(H')_{lk}}{E_k^0 - E_l^0} u_l \qquad (10.19)$$

The second of Eqs. (10.9), derived from the coefficients of the first power of λ in Eq. (10.8), has given us the first-order corrections to the unperturbed energies and eigenfunctions. From the third of Eqs. (10.9), derived from the coefficients of λ^2 in Eq. (10.8), we now derive the second-order corrections to the system energies and wave functions. Into this equation we substitute the now-known ψ_{0k}, ψ_{1k}, E_{0k}, and E_{1k}:

$$H^0 \psi_{2k} + H' \sum_n c_{nk}^{(1)} u_n = E_k^0 \psi_{2k} + H'_{kk} \sum_n c_{nk}^{(1)} u_n + E_{2k} u_k \qquad (10.20)$$

The second-order correction to the kth eigenfunction ψ_{2k} may also be expanded in the unperturbed eigenfunctions u_n:

$$\psi_{2k} = \sum_n c_{nk}^{(2)} u_n \qquad (10.21)$$

and substituted into Eq. (10.20), giving

$$H^0 \sum_n c_{nk}^{(2)} u_n + H' \sum_n c_{nk}^{(1)} u_n = E_k^0 \sum_n c_{nk}^{(2)} u_n + H'_{kk} \sum_n c_{nk}^{(1)} u_n + E_{2k} u_k$$

$$(10.22)$$

If we multiply from the left with u_k^* and integrate, Eq. (10.22) becomes

$$E_k^0 c_{kk}^{(2)} + \sum_n c_{nk}^{(1)} H'_{kn} = E_k^0 c_{kk}^{(2)} + c_{kk}^{(1)} H'_{kk} + E_{2k} \qquad (10.23)$$

The terms $E_k^0 c_{kk}^{(2)}$ cancel out on both sides, and the term $c_{kk}^{(1)} H'_{kk}$ cancels one term of the summation over n on the left-hand side (or, equivalently, we recall that $c_{kk}^{(1)} = 0$ on both sides) and we obtain

$$E_{2k} = \sum_{n \neq k} c_{nk}^{(1)} H'_{kn} = \sum_{n \neq k} \frac{H'_{nk} H'_{kn}}{E_k^0 - E_n^0} = \sum_{n \neq k} \frac{|H'_{nk}|^2}{E_k^0 - E_n^0} \qquad (10.24)$$

The second step above results from the explicit substitution for $c_{nk}^{(1)}$ and the third from the Hermiticity of H' (if H is Hermitian and H^0 is Hermitian, so also is $H' = H - H_0$). We now have the perturbed eigenenergy E_k to the second order, using only the first-order wave function. We see that this term in the energy correction is indeed smaller than the first-order correction by a factor $H'_{kn}/(E_k^0 - E_n^0)$, which is small by the initial assumptions concerning the relative size of H^0 and H'. We note further, however, that there might be a large number of such terms, since a summation over $n \neq k$ is involved. We cannot, in fact, prove a priori that the total second-order correction is small, and we must be alert when using this perturbation theory to ascertain either that H'_{kn} must be finite for only a restricted number of terms or that H'_{kn} drops off as $E_k^0 - E_n^0$ increases. Our present perturbation theory, like any perturbation theory, must be used with discretion.

From Eq. (10.22) we can obtain the second-order expansion coefficients $c_{nk}^{(2)}$ by multiplying on the left by u_l^*, where $l \neq k$, and integrating:

$$E_l^0 c_{lk}^{(2)} + \sum_{n \neq k} c_{nk}^{(1)} H'_{ln} = E_k^0 c_{lk}^{(2)} + H'_{kk} c_{lk}^{(1)} + 0 \qquad (10.25)$$

Solving for $c_{lk}^{(2)}$, we obtain

$$c_{lk}^{(2)} = (E_k^0 - E_l^0)^{-1} \left(\sum_{n \neq k} c_{nk}^{(1)} H'_{ln} - c_{lk}^{(1)} H'_{kk} \right)$$

$$= \sum_{n \neq k} \frac{H'_{ln} H'_{nk}}{(E_k^0 - E_l^0)(E_k^0 - E_n^0)} - \frac{H'_{lk} H'_{kk}}{(E_k^0 - E_l^0)^2} \qquad (10.26)$$

Again our method yields all the $c_{lk}^{(2)}$ except $c_{kk}^{(2)}$, and again this coefficient may be obtained from the normalization requirement upon ψ_k. Working out this normalization, we find that

$$c_{kk}^{(2)} = -\frac{1}{2} \sum_{l \neq k} |c_{lk}^{(1)}|^2 = -\frac{1}{2} \sum_{l \neq k} \frac{|H'_{lk}|^2}{(E_k^0 - E_l^0)^2} \tag{10.27}$$

We now have eigenvalues and eigenfunctions to the second order in perturbation theory. The same analysis can be continued indefinitely, each higher power in λ yielding another equation for determination of the next order of correction to ψ_k and E_k. Usually, second-order perturbation suffices for most purposes, so we close this section with the summary results:

$$E_k = E_k^0 + H'_{kk} + \sum_{n \neq k} \frac{|H'_{nk}|^2}{E_k^0 - E_n^0}$$
$$\psi_k = u_k + \sum_{n \neq k} c_{nk}^{(1)} u_n + \sum_n c_{nk}^{(2)} u_n \tag{10.28}$$

where the relatively complicated $c_{nk}^{(1)}$ and $c_{nk}^{(2)}$ are given by Eqs. (10.17), (10.26), and (10.27).

10.2 STARK EFFECT OF THE LINEAR HARMONIC OSCILLATOR

To illustrate the use of the perturbation theory just derived, we now work out an example, that of the one-dimensional harmonic oscillator in the presence of an electric field. Suppose we place an electric charge of magnitude q upon our particle and place the oscillator in a uniform electric field of magnitude E directed along the x direction and of such a sign as to force the particle in the positive x direction. Our Hamiltonian is now

$$H = \frac{p^2}{2m} + \frac{1}{2} kx^2 - Eqx \tag{10.29}$$

We require that the electric field and the charge are such that the energy of the system is only slightly changed by their presence. Accordingly we can now split H into an unperturbed system H^0 and a perturbation H' with

$$H^0 = \frac{p^2}{2m} + \frac{1}{2} kx^2 \qquad H' = -Eqx \tag{10.30}$$

The eigenfunctions and eigenvalues of H^0 are known to us from the development of Chaps. 5 and 6. In our present notation, they are

$$E_n^0 = (n + \tfrac{1}{2})\hbar\omega_0 \qquad u_n = |n\rangle \tag{10.31}$$

Let us first calculate the first-order perturbation in the linear harmonic oscillator energy levels due to the electric field. According to Eq. (10.15), this is simply

$$E_{1n} = (H')_{nn} = \langle n| -Eqx |n\rangle$$
$$= -Eq \langle n| x |n\rangle \qquad (10.32)$$

Referring to Eq. (6.22), which gives the matrix for x, we observe that all the diagonal elements are zero, so

$$E_{1n} = 0 \qquad (10.33)$$

The eigenenergies of the linear harmonic oscillator are, to first order, unchanged by the presence of the electric field.

The first-order correction to the wave functions and the second-order correction to the eigenenergies involve off-diagonal elements of the perturbing Hamiltonian. Both ψ_{1n} and E_{2n} involve expressions requiring summation over the perturbing elements $(H')_{mn}$. (To avoid confusion between the spring constant k and the quantum number k, we avoid k as an index in this particular illustration of perturbation theory). The elements $(H')_{mn}$ are the elements in the same column as $(H')_{nn}$, but in positions above or below the diagonal. Looking again at the matrix for x [Eq. (6.22)], we observe that for the linear harmonic oscillator there are only two non-zero matrix elements in any column, hence only two terms in the summation for ψ_{1n} [Eq. (10.19)] or E_{2n} [Eq. (10.24)].

$$(H')_{n+1,n} = \langle n+1| -Eqx |n\rangle = -Eq \left(\frac{n+1}{2\alpha}\right)^{1/2}$$

$$(H')_{n-1,n} = \langle n-1| -Eqx |n\rangle = -Eq \left(\frac{n}{2\alpha}\right)^{1/2} \qquad (10.34)$$

Using these matrix elements, we can now write the perturbed wavefunction, correct to first order, as

$$\psi_n = u_n + \frac{(H')_{n+1,n}}{E_n^0 - E_{n+1}^0} u_{n+1} + \frac{(H')_{n-1,n}}{E_n^0 - E_{n-1}^0} u_{n-1}$$

$$= |n\rangle + \frac{-Eq \left(\dfrac{n+1}{2\alpha}\right)^{1/2}}{(n+\frac{1}{2})\hbar\omega_0 - (n+\frac{3}{2})\hbar\omega_0} |n+1\rangle$$

$$+ \frac{-Eq \left(\dfrac{n}{2\alpha}\right)^{1/2}}{(n+\frac{1}{2})\hbar\omega_0 - (n-\frac{1}{2})\hbar\omega_0} |n-1\rangle$$

$$= |n\rangle + \frac{Eq}{\hbar\omega_0}\left[\left(\frac{n+1}{2\alpha}\right)^{1/2} |n+1\rangle - \left(\frac{n}{2\alpha}\right)^{1/2} |n-1\rangle\right] \qquad (10.35)$$

and the eigenenergies, correct to second order, as

$$
\begin{aligned}
E_{2k} &= \frac{|(H')_{n-1,n}|^2}{E_n^0 - E_{n-1}^0} + \frac{|(H')_{n+1,n}|^2}{E_n^0 - E_{n+1}^0} \\
&= \frac{E^2 q^2 n/2\alpha}{\hbar\omega_0} + \frac{E^2 q^2 (n+1)/2\alpha}{-\hbar\omega_0} \\
&= -\frac{E^2 q^2}{2\hbar\omega_0 \alpha} = -\frac{E^2 q^2}{2m\omega_0^2}
\end{aligned}
\tag{10.36}
$$

All the eigenenergies, independent of n, are depressed an identical amount, and the spacing between states remains unaltered. We may, if we wish, proceed to calculate ψ_n, correct to second order, by using Eqs. (10.26) and (10.27) to compute the second-order expansion coefficients $c_{nm}^{(2)}$. However, the utility of the result does not justify the algebra involved, so we will not display this calculation.

The results of our perturbation calculation can, in this case, be checked against the exact solutions, since a simple change of variable will put our Hamiltonian in a form we can treat exactly:

$$
\begin{aligned}
H &= \frac{p^2}{2m} + \frac{1}{2} k x^2 - Eqx \\
&= \frac{p^2}{2m} + \frac{1}{2} k \left(x^2 - \frac{2Eq}{k} x \right) \\
&= \frac{p^2}{2m} + \frac{1}{2} k \left(x - \frac{Eq}{k} \right)^2 - \frac{E^2 q^2}{2k}
\end{aligned}
\tag{10.37}
$$

Introducing the variables

$$
x' = x - \frac{Eq}{k} \qquad p' = \frac{\partial L}{\partial \dot{x}'} = p
\tag{10.38}
$$

we may write our Hamiltonian as

$$
H = \frac{p'^2}{2m} + \frac{1}{2} k x'^2 - \frac{E^2 q^2}{2m\omega^2}
\tag{10.39}
$$

The eigenenergies of this system will be the same as for the linear harmonic oscillator of Chaps. 5 and 6, except for a shifted zero or reference level:

$$
E_n = \left(n + \frac{1}{2} \right) \hbar\omega_0 - \frac{E^2 q^2}{2m\omega_0^2}
\tag{10.40}
$$

and we see our perturbation theory has converged quickly upon the correct answer. Comparison of the perturbed eigenfunctions with the exact eigenfunctions is more difficult because of the more complex variation of the eigenfunctions with a change of argument.

10.3 PERTURBATION THEORY FOR DEGENERATE SYSTEMS The perturbation theory of Sec. 10.1 was derived for nondegenerate systems; the theory fails for degenerate systems because of the regular occurrence of terms such as $(E_k^0 - E_l^0)$ in the denominator of various expressions. Let us see how we formulate perturbation theory for the degenerate case to avoid these difficulties.

Degenerate perturbation theory is best discussed in matrix language. Suppose that our unperturbed Hamiltonian H^0 has, as before, a set of eigenfunctions which we will call u_n but that several of these orthogonal eigenfunctions, (u_k through u_r, for instance) all belong to the same eigenvalue of H^0; that is, $E_k^0 = E_l^0 = \cdots E_r^0$. The energy matrix H^0 is, of course, diagonal in the u_n representation, but the perturbing Hamiltonian H' is in general not diagonal in the u_n representation and may have nonzero entries everywhere in its matrix. Let us write the matrix of the Hamiltonian operator for $H = H^0 + H'$ in the u_n representation, collecting together on the diagonal the equal eigenvalues E_k^0 through E_r^0.

The dashed box of Eq. (10.41) (shown on the following page) contains the region of equal diagonal values E_k^0. The reader must bear in mind that $E_k^0 = E_l^0 = \cdots = E_r^0$; we have retained different subscripts for those equal eigenvalues because we wish to keep track of their associated eigenfunctions. There may be more than one such degenerate box in the full Hamiltonian, and the arguments we shall apply to the one box can be extended to each such box in turn.

The Hamiltonian matrix of Eq. (10.41) is Hermitian, so there must exist a unitary transformation which will diagonalize the whole matrix, giving us the exact eigenvalues as diagonal elements. The required unitary matrix is, of course, of the same dimensions as is the matrix for H; in principle, this dimension is infinite though it is sometimes feasible to truncate the eigenfunction set somewhat and deal with matrices of finite dimension. The task of finding this diagonalizing matrix is a herculean one, requiring the determination of n^2 elements, where n is the dimension of the matrix to be diagonalized. We note, however, that the submatrix contained in the dashed box is itself a Hermitian matrix of finite, often small dimension. Its dimensions are $m \times m$, where m is the order of the degeneracy. This submatrix can be diagonalized by a unitary transformation, which can in turn be represented by an $m \times m$ matrix. Instead of seeking

$$
\begin{bmatrix}
(E_a^0 + H'_{aa}) & H'_{ab} & \cdots & \cdots & H'_{am} & \cdots & \cdots & H'_{as} & H'_{at} \\
 & (E_b^0 + H'_{bb}) & \vdots & \vdots & \vdots & \vdots & \vdots & \vdots & \vdots \\
\vdots & \vdots & (E_k^0 + H'_{kk}) & H'_{kl} & H'_{km} & \cdots & H'_{kr} & \vdots & \vdots \\
\vdots & \vdots & H'_{lk} & (E_l^0 + H'_{ll}) & H'_{lm} & \cdots & H'_{lr} & \vdots & \vdots \\
H'_{ma} & \vdots & H'_{mk} & H'_{ml} & (E_m^0 + H'_{mm}) & \cdots & H'_{mr} & \vdots & \vdots \\
\vdots & \vdots & H'_{rk} & H'_{rl} & H'_{rm} & \cdots & (E_r^0 + H'_{rr}) & \vdots & \vdots \\
\vdots & \vdots & \vdots & \vdots & \vdots & \cdots & \vdots & (E_s^0 + H'_{ss}) & \vdots \\
H'_{ta} & \vdots & \vdots & \vdots & \vdots & \cdots & \vdots & \cdots & (E_t^0 + H'_{tt})
\end{bmatrix}
\tag{10.41}
$$

the transformation which diagonalizes the whole of the H matrix, let us reduce our objective to finding a transformation which diagonalizes the $m \times m$ region of the H matrix embracing the degenerate eigenvalues of H^0. Schematically the unitary matrix we seek may be represented as

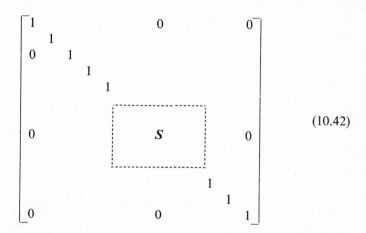

$$(10.42)$$

where the diagonal entries are unity and the off-diagonal entries are zero outside of the $m \times m$ box corresponding to rows and columns k through r of our original H matrix. The transformed Hamiltonian matrix $\mathbf{SHS}^{-1}$ will now take the form of Eq. (10.43a) (shown on the following page).

The eigenvalues of H, correct to first order in H', now appear uniformly along the diagonal of this matrix, and we have solved the first-order perturbation problem for the degenerate case. The primes on the subscripts k' through r' are included to take cognizance of the fact that the wave functions spanning this space, $u_k, u_l, \ldots, u_r$, have been scrambled by the unitary transformation to form a new set of basis functions, linear combinations of the old, which we shall label $u_{k'}, u_{l'}, \ldots, u_{r'}$. The new wave functions are related to the old by

$$
\begin{bmatrix} u_{k'} \\ u_{l'} \\ u_{m'} \\ \cdot \\ \cdot \\ \cdot \\ u_{r'} \end{bmatrix}
=
\begin{bmatrix} & & \\ & \tilde{S}^{-1} & \\ & & \end{bmatrix}
\begin{bmatrix} u_k \\ u_l \\ u_m \\ \cdot \\ \cdot \\ \cdot \\ u_r \end{bmatrix}
\qquad (10.43b)
$$

$$
\begin{bmatrix}
(E_a^0+H'_{aa}) & H'_{ab} & \cdots & \cdots & H'_{am'} & \cdots & \cdots & H'_{as} & H'_{at} \\
\vdots & (E_b^0+H'_{bb}) & \vdots & \vdots & \vdots & \vdots & \vdots & \vdots & \vdots \\
\vdots & \vdots & (E_k^0+E_{1k'}) & 0 & 0 & 0 & \cdots & \vdots & \vdots \\
H'_{l'a} & \vdots & 0 & (E_l^0+E_{1l'}) & 0 & 0 & \cdots & \vdots & \vdots \\
H'_{m'a} & \vdots & 0 & 0 & (E_m^0+E_{1m'}) & 0 & \cdots & \vdots & \vdots \\
\vdots & \vdots & 0 & 0 & 0 & (E_r^0+E_{1r'}) & \vdots & \vdots & \vdots \\
\vdots & \vdots & \vdots & \vdots & \vdots & \vdots & (E_s^0+H'_{ss}) & \vdots \\
H'_{ta} & \vdots & \vdots & \vdots & \vdots & \vdots & \cdots & (E^0+H'_{tt})
\end{bmatrix}
$$

$$(10.43a)$$

where S is the unitary matrix which transformed the $m \times m$ Hermitian submatrix into diagonal form

$$
S\begin{bmatrix}
(H^0 + H') & H' & H' \\
\cdots & (H^0 + H') & \cdots \\
\cdots\cdots\cdots\cdots\cdots\cdots\cdots\cdots \\
H' & \cdots & (H^0 + H')
\end{bmatrix}S^{-1}
$$

$$
= \begin{bmatrix}
(E_k^0 + E_{1k'}) & \cdots & 0 \\
\cdots & (E_{l'}^0 + E_{1l'}) & \cdots \\
\cdots\cdots\cdots\cdots\cdots\cdots\cdots\cdots\cdots \\
0 & \cdots & (E_{r'}^0 + E_{1r'})
\end{bmatrix} \quad (10.44)
$$

Within the submatrix, the elements E_k^0, $E_{l'}^0$, etc., remain equal to one another and to the E_k^0, E_l^0, etc., of the unperturbed case. To each of these equal diagonal elements have been added the first-order energy corrections $E_{1k'}$, $E_{1l'}$, etc., which will in general be different from one another. Note further that the elements of H' outside the $m \times m$ box but in rows or columns k through r will also be altered by the redefinition of the basis functions for those rows and columns.

The task of finding the eigenvalues of a degenerate Hamiltonian, correct to first order in the perturbation, can then be reduced to the task of finding the $m \times m$ unitary transformation S which diagonalizes the $m \times m$ region of the full Hamiltonian embracing the m-fold degeneracy. Let us therefore turn our attention to the techniques available for diagonalizing our $m \times m$ matrix. It will be characteristic of the matrix S which we seek that

$$
SHS^{-1} = \begin{bmatrix}
\lambda_1 & \cdots & \cdots & \cdots & \cdots & \cdots & 0 \\
\cdots & \lambda_2 & \cdots & \cdots & \cdots & \cdots & \cdots \\
\cdots & \cdots & \lambda_3 & \cdots & \cdots & \cdots & \cdots \\
\cdots\cdots\cdots\cdots\cdots\cdots\cdots\cdots \\
\cdots & \cdots & \cdots & \cdots & \lambda_k & \cdots & \cdots \\
\cdots\cdots\cdots\cdots\cdots\cdots\cdots\cdots \\
0 & \cdots & \cdots & \cdots & \cdots & \cdots & \lambda_m
\end{bmatrix} \quad (10.45)
$$

where the λ_i are the eigenvalues of H. The diagonalized Hamiltonian has as its basis vectors the transformed functions $v_1, v_2, v_3, \ldots, v_m$, which are obtained from the original basis functions $u_1, u_2, u_3, \ldots u_m$ by

$$
\begin{bmatrix} v_1 \\ v_2 \\ v_3 \\ \cdot \\ \cdot \\ \cdot \\ v_m \end{bmatrix} = \tilde{S}^{-1} \begin{bmatrix} u_1 \\ u_2 \\ u_3 \\ \cdot \\ \cdot \\ \cdot \\ u_m \end{bmatrix}
\tag{10.46}
$$

The eigenvectors of a diagonal matrix are easy to identify; they are column vectors with all entries zero except one, and that one equal to unity. The eigenfunction corresponding to the eigenvalue λ_k is therefore easy to write in the v_n representation, and the eigenvalue equation, in matrix form, is

$$
\begin{bmatrix} \lambda_1 & \cdots & \cdots & \cdots & \cdots & \cdots & \cdots & \cdots & 0 \\ \cdots & \lambda_2 & \cdots & \cdots & \cdots & \cdots & \cdots & \cdots & \cdots \\ & & & & & & & & \\ \cdots & \cdots & \cdots & \cdots & \lambda_k & \cdots & \cdots & \cdots & \cdots \\ & & & & & & & & \\ 0 & \cdots & \cdots & \cdots & \cdots & \cdots & \cdots & \cdots & \lambda_m \end{bmatrix} \begin{bmatrix} 0 \\ 0 \\ \cdot \\ \cdot \\ \cdot \\ 1 \\ \cdot \\ \cdot \\ 0 \end{bmatrix} = \lambda_k \begin{bmatrix} 0 \\ 0 \\ \cdot \\ \cdot \\ \cdot \\ 1 \\ \cdot \\ \cdot \\ 0 \end{bmatrix}
\tag{10.47}
$$

Transforming this equation back to our original nondiagonal representation, we have

$$
S^{-1} \begin{bmatrix} \lambda_1 & \cdots & \cdots & \cdots & \cdots & \cdots & \cdots & 0 \\ \cdots & \lambda_2 & \cdots & \cdots & \cdots & \cdots & \cdots \\ & & & & & & & \\ \cdots & \cdots & \cdots & \cdots & \lambda_k & \cdots & \cdots & \cdots \\ & & & & & & & \\ 0 & \cdots & \cdots & \cdots & \cdots & \cdots & \lambda_m \end{bmatrix} SS^{-1} \begin{bmatrix} 0 \\ 0 \\ \cdot \\ \cdot \\ \cdot \\ 1 \\ \cdot \\ \cdot \\ 0 \end{bmatrix} = \lambda_k S^{-1} \begin{bmatrix} 0 \\ 0 \\ \cdot \\ \cdot \\ \cdot \\ 1 \\ \cdot \\ \cdot \\ 0 \end{bmatrix}
\tag{10.48}
$$

or
$$H \begin{bmatrix} c_1 \\ c_2 \\ c_3 \\ \cdot \\ \cdot \\ \cdot \\ c_n \end{bmatrix} = \lambda_k \begin{bmatrix} c_1 \\ c_2 \\ c_3 \\ \cdot \\ \cdot \\ \cdot \\ c_n \end{bmatrix} \qquad (10.49)$$

The column vector is still an eigenvector of the Hamiltonian, belonging to the eigenvalue λ_k, though its character as an eigenvector k is not obvious when it is written, as in Eq. (10.49), in a basis system in which H is not diagonal. Equation (10.49) may be rewritten

$$\begin{bmatrix} & & \\ & H - \lambda_k I & \\ & & \end{bmatrix} \begin{bmatrix} c_1 \\ c_2 \\ c_3 \\ \cdot \\ \cdot \\ \cdot \\ c_n \end{bmatrix} = 0 \qquad (10.50)$$

Since the c_i are in general nonvanishing, Eq. (10.50) can be true only if the determinant of the matrix is zero.

$$\text{Det}(H - \lambda_k I) = 0 \qquad (10.51)$$

The determinant of the $m \times m$ matrix is a polynomial of degree m in λ.

$$\lambda^m + \lambda^{(m-1)} \left(\sum_n H_{nn} \right) + \cdots + C = 0 \qquad (10.52)$$

The m roots of this equation—known as the *secular equation of the Hamiltonian*—are the m possible values of λ_k, the full set of eigenvalues of the Hamiltonian, correct to first order in the perturbation H'.

Once the λ_k have been established, the diagonalizing transformation can also be computed. If we insert in Eq. (10.50) one of the known values λ_k, we have a matrix equation which is equivalent to m simultaneous linear equations in m unknowns, the c_i. The m simultaneous equations can be solved for the m c_i, and we then know, in the u_n representation, the eigenvector corresponding to λ_k. But we also know the same eigenvector in the

v_n representation [Eq. (10.47)], and we know that the eigenvectors in the two representations are connected by the transformation S.

$$
\begin{bmatrix} c_1 \\ c_2 \\ c_3 \\ \cdot \\ \cdot \\ \cdot \\ c_n \end{bmatrix} = S^{-1} \begin{bmatrix} 0 \\ 0 \\ 0 \\ \cdot \\ \cdot \\ \cdot \\ 1 \\ \cdot \\ \cdot \\ \cdot \\ 0 \\ 0 \end{bmatrix}
\tag{10.53}
$$

From the definition of matrix multiplication, we see that the components c_i of the eigenvector belonging to λ_k constitute the kth column of the unitary transformation S^{-1}. Each of the eigenvalues λ_n generates by this procedure one column of S^{-1}; the m eigenvalues all together generate the m columns of the complete S^{-1} matrix. If m is small, the labor involved in solving the simultaneous equation sets is not large, and the S^{-1} matrix is relatively easily generated. If m is large, the labor involved becomes enormous, but the scientific computer may again come to the rescue. Programs which will diagonalize matrices are generally available, and these programs generally also provide the eigenvectors of the matrix. Knowing these eigenvectors is tantamount to knowing S^{-1}, as has been shown above.

Once our Hamiltonian has been transformed to the form of Eq. (10.43a), the eigenenergies are known to first order, but not second order, in the perturbation. If the $E_{1m'}$ are all different, i.e., if all degeneracies are lifted by the first-order perturbation, we may proceed to calculate second-order corrections by the nondegenerate perturbation theory of Sec. 10.1. If not all degeneracies are removed by the first-order corrections, we must proceed with somewhat more caution. There are no matrix elements of H' connecting the degenerate eigenfunctions, since we have eliminated all these in diagonalizing the submatrix, but there may well be non-zero elements of H' connecting degenerate states to some common state (or states) outside the previously degenerate manifold. The calculation of the second-order energy correction in such cases is relatively complex, and will not be developed here. The reader is referred to a more advanced textbook for a discussion of second-order degenerate perturbation theory.

10.4 ZEEMAN EFFECT IN HYDROGEN Let us again illustrate our theory with an example: the hydrogen atom placed in a magnetic field **H**. For the purpose of the present illustration, we shall consider the electron to be spinless so that we may use the nonrelativistic solutions and the **L** matrices of Chap. 9.

The Hamiltonian, including the magnetic field, will be

$$H = \frac{p^2}{2m} - \frac{Ze^2}{r} + g\beta \mathbf{L} \cdot \mathbf{H} \tag{10.54}$$

where $g\beta$ is a constant conventionally used to convert the angular momentum **L** into a magnetic moment **μ**. We again separate the Hamiltonian into an unperturbed portion H^0 and a perturbing portion H'.

$$H^0 = \frac{p^2}{2m} - \frac{Ze^2}{r} \qquad H' = g\beta \mathbf{L} \cdot \mathbf{H} \tag{10.55}$$

The eigenfunctions of H^0 are, of course, the hydrogenic wave functions ψ_{nlm}. Let us write the matrix for the Hamiltonian of Eq. (10.54) in this basis system. We will arrange the eigenfunctions in order of increasing n and l, and the Hamiltonian matrix will look schematically as given in Eq. (10.56) (shown on the following page).

H^0 gives, of course, only diagonal entries, which are multiply degenerate for $n > 1$. The various components of **L** will generate nonzero elements within the boxes along the diagonal. Each box is spanned by a set of $Y_l^{\pm m}$ belonging to some specific l, and is $(2l + 1) \times (2l + 1)$ in dimension. All matrix entries outside these boxes will be zero.[1] We can see the nature of these diagonal boxes from

$$H' = g\beta \mathbf{L} \cdot \mathbf{H} = g\beta(L_x H_x + L_y H_y + L_z H_z)$$

$$H' = g\beta[H_x(L_x) + H_y(L_y) + H_z(L_z)] \tag{10.57}$$

where H_x, H_y, and H_z are scalar multipliers specifying the magnitude of the x, y, and z components of **H**, respectively, and L_x, L_y, and L_z are the matrices of Chap. 9.

Suppose our applied magnetic field is along the z direction. Then

$$H' = g\beta H L_z \tag{10.58}$$

---

[1] The assumption that $g\beta$ was a constant, the same for all $R(r)$, suppresses all changes in the radial wave function caused by the presence of H. Actually there are small changes in the radial distribution of charge caused by the magnetic field, which will give nonzero matrix elements between wave functions of the same l but different n. We are ignoring these generally small effects in the present treatment.

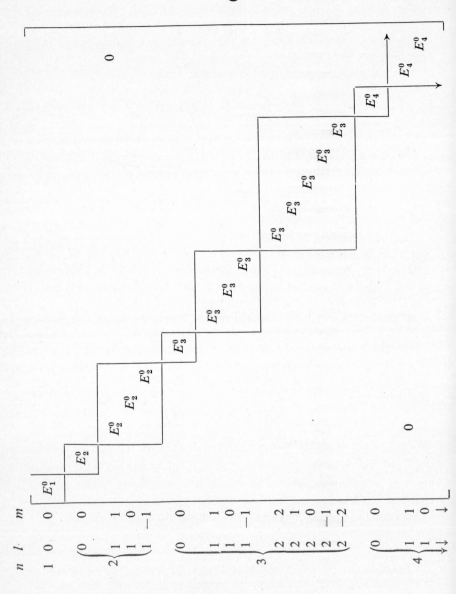

$$(10.56)$$

and the matrix of Eq. (10.56) becomes

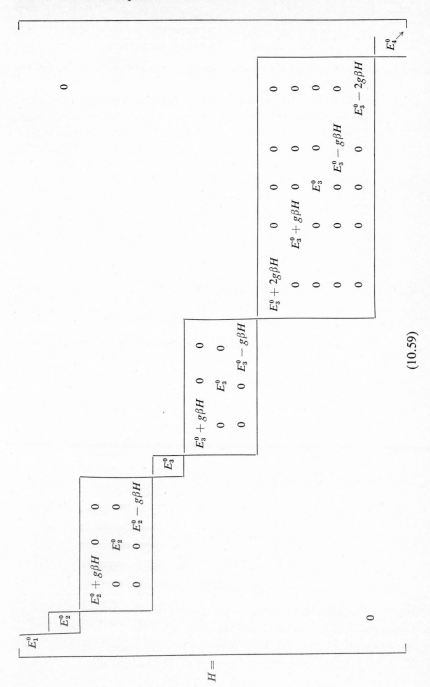

$$(10.59)$$

This matrix is already diagonal (since L_z commutes with the Hamiltonian), so no further manipulation is required. Suppose, however, that we apply the magnetic field along the x direction, giving

$$H' = g\beta H L_x \tag{10.60}$$

The Hamiltonian matrix [Eq. (10.61)] is shown on the opposite page.

We now have off-diagonal elements connecting states of the same energy. Each box along the diagonal encloses a region where such entries appear. Let us now find the eigenvalues and the diagonalizing transformation for one of these regions. We will choose one of the 3×3 boxes corresponding to $l = 1$ and to any n. Such a box is of the form

$$\begin{bmatrix} E_n^0 & d & 0 \\ d & E_n^0 & d \\ 0 & d & E_n^0 \end{bmatrix} = H \tag{10.62}$$

where
$$d = \frac{g\beta H}{\sqrt{2}} \tag{10.63}$$

We first find the eigenvalues of this submatrix, its diagonal entries when it is in diagonal form. To do so, we use the formalism of the previous section, setting

$$\text{Det} \begin{bmatrix} E_n^0 - \lambda & d & 0 \\ d & E_n^0 - \lambda & d \\ 0 & d & E_n^0 - \lambda \end{bmatrix} = 0 \tag{10.64}$$

There results the equation in λ

$$(E_n^0 - \lambda)^3 - 2(E_n^0 - \lambda) d^2 = 0 \tag{10.65}$$

which has the roots

$$\begin{aligned} \lambda_1 &= E_n^0 + \sqrt{2}d = E_n^0 + g\beta H \\ \lambda_2 &= E_n^0 + 0 \quad\;\; = E_n^0 \\ \lambda_3 &= E_n^0 - \sqrt{2}d = E_n^0 - g\beta H \end{aligned} \tag{10.66}$$

We see that these are the same eigenvalues obtained for the magnetic field applied in the z direction, and a little reflection suffices to convince us that the effect of adding a magnetic field to our isotropic Hamiltonian would have to be independent of the direction of the applied field.

$$H = \begin{pmatrix}
E_1^0 & & & & & & & & & & \\
& E_2^0 & \dfrac{g\beta H}{\sqrt 2} & 0 & & & & & & & \\
& \dfrac{g\beta H}{\sqrt 2} & E_2^0 & \dfrac{g\beta H}{\sqrt 2} & & & & & & \Large 0 & \\
& 0 & \dfrac{g\beta H}{\sqrt 2} & E_2^0 & & & & & & & \\
& & & & E_3^0 & & & & & & \\
& & & & & E_3^0 & \dfrac{g\beta H}{\sqrt 2} & 0 & & & \\
& & & & & \dfrac{g\beta H}{\sqrt 2} & E_3^0 & \dfrac{g\beta H}{\sqrt 2} & & & \\
& & & & & 0 & \dfrac{g\beta H}{\sqrt 2} & E_3^0 & & & \\
& & & & & & & & E_3^0 & g\beta H & 0 & 0 & 0 \\
& \Large 0 & & & & & & & g\beta H & E_3^0 & \sqrt 6/2\,g\beta H & 0 & 0 \\
& & & & & & & & 0 & \sqrt 6/2\,g\beta H & E_3^0 & \sqrt 6/2\,g\beta H & 0 \\
& & & & & & & & 0 & 0 & \sqrt 6/2\,g\beta H & E_3^0 & g\beta H \\
& & & & & & & & 0 & 0 & 0 & g\beta H & E_3^0 \\
& & & & & & & & & & & & & E_4^0
\end{pmatrix}$$

$$(10.61)$$

Let us ask further for the transformation which diagonalizes the matrix of Eq. (10.62). We seek S such that

$$S\begin{bmatrix} E_n^0 & d & 0 \\ d & E_n^0 & d \\ 0 & d & E_n^0 \end{bmatrix} S^{-1} = \begin{bmatrix} E_n^0 + \sqrt{2}d & 0 & 0 \\ 0 & E_n^0 & 0 \\ 0 & 0 & E_n^0 - \sqrt{2}d \end{bmatrix} \quad (10.67)$$

Following the discussion of Sec. 10.3, we write the eigenvectors associated with the three eigenvalues as

$$\begin{bmatrix} a_{11} \\ a_{21} \\ a_{31} \end{bmatrix} = S^{-1} \begin{bmatrix} 1 \\ 0 \\ 0 \end{bmatrix} \qquad \text{belonging to } \lambda_1 = E_n^0 + \sqrt{2}d \quad (10.68a)$$

$$\begin{bmatrix} a_{12} \\ a_{22} \\ a_{32} \end{bmatrix} = S^{-1} \begin{bmatrix} 0 \\ 1 \\ 0 \end{bmatrix} \qquad \text{belonging to } \lambda_1 = E_n^0 \quad (10.68b)$$

and

$$\begin{bmatrix} a_{13} \\ a_{23} \\ a_{33} \end{bmatrix} = S^{-1} \begin{bmatrix} 0 \\ 0 \\ 1 \end{bmatrix} \qquad \text{belonging to } \lambda_1 = E_n^0 - \sqrt{2}d \quad (10.68c)$$

where the a_{ij} are the matrix elements of S^{-1} (not S). For these eigenvectors, we know that

$$\begin{bmatrix} E_n^0 & d & 0 \\ d & E_n^0 & d \\ 0 & d & E_n^0 \end{bmatrix} \begin{bmatrix} a_{1i} \\ a_{2i} \\ a_{3i} \end{bmatrix} = \lambda_i \begin{bmatrix} a_{1i} \\ a_{2i} \\ a_{3i} \end{bmatrix} \quad (10.69)$$

Equation (10.69) may be rewritten

$$\begin{bmatrix} E_n^0 - \lambda_i & d & 0 \\ d & E_n^0 - \lambda_i & d \\ 0 & d & E_n^0 - \lambda_i \end{bmatrix} \begin{bmatrix} a_{1i} \\ a_{2i} \\ a_{3i} \end{bmatrix} = 0 \quad (10.70)$$

which is a set of three linearly independent equations in three unknowns, the a_{ni}. Let us calculate one set of these a_{ni}, those belonging to $\lambda_1 = E_n^0 + \sqrt{2}d$. The set of determinative equations are

$$\begin{aligned} -\sqrt{2}d \; a_{11} + \quad d \; a_{21} + \quad 0 \quad &= 0 \\ d \; a_{11} - \sqrt{2}d \; a_{21} + \quad d \; a_{31} &= 0 \quad (10.71) \\ 0 \quad + \quad d \; a_{21} - \sqrt{2}d \; a_{31} &= 0 \end{aligned}$$

Solving these equations for a_{11}, a_{21}, and a_{31}, subject to the constraint that

$$\sum_{n=1}^{3} |a_{n1}|^2 = 1 \tag{10.72}$$

(preserving normalization of ψ), we obtain

$$a_{11} = \frac{1}{2} \qquad a_{21} = \frac{1}{\sqrt{2}} \qquad a_{31} = \frac{1}{2} \tag{10.73}$$

Proceeding similarly for λ_2 and λ_3, we obtain

$$S^{-1} = \begin{bmatrix} \dfrac{1}{2} & \dfrac{1}{\sqrt{2}} & \dfrac{1}{2} \\[2ex] \dfrac{1}{\sqrt{2}} & 0 & -\dfrac{1}{\sqrt{2}} \\[2ex] \dfrac{1}{2} & -\dfrac{1}{\sqrt{2}} & \dfrac{1}{2} \end{bmatrix} = S \tag{10.74}$$

and we have the desired transformation. In arriving at S^{-1}, we have made some arbitrary decisions concerning the phase factor multiplying each column in the matrix as we assemble it from the eigenvectors. We have chosen the phase factors in such a way that the determinant of S^{-1} is $+1$. This is an arbitrary but convenient convention. The transformation produced here is that which diagonalizes L_x if L_x is originally written in a representation based on the eigenfunctions of L_z (called therefore the L_z representation).

In the present example there are no matrix elements outside the boxes along the diagonal, so diagonalizing these boxes solves the perturbation problem completely—not only in first order. Ordinarily there will be matrix elements outside the degenerate boxes, and account must be taken of these in calculating the second-order correction to the eigenenergies.

Summary

Most of the real problems that the reader will ever have to solve using quantum mechanics, will be perturbation problems. This chapter and the following chapter on time-dependent perturbation theory are therefore the most important chapters in this book.

If the Hamiltonian does not contain the time, we know that there exists a set of eigenfunctions which will diagonalize the Hamiltonian, giving the desired eigenvalues as diagonal entries in the Hamiltonian matrix. If in writing the Hamiltonian matrix we use not the correct eigenfunctions as a basis but rather an almost correct basis set, the Hamiltonian matrix will have large entries on the diagonal (almost equal to the true eigenvalues) and smaller entries in the off-diagonal positions. Time-independent perturbation theory is a collection of techniques for ascertaining what the diagonal elements of the Hamiltonian would be if diagonalized without actually going through a full diagonalization procedure.

If the Hamiltonian is nondegenerate, the exact eigenvalues and eigenfunctions may be obtained from the approximate ones by a straightforward procedure summarized in Eq. (10.28). To second order in the perturbation,

$$E_k = E_k^0 + H_{kk}' + \sum_{n \neq k} \frac{|H_{nk}'|^2}{E_k^0 - E_n^0}$$

The wave functions, correct to any given order, will always allow the calculation of the eigenenergies to one higher order.

If the Hamiltonian is degenerate, the degenerate manifolds must be diagonalized exactly to yield the eigenenergies correct to first order. The degenerate manifolds are often of small dimension.

The transformation which diagonalizes a degenerate manifold of the Hamiltonian also produces the required eigenfunctions, correct to first order within the manifold, from the original inexact set.

Problems

10.1 A one-dimensional oscillator has the Hamiltonian

$$H = \frac{p^2}{2m} + \frac{1}{2} k_1 x^2 + k_2 x^4 \qquad \text{where } k_2 \ll k_1$$

Write the eigenenergies of the perturbed system correct to first and second order, and the perturbed wave functions correct to first order.

For sufficiently large x (for highly excited states), the x^4 term will overtake the x^2 term in importance, and perturbation theory based on the simple harmonic oscillator will fail. Obtain a criterion for the domain of validity of the perturbation theory.

10.2 Consider the isotropic two-dimensional harmonic oscillator

$$H^0 = \frac{p_x^2}{2m} + \frac{p_y^2}{2m} + \frac{1}{2} k(x^2 + y^2)$$

We now introduce a perturbation of the form

$$H' = Cxy$$

Write the energy matrix for $H = H^0 + H'$ for the ground and the first two excited states of the oscillator.

Solve for the eigenenergies of these states to second order in the perturbation.

What are the eigenfunctions of the first excited state which diagonalize the energy submatrix for that state?

10.3 The harmonically bound particle in a two-dimensional harmonic oscillator carries a charge $+q$. A magnetic field is applied to the system in a direction perpendicular to the plane in which the particle oscillates.

Calculate the first several eigenenergies and eigenfunctions of the particle for (a) $k_x \neq k_y$ (nonisotropic oscillator) and (b) $k_x = k_y$ (isotropic oscillator).

10.4 The Hamiltonian of the hydrogen atom including spin may be written

$$H = \frac{\mathbf{p}^2}{2m} + V(\mathbf{r}) + \lambda \mathbf{L} \cdot \mathbf{S}$$

This differs from the Hamiltonian of Chap. 9 only by the addition of the $\lambda \mathbf{L} \cdot \mathbf{S}$ term, which we regard as a perturbation on the spinless Hamiltonian.

  a Consider the states for which $L = 1$ and $S = \frac{1}{2}$. How many such states are there?

  b Write the set of wave functions spanning this space in L, L_z, S, and S_z quantization.

  c Using these wave functions, write the matrix for $\lambda \mathbf{L} \cdot \mathbf{S}$.

  d Diagonalize the $\lambda \mathbf{L} \cdot \mathbf{S}$ matrix and produce the wave functions which are a basis for the diagonalized matrix.

  e If we apply now a magnetic field $\mathbf{H}$ in the z direction, we add a further energy of the form

$$H' = g_L \beta \mathbf{L} \cdot \mathbf{H} + g_S \beta \mathbf{S} \cdot \mathbf{H}$$

Calculate eigenenergies of the system to first order in the applied field H within the manifold $L = 1$, $S = \frac{1}{2}$ treated above. Consider the interaction with the magnetic field to represent an energy substantially smaller than that associated with the $\mathbf{L} \cdot \mathbf{S}$ interaction. Draw the energy levels for small $\mathbf{H}$.

10.5 The electrostatic interaction of an atom with its surrounding atoms or ions in a solid may be represented by an operator involving only the angular-momentum operators. The ground (lowest lying in energy) state of the Yb^{3+} free ion has $L = 3$, $S = \frac{1}{2}$, and $J = \frac{7}{2}$. If this ion is placed in a crystal in a site such that its environment has cubic symmetry, the energy of interaction with its neighbors may be written

$$H' = C_4[35J_z^4 - 30J(J + 1)J_z^2 + 25J_z^2 - 6J(J + 1) + 3J^2(J + 1)^2]$$

$$+ \tfrac{5}{2}C_4(J_+^4 + J_-^4)$$

Show that this perturbation splits the eightfold degenerate free-ion state into two doublets and a quartet.

Bibliography

Time-independent perturbation theory is discussed in substantially every quantum mechanics textbook. Several useful references are:

Schiff, L. I.: "Quantum Mechanics," 2d ed., chap. 7, McGraw-Hill Book Company, New York, 1955.

Messiah, A.: "Quantum Mechanics," vol. 2, chap. 16, Interscience Publishers, Inc., New York, 1962.

Dicke, R. H., and J. P. Wittke: "Introduction to Quantum Mechanics," Chap. 14, Addison-Wesley Publishing Company, Inc., Reading, Mass., 1960.

Merzbacher, E.: "Quantum Mechanics," chap. 16, John Wiley & Sons, Inc., New York, 1961.

CHAPTER 11

Time-Dependent

Perturbation Theory:

Interaction With Radiation

11.1 FORMULATION OF THE PROBLEM In the preceding sections we have developed techniques for treating quantum-mechanically the properties of systems whose Hamiltonian did not contain an explicit time dependence. Such systems possess a set of energy eigenvalues which do not vary with time. If the Hamiltonian does not contain time-dependent terms, the associated Schrödinger equation is always separable in time and spatial coordinates, and a set of system eigenfunctions exists such that

$$\Psi_n(\mathbf{r},t) = \psi_n(\mathbf{r})e^{-(i/\hbar)E_n t} \tag{11.1}$$

These eigenfunctions are products of a spatial eigenfunction (an eigenfunction of the Hamiltonian operator) and a harmonic time function whose frequency is determined by the corresponding eigenvalue of the Hamiltonian operator. If a general state function for the system is expanded in these eigenfunctions, the expansion coefficients are constants independent of time, as was shown in Chap. 3. If the state function is known at any reference time, these expansion coefficients can be determined, and the expectation value of any observable calculated at any subsequent time. Though the actual determination of eigenfunctions and eigenvalues may be difficult, we know in principle how to tackle such systems quantum-mechanically.

If the Hamiltonian of the system contains time explicitly, we are not in so fortunate a situation. The eigenvalues of the Hamiltonian will not be independent of time, the time dependence of the eigenfunctions is not obvious, and the behavior of expectation values with time is even less obvious. In general, no complete convergent machinery exists for the solution of problems involving a time-dependent Hamiltonian.

234 Basic Quantum Mechanics

Techniques have been developed, however, for solving certain special cases. One of these, the adiabatic approximation, works for systems where the variation with time of the Hamiltonian is very slow compared with the frequency of any of the eigenstates and with the difference frequency between eigenstates, $(E_n - E_m)/\hbar$. Consider, for example, a simple harmonic oscillator whose spring constant is very slowly changed at a rate that is very slow compared with ω_0. Clearly, a good approximation to the actual solutions of the problem will be given if the time-varying spring constant $k(t)$ is simply inserted into the solutions already known for the case where k is rigorously constant with time.

For another class of systems involving time-dependent Hamiltonians, the time-dependent portions of the Hamiltonian can be sequestered from the time-independent parts, and we arrive at a Hamiltonian which is the sum of two parts.

$$H(t) = H^0 + H'(t) \tag{11.2}$$

H' may or may not be small compared with H^0. There is, fortunately, a large class of problems of real physical and technological importance for which H' *is* small, and most of what follows will be directed toward such problems. The electric and magnetic fields which man is capable of generating are usually small compared with those which exist within atomic systems, so the radio-frequency, microwave, infrared, and optical susceptibilities (both electric and magnetic) of solid, liquid, or gaseous atomic systems can generally be calculated from a Hamiltonian such as Eq. (11.2). For these cases, the time-independent fields of atomic origin define H^0, and the much weaker applied alternating fields give rise to H'.

Consider, then, that we do have a system whose Hamiltonian can be divided as is done in Eq. (11.2). We shall assume that we know the eigenfunctions $u_n(\mathbf{r})$ and eigenenergies E_n of the time-independent part H^0. These are not the correct eigenfunctions for the full Hamiltonian, including the time-dependent part, but they are the best that we have, so let us use the eigenfunctions of H^0 as a basis set for describing our state functions. Writing some general state functions in this basis, we have

$$\Psi(\mathbf{r},t) = \sum_n c_n(t)u_n(\mathbf{r})e^{-(i/\hbar)E_n t} \tag{11.3}$$

The expansion coefficients will now certainly be functions of time, as we may verify by substituting the expansion of Eq. (11.3) back into the general time-dependent Schrödinger equation,

$$H\Psi(\mathbf{r},t) = -\frac{\hbar}{i}\frac{\partial}{\partial t}\Psi(\mathbf{r},t) \tag{11.4}$$

We then obtain

$$H^0 \sum_n c_n(t)u_n e^{-(i/\hbar)E_n t} + H' \sum_n c_n(t)u_n e^{-(i/\hbar)E_n t}$$

$$= -\frac{\hbar}{i}\frac{\partial}{\partial t}\sum_n c_n(t)u_n e^{-(i/\hbar)E_n t} \quad (11.5)$$

or

$$\sum_n E_n c_n(t)u_n e^{-(i/\hbar)E_n t} + H' \sum_n c_n(t)u_n e^{-(i/\hbar)E_n t}$$

$$= -\frac{\hbar}{i}\sum_n \dot{c}_n(t)u_n e^{-(i/\hbar)E_n t} + \sum_n E_n c_n(t)u_n e^{-(i/\hbar)E_n t} \quad (11.6)$$

The first and last terms cancel, leaving

$$-\frac{\hbar}{i}\sum_n \dot{c}_n(t)u_n e^{-(i/\hbar)E_n t} = H' \sum_n c_n(t)u_n e^{-(i/\hbar)E_n t} \quad (11.7)$$

Multiplying from the left by $u_k^* e^{+(i/\hbar)E_k t}$ and integrating over the relevant volume, we obtain

$$-\frac{\hbar}{i}\dot{c}_k(t) = \sum_n H'_{kn}(\mathbf{r},t)c_n(t) \quad (11.8)$$

where
$$H'_{kn}(\mathbf{r},t) = \int u_k^*(\mathbf{r})e^{+(i/\hbar)E_k t}H'(\mathbf{r},t)u_n(\mathbf{r})e^{-(i/\hbar)E_n t}\,d\mathbf{r} \quad (11.9)$$

Up to this point we have made no assumptions concerning the relative sizes of H^0 and H', and Eq. (11.9) is therefore rigorous, presuming only that H is separable into a time-dependent and a time-independent portion. To make progress beyond this point, however, we must now make special assumptions concerning the form of H', the state of the system at some reference time, and the relative sizes of H^0 and H'.

We shall consider at some length the case where H' is harmonic in time and is small compared with H^0, because a large number of situations of great practical interest fall into this category; for example, the interaction of radiation and matter, in all its ramifications: microwave, infrared, and optical spectroscopy; masers and lasers; optical properties of solids; photoemission and photoconductivity; radio-frequency permeabilities and susceptibilities, etc. We shall consider at somewhat less length a second case in which H' is time dependent only in that it is "turned on" at some specific time. Many scattering problems can be treated within this framework.

Let us first see what progress we can make beyond the general equation [Eq. (11.8)] if we consider only small perturbations, that is, assume $H' \ll H^0$.

If H' is small, the time variation of the various $c_n(t)$ will be slow; in the limit that $H' \to 0$, the $c_n(t)$ become constants. Suppose further that we know the $c_n(t)$ at some time t_0. The $c_n(t_0)$ specify, of course, the initial conditions of the system. If the $c_n(t)$ are slowly varying functions of time, we will incur little error in calculating the $\dot{c}_k(t)$ for times not too far removed from t_0 if we simply replace the $c_n(t)$ in the right-hand side of Eq. (11.8) by the $c_n(t_0)$ which we know.

$$\dot{c}_k(t) = -\frac{i}{\hbar} \sum_n H'_{kn}(\mathbf{r},t)c_n(t_0) \tag{11.10}$$

Integrating with respect to time, we obtain

$$c_k^{(1)}(t) - c_k(t_0) = -\frac{i}{\hbar} \sum_n \int_{t_0}^{t} H'_{kn}(\mathbf{r},t)c_n(t_0)\, dt \tag{11.11}$$

Equation (11.11) gives us the first-order approximation to $c_k(t)$, as is indicated by the superscript (1). If a more accurate determination of $c_k(t)$ is needed, we can iterate the procedure by substituting the $c_n^{(1)}(t)$, as determined above, into the right-hand side of Eq. (11.8). We obtain then

$$c_n^{(2)}(t) - c_k(t_0) = -\frac{i}{\hbar} \sum_n \int_{t_0}^{t} H'_{kn}(\mathbf{r},t)c_n^{(1)}(t)\, dt \tag{11.12}$$

where the superscript (2) indicates that the expansion coefficient is now correct to second order in the time variation. $c_k^{(2)}(t)$ is not a second-order correction to $c_k^{(1)}(t)$, but is the expansion coefficient correct to second order. Successive iterations allow us, mostly in principle, to extend this procedure to arbitrary accuracy and for an arbitrary extent of time and to follow the change of the state function with time under the influence of the time-dependent perturbation H'.

11.2 THE HARMONIC PERTURBATION AND TRANSITION PROBABILITIES

As remarked above, the time harmonic perturbation is of considerable interest in both physics and physical electronics. A great deal of what we know about the structure of materials has been obtained through spectroscopy of some sort—the observation of the interaction of materials with applied radiation. Often this interaction shows resonant characteristics, that is, the material absorbs or emits radiation very strongly in certain very narrow frequency regions. Time-dependent perturbation theory enables us to make the connection between this interaction and the intrinsic properties of the material, its quantum-mechanical structure.

Let us consider a perturbation harmonic in time, that is, of the form

$$H'(\mathbf{r},t) = H'(\mathbf{r}) \cos \omega t \qquad (11.13)$$

We may then write the matrix elements of $H'(\mathbf{r},t)$ in the representation supplied by the eigenfunctions of H^0 as

$$H'_{kn}(\mathbf{r},t) = \int u_k^*(\mathbf{r}) H'(\mathbf{r}) u_n(\mathbf{r}) \, d\mathbf{r} e^{(i/\hbar)(E_k - E_n)} \cos \omega t$$

$$= H'_{kn} \frac{e^{i(\omega_{kn}+\omega)t} + e^{i(\omega_{kn}-\omega)t}}{2} \qquad (11.14)$$

where
$$\omega_{kn} = \frac{E_k - E_n}{\hbar} \qquad (11.15)$$

and H'_{kn} refers to the matrix element obtained by integration over the spatial coordinates.

Substituting $H'_{kn}(\mathbf{r},t)$ from Eq. (11.13) into Eq. (11.8) gives us a set of n first-order differential equations in the n unknown $c_n(t)$, and if we further know the $c_n(t)$ at some reference time t_0, we can, in principle at least, solve for the n unknowns completely. For systems involving only a few levels (up to four), such calculations have indeed been made and the explicit $c_n(t)$ obtained. In the more general case, however, we are forced to introduce some approximations and assumptions at this point in order to make further progress.

We shall first assume that $H' \ll H^0$ and that the relevant theory of the previous section applies. As remarked earlier, this approximation is usually a valid one when we consider the effect of man-made radiation incident upon atomic systems and the effect this radiation causes on a microscopic (atomic or molecular) scale. We then have for the harmonic perturbation

$$c_k(t) - c_k(t_0) = -\frac{i}{\hbar} \sum_n \int_{t_0}^{t} H'_{kn} \frac{e^{i(\omega_{kn}+\omega)t} + e^{i(\omega_{kn}-\omega)t}}{2} c_n(t_0) \, dt \quad (11.16)$$

The implications of this expression can best be illustrated by consideration of a rather special initial state, one which is an eigenfunction of H^0. Let us also take $t_0 = 0$ to simplify the notation of the various integrals and coefficients. The initial conditions are then

$$c_n(t = 0) = 1 \qquad c_k(t = 0) = 0 \qquad k \neq n \qquad (11.17)$$

We are asking essentially the following question: If a system is in an initial state corresponding to an eigenstate of H^0, how fast is this state converted to other eigenstates by the action of H'? If H' were vanishingly small, the system would remain in the initial eigenstate indefinitely. The presence of the perturbation causes a change in the state function, which must be recognized by a change in the state expansion coefficients, the $c_k(t)$. Presumably some of the $c_k(t)$ will increase more rapidly than others, indicating some systematic change in the state function under the action of the perturbation. If our actual system is in a more complicated initial state than the one we are considering here, we can construct its behavior by a superposition process—a straightforward but not necessarily trivial operation.

The assumption of our very simple initial state reduces the summation of Eq. (11.16) to just one term, so for any state $k \neq n$, we have

$$c_k(t) = -\frac{i}{\hbar} \int_0^t H'_{kn} \frac{e^{i(\omega_{kn}+\omega)t} + e^{i(\omega_{kn}-\omega)t}}{2} \, dt \qquad (11.18)$$

The integral is readily completed, giving, for the harmonic perturbation,

$$c_k(t) = -\frac{H'_{kn}}{2\hbar} \left[\frac{e^{i(\omega_{kn}+\omega)t} - 1}{\omega_{kn} + \omega} + \frac{e^{i(\omega_{kn}-\omega)t} - 1}{\omega_{kn} - \omega} \right] \qquad (11.19)$$

The probability of finding the system (initially in the eigenstate ψ_n of H^0) in some other eigenstate ψ_k at time t is given by $|c_k(t)|^2$. We note that the right-hand side of Eq. (11.19) has poles at $\omega = \pm\omega_{kn}$ and that $c_k(t)$ and $|c_k(t)|^2$ will be large or appreciable primarily when this "resonance condition" $\omega_{kn} = \pm\omega$ is satisfied. The perturbation frequency ω is a positive number, but ω_{kn} can be either positive or negative, depending on whether $E_k > E_n$ or $E_k < E_n$. If ψ_k lies above ψ_n in energy (ω_{kn} positive), $|c_k(t)|^2$ will become appreciable when $\omega \approx |\omega_{kn}|$ because of the resonant denominator in the second term of Eq. (11.19) and will be negligible for all other ω. If ψ_k lies below ψ_n in energy (ω_{kn} negative) $|c_k(t)|^2$ will become appreciable when $\omega \approx |\omega_{kn}|$ because of the resonant denominator in the first term of Eq. (11.19) and will be negligible for all other ω. The two terms are never simultaneously important except in the limit $\omega_{kn} \rightarrow 0$, which we will discuss later as the "constant" perturbation.

If $E_k > E_n$ and the perturbation causes $|c_k(t)|^2$ to grow at the expense of $|c_n(t)|^2$, the expectation value of the energy of the system is increasing. In the case where H^0 represents an unperturbed atomic system and H' represents an incident radiation field, we would describe the above situation by saying that the atomic system is absorbing energy from the radiation field. If $E_k < E_n$ and $|c_k(t)|^2$ is growing at the expense of $|c_n(t)|^2$, the atomic system is surrendering energy to the radiation field; it is undergoing stimulated emission.

We may calculate $|c_k(t)|^2$ directly from Eq. (11.19), recognizing that only one of the two terms will be important at any time and that interference effects between the two terms therefore need not be considered.

$$|c_k(t)|^2 = \frac{|H'_{kn}|^2}{4\hbar^2} \left| \frac{e^{i(\omega_{kn}\pm\omega)t} - 1}{\omega_{kn} \pm \omega} \right|^2$$

$$= \frac{|H'_{kn}|^2}{4\hbar^2} \left| \frac{2 - 2\cos(\omega_{kn} \pm \omega)t}{(\omega_{kn} \pm \omega)} \right|^2$$

$$= \frac{|H'_{kn}|^2}{4\hbar^2} \frac{\sin^2\left(\dfrac{\omega_{kn} \pm \omega}{2}\right)t}{\left(\dfrac{\omega_{kn} \pm \omega}{2}\right)^2}$$

$$= \frac{|H'_{kn}|^2}{4\hbar^2} \frac{\sin^2 \beta t}{(\beta)^2} \tag{11.20}$$

where $$\beta = \frac{\omega_{kn} \pm \omega}{2} \tag{11.21}$$

The function $\sin^2 \beta t/\beta^2$ is plotted in Fig. 11.1 and may be seen to be very sharply peaked around $\beta = 0$. The maximum of the peak at $\beta = 0$ is equal to t^2, and the width of the peak is proportional to $1/t$, so the area under the curve is proportional to t. As t increases, the central peak gets narrower and narrower; the function $\sin^2 \alpha/\alpha^2$ is in fact one form of the Dirac delta function.

If the perturbing source is set exactly to ω_{kn}, so that $\beta \equiv 0$, $|c_k(t)|^2$ will increase quadratically with time. If ω is set ever so slightly away from the "resonance" frequency ω_{kn}, $\beta = \varepsilon$, the growth of $|c_k(t)|^2$ will be initially large, will pass through zero when $t = \pi/\varepsilon$ (as the first zero of $\sin^2 \beta t/\beta^2$ occurs), rise to some small value, pass through zero again at $t = 2\pi/\varepsilon$ etc., with the growth rate becoming ever smaller. The major increase in $|c_k(t)|^2$ comes as a transient effect when the perturbation is first turned on. Both these predictions violate our intuition as to what should happen. We would expect that the initial rate of growth of $|c_k(t)|^2$ should be linear in time; doubling the time of perturbation, doubling the growth of the new eigenstate. The essentially zero width of the effective ω also seems physically implausible. Both these implausibilities are rooted in the implicit assumption in our derivation that the energy levels involved are arbitrarily sharply defined, that the width E of any level is vanishingly small, and that the energy denominator of $|c_k(t)|^2$ has a pole of infinite height and zero width at $\omega = \omega_{kn}$.

We have never before had to introduce the idea of finite width of energy levels, so we might well ask why it is necessary to do so now. We must do so precisely because our Hamiltonian contains time-dependent terms. If the Hamiltonian does not have any time-dependent terms, it may have perfectly well-defined, arbitrarily narrow time-independent energy levels. When we introduce a small time-dependent term, as we do in a Hamiltonian of the form of Eq. (11.2), we introduce a modulation of these eigenvalues. If the $H'(t)$ term is small compared with H^0, there will be some small excursion of the corresponding eigenvalues of H^0 alone. The result of an energy measurement will depend upon the exact time at which the measurement is made. The eigenfunctions of H^0 are still a useful and complete basis for the description of the system, but there is now not one unique eigenvalue associated with each eigenstate but rather a small spread of eigenvalues. We may think of the eigenstates as acquiring a finite width in energy because of the time-dependent perturbation. One result of the spreading of the eigenenergies is the blurring of the delta function at $\omega = \omega_{kn}$, since ω_{kn} is no longer a clearly and unambiguously defined constant, so we should reexamine our derivation of $|c_k(t)|^2$.

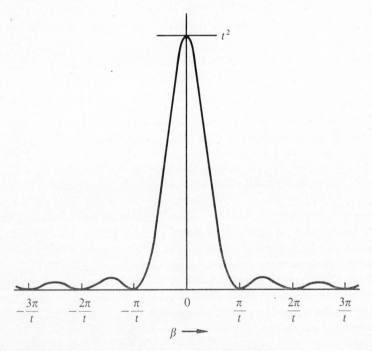

Fig. 11.1 $\sin^2 \beta t / \beta^2$ *versus* β.

We lead up to our final answer by first considering a second kind of situation, one for which we have an initial state of energy E_n and a continuum of states in the region around E_k, where $(E_k - E_n)/\hbar = \omega_{kn}$. The density of states in the vicinity of E_k may be characterized by some density of states function $\rho(E)$. Let us now apply a harmonic perturbation of frequency $\omega = \omega_{kn}$ and ask for the total increment in the $|c_l(t)|^2$ of all states other than the initial state. This is a measure of the total probability of finding the system at time t in a state other than the original state. This total probability is given by

$$\sum_l |c_l(t)|^2 = \int_{-\infty}^{+\infty} \frac{|H'_{ln}|^2}{4\hbar^2} \frac{\sin^2 \beta t}{\beta^2} \rho(E_l)\, dE_l \qquad (11.22)$$

where now

$$\beta = \frac{\omega'_{ln} \pm \omega}{2} = \frac{\omega'_{ln} \pm \omega_{kn}}{2}$$

$$= \frac{E_l - E_n}{2\hbar} \pm \frac{E_k - E_n}{2\hbar}$$

$$= \frac{E_l - E_k}{2\hbar} \qquad (11.23)$$

since we have set our harmonic perturbation to the frequency $\omega = \omega_{kn}$. We use an integral in Eq. (11.22) because we have assumed a continuum of states in the vicinity of E_k. In view of the relation between β and E_l given in Eq. (11.23), we can convert our variable of integration from dE_l to $d\beta$ and rewrite Eq. (11.22) as

$$\sum_l |c_l(t)|^2 = \int_{-\infty}^{+\infty} \frac{|H'_{ln}|^2}{4\hbar^2} \rho(E_l) t^2 \frac{\sin^2 \beta t}{(\beta t)^2} \frac{2\hbar}{t}\, d(\beta t) \qquad (11.24)$$

The time t will be held constant during the integration over energy, that is, during the summation over states. The function $\sin^2 \beta t/(\beta t)^2$ is a very rapidly varying function of β, and is, as remarked before, one form of the Dirac delta function, having a sharp peak at $\beta = 0$. We may therefore assign to $|H'_{ln}|^2$ and $\rho(E_l)$, which we presume to be slowly varying functions of E_l compared with the delta function, their values at the peak of the delta function: $|H'_{kn}|^2$ and $\rho(E_k)$, respectively. The integral can then be readily evaluated; it is

$$\sum_l |c_l(t)|^2 = \frac{|H'_{kn}|^2}{2\hbar} \rho(E_k)\pi t \qquad (11.25)$$

The only states which the perturbation of $\omega = \omega_{kn}$ will cause to be populated .are in the immediate vicinity of E_k, and the probability of finding the system in one of these states increases linearly with the length of time the perturbation is applied. Since the probability increases linearly with time, we may speak of a *transition rate* or *transition probability*

$$w_{kn} = \frac{\pi |H'_{kn}|^2}{2\hbar} \rho(E_k) \qquad (11.26)$$

The transition probability is proportional to the square of the matrix element of the perturbing term and to the density of terminal states available. Equation (11.26), an important equation in quantum mechanics, is one form of Fermi's "Golden Rule." Note that Eq. (11.26) applies only "on resonance," i.e., for states near E_k where the applied frequency ω is equal to ω_{kn}.

Let us return now to the earlier problem, that of calculating the transition probability between two discrete states of finite width. We may borrow directly from the results immediately above by simply regarding the terminal state of finite width as a continuum of states in the vicinity of E_k, with a probability distribution such that the total number of states in the vicinity of E_k is exactly unity. We then simply insert $\rho(E_k) = 1$ into Eq. (11.26), and have, for the transition probability from state ψ_n to state ψ_k,

$$w_{kn} = \frac{\pi}{2\hbar} |H'_{kn}|^2 \qquad (11.27)$$

If our system is initially entirely in state ψ_n of energy E_n and subject to a harmonic perturbation of frequency ω, the probability of finding the system at some later time t in state ψ_k of energy E_k increases linearly with time at the rate given by Eq. (11.27) if $(E_k - E_n)/\hbar = \pm\omega$, and is substantially zero otherwise. It is Eq. (11.27), not Eq. (11.20), which we should use in computing the effect of a harmonic perturbation upon a real system having discrete energy levels; Eq. (11.20) is appropriate only to a hypothetical system whose energy levels have zero width.

11.3 THE HARMONIC PERTURBATION, MASERS, LASERS, AND SPEC-TROSCOPY   The transition probability between states k and n given in Eq. (11.26) applies only when the frequency of the perturbing $H'(t)$ coincides with $\omega_{kn} = |E_k - E_n|/\hbar$. Otherwise, the transition probability is substantially zero. Note further that the transition probability w_{kn} is equal to the transition probability w_{nk} from the Hermiticity of H'_{kn}. The probability of inducing a transition from state n to state k is exactly equal to the probability of inducing a transition from state k to state n, and which way the transition goes depends entirely on the initial conditions of the system, the $c_n(0)$. For instance, if a system is known to be in state

ψ_n at $t = 0$, the only transition possible, if $\omega = \omega_{kn}$, will be from state ψ_n to state ψ_k, and if the system is known to be in state ψ_k at $t = 0$, the only transition possible will be from state ψ_k to state ψ_n. If the system is initially in some mixed state, where both $c_k(0)$ and $c_n(0)$ are nonzero, both types of transitions will take place with a relative probability given by the $|c_i(0)|^2$, where $c_i(0)$ is the expansion coefficient of the *initial* state. If $E_k > E_n$, the system will, on the average, absorb energy from the perturbing field when $|c_n(0)|^2 > |c_k(0)|^2$ and contribute energy to the perturbing field (through induced emission) when $|c_k(0)|^2 > |c_n(0)|^2$. This fact underlies all the maser-laser family of coherent electromagnetic generators.

If an atomic or molecular system possesses a discrete set of energy levels and is irradiated by an electromagnetic radiation of arbitrary frequency ω, there will be in general no transition induced with any appreciable probability and no energy absorbed from or contributed to the incident wave. The material will be transparent at the frequency ω. If ω is slowly varied until it coincides with one of the ω_{kn}, transitions will be induced and absorption from the perturbing wave will occur (we assume now that $|c_k(0)|^2 < |c_n(0)|^2$ if $E_k > E_n$, the usual case in thermal equilibrium). Let us refer now to Fig. 11.2, which gives the energy level scheme of some imaginary material.

Suppose first (Fig. 11.2*a*) that the system is entirely in the lowest state ($c_0(0) = 1$, all $c_{n>0}(0) = 0$), which is often the case for atomic systems at low temperature. The transitions indicated by the arrows will occur as the incident radiation is swept in frequency from zero to the highest frequency involved, provided the spatial matrix elements H'_{k0} are nonzero. In the hypothetical absorption spectrum for this system, drawn below the energy-level scheme in Fig. 11.2, the H'_{k0} are all assumed to be equal.

Suppose next that $|c_0(0)|^2 = \frac{2}{3}$ and $|c_1(0)|^2 = \frac{1}{3}$, that is, that the first "excited" state has become appreciably populated, perhaps because of a rise in the temperature. Now discrete absorptions will occur, originating on both E_0 and E_1, and the absorption spectrum will be as sketched in Fig. 11.2*b*. Note that additional absorptions have appeared and that the absorption corresponding to w_{01} has been greatly reduced because of the competition from the radiative transition w_{10} at the same frequency. We see that by observing the absorption spectrum of a material and by measuring the frequency, intensity, and temperature dependence of the intensity of the absorptions we can characterize completely the energy levels of the system. The appropriate frequency to cause transitions may be in the radio-frequency, microwave, infrared, optical, or x-ray regions of the spectrum, but the principle of interpretation is the same. The study of the response of a physical system to a harmonic perturbation, usually but not necessarily an electromagnetic wave, is known as *spectroscopy*, and is perhaps the most incisive tool available for studying the structure of systems on an atomic and molecular scale. The necessity of explaining the optical spectra of atoms was one of the prime motivating factors in the formulation of quantum mechanics, and Schrödinger's success in explaining the spectrum of hydrogen with his new wave mechanics effected the almost instantaneous acceptance of the validity of his approach.

Spectroscopy yields the energy differences between states, rather than the absolute position of levels. Other evidence, usually the temperature dependence of absorption intensities, must be adduced if the eigenenergy spectrum of the system, arranged in proper order, is to be finally obtained. The subject of statistical mechanics deals with, among other things, the relative population of different energy states as a function of temperature. Different kinds of statistics apply to different kinds of systems, but it is generally true that a system in equilibrium with its environment at any

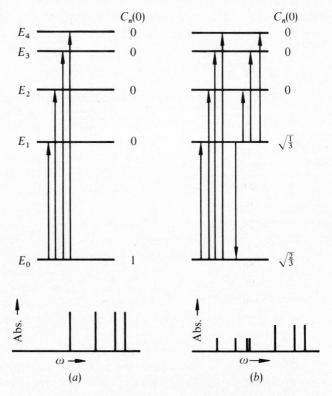

Fig. 11.2 *Absorption spectrum of hypothetical system.*

temperature will have lower energy states more generously populated than higher energy states. If $E_k > E_n$, then $|c_k|^2 < |c_n|^2$ in thermal equilibrium. If radiation (a harmonic perturbation) is incident upon a system in thermal equilibrium, there will be net absorption from the radiation by the atomic system. If the perturbation is continued for some time or with some considerable strength, the thermal equilibrium will be eventually upset, and higher energy states may acquire populations appreciably in excess of their thermal equilibrium values. If $|c_k|^2 > |c_n|^2$ (for $E_k > E_n$) under the influence of the perturbation, "population inversion" has been accomplished, and the system will surrender energy to a perturbing field of frequency ω_{kn}, amplifying the perturbing wave. If the population inversion is of sufficient magnitude and if certain other conditions are met, an atomic oscillator of the maser-laser class may be created. The various masers and lasers differ primarily in the schemes used to obtain population inversion and in the frequencies ω_{kn} at which it is possible to obtain amplification or oscillation.

11.4 QUANTITATIVE EXAMPLE: PARAMAGNETIC RESONANCE ABSORPTION Let us illustrate the harmonic time-dependent perturbation with a specific example: the paramagnetic resonance absorption of an atom placed in a static magnetic field. We will treat here the hypothetical spinless hydrogen atom so that we may borrow directly the eigenfunction and eigenvalue solutions of earlier chapters. Our Hamiltonian will therefore be

$$H = -\frac{\hbar^2}{2m} \nabla^2 - \frac{Ze^2}{r} + g\beta(\mathbf{L} \cdot \mathbf{H_0}) + g\beta(\mathbf{L} \cdot \mathbf{H_1} \cos \omega t) \quad (11.28)$$

where $\mathbf{H_0}$ is the static magnetic field and $\mathbf{H_1}$ is the radio-frequency magnetic field. The first two terms of Eq. (11.28) are the Hamiltonian of the free hydrogen atom, treated in Chap. 9. The energy levels of this atom are, we recall, multiply degenerate. Applying the static magnetic field $\mathbf{H_0}$ removes some of this degeneracy, as discussed in Chap. 10. Let us call the direction of $\mathbf{H_0}$ the *z direction*. In a paramagnetic resonance experiment, the harmonic field is usually applied in a direction perpendicular to the static field. Let us call this direction the *x direction*. The Hamiltonian of Eq. (11.28) then becomes

$$H = -\frac{\hbar^2}{2m} \nabla^2 - \frac{Ze^2}{r} + g\beta L_z H_0 + g\beta H_1 L_x \cos \omega t \quad (11.29)$$

We have solved the time-independent part of this Hamiltonian earlier, so we know the eigenfunctions and eigenenergies exactly. Let us write the Hamiltonian matrix, including the time-independent harmonic term, in the L^2, L_z representation, the basis system in which both L^2 and L_z are diagonal. The Hamiltonian matrix will again be composed of a string of submatrices of various dimension along the diagonal. Let us write down in Eq. (11.30) one submatrix out of this whole matrix and concentrate on it. Neither H_0 nor H_1 introduces matrix elements which "couple" these submatrices together, so we may examine each submatrix separately. We choose a submatrix corresponding to $L = 2$, implying that $n \geq 3$.

$$
\begin{bmatrix}
E_n^0 + 2g\beta H_0 & g\beta H_1 \cos\omega t & 0 & 0 & 0 \\
g\beta H_1 \cos\omega t & E_n^0 + g\beta H_0 & (\sqrt{6}/2)g\beta H_1 \cos\omega t & 0 & 0 \\
0 & (\sqrt{6}/2)g\beta H_1 \cos\omega t & E_n^0 & (\sqrt{6}/2)g\beta H_1 \cos\omega t & 0 \\
0 & 0 & (\sqrt{6}/2)g\beta H_1 \cos\omega t & E_n^0 - g\beta H_0 & g\beta H_1 \cos\omega t \\
0 & 0 & 0 & g\beta H_1 \cos\omega t & E_n^0 - 2g\beta H_0
\end{bmatrix}
$$

$$(11.30)$$

We note that H_{kn}' has only three values: $g\beta H_1$, $(\sqrt{6}/2)g\beta H_1$, and 0. The nonzero values of H_{kn}' occur between states of L_z and $L_z \pm 1$, so the r-f field will induce transition only between states differing by 1 unit in their L_z quantum number and therefore differing in energy only by $\pm g\beta H_0$. For this system then, all the absorptions occur at the same frequency:

$$\omega = \frac{g\beta H_0}{\hbar} \tag{11.31}$$

The transition probabilities for the "allowed" transition are

$$w(-2 \to -1) = w(-1 \to -2) = w(2 \to 1) = w(1 \to 2) = \frac{\pi}{2\hbar}g^2\beta^2 H_1^2 \tag{11.32}$$

$$w(-1 \to 0) = w(0 \to -1) = w(1 \to 0) = w(0 \to 1) = \frac{\pi}{2\hbar}\frac{6}{4}g^2\beta^2 H_1^2$$

where the parentheses after the w's indicate the L_z values of the initial and final states involved in the transition. If the populations of the various L_z states were to be the same, there would be no net absorption by the system, even at $\omega = g\beta H_0/\hbar$, for the reasons cited in the preceding section. However, for a system in thermal equilibrium at any finite temperature, the ratio of the populations of successive L_z states belonging to the same E_n^0 will be given by

$$\frac{|c(L_z = n + 1)|^2}{|c(L_z = n)|^2} = e^{-g\beta H_0/kT} \tag{11.33}$$

and there will, in general, be a net absorption at the resonance frequency. The absorption will increase as the temperature decreases, as we can see from Eq. (11.33), because of the increased difference in state population. The rate at which energy will be initially absorbed because of transitions between any particular pair of states will be given by the transition probability times the difference in population times the energy difference between states:

$$P = \frac{\pi}{2\hbar} |H'_{kn}|^2 (|c_k(0)|^2 - |c_n(0)|^2) \hbar \omega_{kn} \qquad (11.34)$$

For the paramagnetic case,

$$|c_n(0)|^2 - |c_{n+1}(0)|^2 = |c_n(0)|^2 (1 - e^{-g\beta H_0/kT}) \qquad (11.35)$$

In the temperature domain where $kT \gg g\beta H_0$, which would be for any temperature above about $5°K$ for ordinary microwave frequencies, we may approximate the exponential by $1 - (g\beta H_0/kT)$ and obtain

$$|c_n(0)|^2 - |c_{(n+1)}(0)|^2 = |c_n(0)|^2 \frac{g\beta H_0}{kT} \qquad (11.36)$$

showing that the rate at which the system would absorb energy from the perturbing field is inversely proportional to the temperature.

In the example we have given, there is only one frequency ω (for a given H_0) or one field H_0 (for a given ω) at which energy absorption will take place, and our hypothetical experiment would give us only one piece of information about the atom: the value of the constant $g\beta$. The extreme simplicity of our result reflects the simple model we have used for our atom. Had we introduced the electron's spin into the picture, we would have the energy of the spin's interaction with the orbital angular momentum and with the external magnetic fields to consider. The static portion of the Hamiltonian, whose eigenfunctions and eigenvalues we would need in order to solve the time-dependent perturbation problem, would be

$$H = -\frac{\hbar^2}{2m} \nabla^2 - \frac{Ze^2}{r} + \lambda \mathbf{L} \cdot \mathbf{S} + g_l \beta \mathbf{L} \cdot \mathbf{H}_0 + g_s \beta \mathbf{S} \cdot \mathbf{H}_0 \quad (11.37)$$

and the time-dependent perturbation would be

$$H' = \beta(g_l \mathbf{L} + g_s \mathbf{S}) \cdot \mathbf{H}_1 \cos \omega t \qquad (11.38)$$

Further, the atom would normally be situated in a crystal, and the electric fields generated by its neighbors would have to be included in the static Hamiltonian. If all these effects are included, we find that the paramagnetic resonance absorption spectrum provides a means for evaluating all the interaction constants appearing in the Hamiltonian, since the inter-actions will generally serve to shift the energy levels of the atoms, hence the absorption frequencies.

11.5 THE INTERACTION OF ATOMIC SYSTEMS WITH RADIATION In the preceding section a time-varying magnetic field was added to the Hamiltonian quite arbitrarily and treated as the sole perturbation active. However, we know from Maxwell's equations that there must be a harmonically varying electric field associated with a harmonic magnetic field. In this section we shall introduce electromagnetic fields into our Hamiltonian in a more nearly consistent and correct fashion.

As we showed in the section of Chap. 2 in which we reviewed classical mechanics, the Hamiltonian of a particle moving in the presence of electric and magnetic fields can be written

$$H = \frac{\left(\mathbf{p} - \frac{e}{c}\mathbf{A}\right)^2}{2m} + V(\mathbf{r}) \tag{11.39}$$

where $\mathbf{A}$ is the vector potential which, in conjunction with the scalar potential φ, determines all the electric and magnetic fields present.

$$\mathbf{E} = -\frac{1}{c}\frac{\partial \mathbf{A}}{\partial t} - \nabla\varphi \qquad \mathbf{B} = \nabla \times \mathbf{A} \tag{11.40}$$

The choice of $\mathbf{A}$ and φ leading to the fields $\mathbf{E}$ and $\mathbf{B}$ is not unique; an infinite set of combinations $\mathbf{A}'$ and φ' exist, leading to the same fields. These various choices of $\mathbf{A}$ and φ are related by what are called *gauge transformations*. For a region of space not containing currents or net charge, it is always possible to choose $\mathbf{A}$ and φ such that

$$\varphi = 0 \qquad \nabla \cdot \mathbf{A} = 0 \tag{11.41}$$

For this particular choice of $\mathbf{A}$ and φ

$$\mathbf{E} = -\frac{1}{c}\frac{\partial \mathbf{A}}{\partial t} \qquad \mathbf{B} = \nabla \times \mathbf{A} \tag{11.42}$$

The vector potential describing a plane wave of frequency ω propagating in the positive y direction with its $\mathbf{E}$ vector polarized parallel to the z axis and its $\mathbf{H}$ vector polarized parallel to the x axis is

$$\mathbf{A}(\mathbf{r},t) = A\mathbf{z}_0 \sin(\mathbf{k} \cdot \mathbf{r} - \omega t) \tag{11.43}$$

where $\mathbf{k}$ is the propagation vector

$$\mathbf{k} = \frac{\omega}{c}\, \mathbf{y}_0 \qquad (11.44)$$

($\mathbf{x}_0$, $\mathbf{y}_0$, and $\mathbf{z}_0$ are unit vectors in the positive x, y, and z directions).

Inserting the vector potential $\mathbf{A}(\mathbf{r},t)$ of Eq. (11.43) into the formulas of Eq. (11.42)

$$\mathbf{E} = \frac{\omega}{c}\, A\mathbf{z}_0 \cos(ky - \omega t) \qquad \mathbf{B} = \frac{\omega}{c}\, A\mathbf{x}_0 \cos(ky - \omega t) \quad (11.45)$$

Returning now to our Hamiltonian, we may rewrite Eq. (11.39) as

$$H = \frac{p^2}{2m} + V(\mathbf{r}) - \frac{e}{2mc}\,(\mathbf{p} \cdot \mathbf{A} + \mathbf{A} \cdot \mathbf{p}) + \frac{e^2}{2mc^2}\, A^2 \qquad (11.46)$$

This Hamiltonian we now regard as composed of two parts, the unperturbed Hamiltonian $p^2/2m + V(\mathbf{r})$ and the perturbing terms in $e\mathbf{p} \cdot \mathbf{A}/c$, $e\mathbf{A} \cdot \mathbf{p}/c$, and e^2A^2/c^2. We observe that the last term is one order higher in the small parameter $e A/\mathbf{p}c$ than the other two terms and is correspondingly smaller and of less importance. We therefore drop it at this time and consider only the terms in $\mathbf{p} \cdot \mathbf{A}$ and $\mathbf{A} \cdot \mathbf{p}$ when forming the perturbing Hamiltonian H'.

The reader will note that we are retaining a classical picture of the radiation field. To treat the problem of the interaction of a mechanical system with electromagnetic radiation in a truly consistent quantum-mechanical fashion, we would have to introduce the Hamiltonian of the radiation field and quantize the radiation field by introducing the appropriate commutation relations for its conjugate variables. We regard this problem, the formulation of quantum electrodynamics, as outside the domain of this book, referring the reader to one of the references at the end of this chapter for further enlightenment on this subject. In this book we choose a semiclassical approach in which we solve for the properties of the mechanical system quantum mechanically but treat the radiation field classically. In so doing we lose one important feature of the real system: we lose the zero-point fluctuations of the electromagnetic field and the "spontaneous emission" they induce in the mechanical system.

Considering now the quantum-mechanical problem of the mechanical system, we have the Hamiltonian

$$H = \frac{p^2}{2m} + V(\mathbf{r}) - \frac{e}{2mc}\,(\mathbf{p} \cdot \mathbf{A} + \mathbf{A} \cdot \mathbf{p})$$
$$= H^0 + H' \qquad (11.47)$$

The interaction term is, from this point of view, the perturbation acting upon the mechanical system. The perturbing term can be put into some-what simpler form since our choice of gauge ($\nabla \cdot \mathbf{A} = 0$) causes the operators for $\mathbf{p}$ and $\mathbf{A}$ to commute. Making the usual gradient-operator association with $\mathbf{p}$ and using a well-known theorem on vector identities, we see that

$$\mathbf{p} \cdot \mathbf{A}\psi = \frac{\hbar}{i}\nabla \cdot \mathbf{A}\psi = \frac{\hbar}{i}(\nabla \cdot \mathbf{A})\psi + \frac{\hbar}{i}\mathbf{A} \cdot \nabla\psi$$

$$= \mathbf{A} \cdot \mathbf{p}\psi \qquad (11.48)$$

We may therefore combine the two terms of the perturbing Hamiltonian to obtain

$$H' = -\frac{e}{mc}\mathbf{A} \cdot \mathbf{p} \qquad (11.49)$$

We are now in a position to consider the response of an atomic system to an incident electromagnetic wave. Let us choose this wave to be that described by the vector potential of Eq. (11.43). Since $\mathbf{A}$ is in the z direction and $\mathbf{k}$ is in the y direction, our perturbing term becomes

$$H' = -\frac{e}{mc}Ap_z \sin(ky - \omega t)$$

$$= -\frac{e}{2imc}Ap_z[e^{i(ky-\omega t)} - e^{-i(ky-\omega t)}] \qquad (11.50)$$

Consider now the transitions this perturbation will cause between two eigenstates $\Psi'_k(\mathbf{r},t)$ and $\Psi'_n(\mathbf{r},t)$ of the unperturbed Hamiltonian H^0. These states will be of the usual form

$$\Psi'_k(\mathbf{r},t) = \psi_k(\mathbf{r})e^{-(i/\hbar)E_k t}$$
$$\Psi'_n(\mathbf{r},t) = \psi_n(\mathbf{r})e^{-(i/\hbar)E_n t} \qquad (11.51)$$

The transition probability between these states is given, when $\omega = \omega_{kn}$, by the transition probability expression of Eq. (11.27), where now

$$H'_{kn} = -\frac{eA}{2imc}\int \psi_k^*(\mathbf{r})p_z e^{iky}\psi_n(\mathbf{r})\,d\mathbf{r} \qquad (11.52)$$

for $\omega = +\omega_{kn}$, and

$$H'_{kn} = \frac{eA}{2imc}\int \psi_k^*(\mathbf{r})p_z e^{-iky}\psi_n(\mathbf{r})\,d\mathbf{r} \qquad (11.53)$$

when $\omega = -\omega_{kn}$. These elements are very similar in form, so it will suffice to examine one of them, the first, in detail.

The wave functions $\Psi'_k(\mathbf{r})$ and $\Psi'_n(\mathbf{r})$ are wave functions of an atomic or molecular system. If we take the origin of coordinates at the center of the atom or molecule, $\Psi'_k(\mathbf{r})$ and $\Psi'_n(\mathbf{r})$ will have appreciable magnitude for a radius of only a few angstroms around the origin and will drop to substantially zero outside this region. The wavelength of the incident radiation, on the other hand, is most certainly much longer than a few angstroms. If ω is an optical frequency, the wavelength is typically several thousand Å; if ω is in the infrared spectral region, the wavelength is tens of thousands of Å; if ω is a microwave frequency, its wavelength is on the order of centimeters. Consequently e^{iky} will vary only slightly over the region where $\Psi'_k(\mathbf{r})$ or $\Psi'_n(\mathbf{r})$ are appreciable. We may then without serious error replace e^{iky} in the integral by its expansion in the small quantity ky:

$$e^{iky} = 1 + iky + \tfrac{1}{2}(iky)^2 \cdots \qquad (11.54)$$

and save only the first few terms in the expansion. We obtain then the matrix element

$$H'_{kn} = -\frac{A}{2imc}\int \psi_k^*(\mathbf{r})ep_z\psi_n(\mathbf{r})\,d\mathbf{r}$$

$$-\frac{kA}{2mc}\int \psi_k^*(\mathbf{r})ep_z y\psi_n(r)\,d\mathbf{r}$$

$$+\frac{k^2 A}{4imc}\int \psi_k^*(\mathbf{r})ep_z y^2\psi_n(\mathbf{r})\,d\mathbf{r} \qquad (11.55)$$

Since the parameter ky is small, on the order of 10^{-2} or 10^{-3}, the second term in H'_{kn} is very much smaller than the first, and the third smaller again by the same factor. The smaller terms are important only if the integral of the leading terms is zero, as sometimes is the case. The transitions caused by the radiation field through the perturbation H' are classified as electric dipole, magnetic dipole, electric quadrupole, etc., depending on the form of the important term in H'_{kn}.

The first integral of Eq. (11.55) gives the electric dipole interaction, since it corresponds to a term of the form $\mathbf{E}\cdot\mathbf{d}$, where $\mathbf{E}$ is the electric field and $\mathbf{d}$ is the dipole moment $\langle e\mathbf{r}\rangle$ of the charge distribution of the atom or molecule. It is not obvious that the integral corresponds, as alleged, to a term of the form $\mathbf{E}\cdot\mathbf{d}$, so we now engage in a bit of manipulation to put the leading term of Eq. (11.55) into such form. We first make a substitution for p_z. From Hamilton's canonical equation, we know that

$$\dot{z} = \frac{\partial H}{\partial p_z} = \frac{p_z}{m} \qquad (11.56)$$

where we have used the specific form of H^0 appropriate to this problem. We may therefore rewrite the leading term of Eq. (11.55) as

$$H'_{kn}\text{ (electric dipole)} = -\frac{A}{2imc}e(p_z)_{kn} = -\frac{A}{2ic}e(\dot{z})_{kn} \qquad (11.57)$$

We may evaluate $(\dot{z})_{kn}$ from

$$(\dot{z})_{kn} = \int \psi_k^*(\mathbf{r})\dot{z}\psi_n(\mathbf{r})\, d\mathbf{r}$$

$$= \int \psi_k^*(\mathbf{r})\frac{i}{\hbar}[H,z]\psi_n(\mathbf{r})\, d\mathbf{r}$$

$$= \frac{i(E_k - E_n)}{\hbar}\int \psi_k^*(\mathbf{r})z\psi_n(\mathbf{r})\, d\mathbf{r}$$

$$= i\omega_{kn}z_{kn} \tag{11.58}$$

We have then

$$H_{kn}'\ (\text{electric dipole}) = -\frac{A\omega}{2c}\, ez_{kn} \tag{11.59}$$

Referring back to Eq. (11.45) we note that the harmonic E field was of magnitude $A\omega/c$ and was directed along the z axis, so we may rewrite H_{kn}' once more as

$$H_{kn}'\ (\text{electric dipole}) = Eez_{kn}/2 \tag{11.60}$$

The character of this energy as an electric dipole is now apparent. It is a rather particular kind of electric dipole interaction, however. The electric dipole involved is not that of state Ψ_k nor of state Ψ_n but rather the matrix element of the electric dipole operator connecting states Ψ_k and Ψ_n.

The second integral of Eq. (11.55) for H_{kn}' gives rise to perturbations of magnetic dipole and electric quadrupole nature. Both these elements are of the same order of magnitude and are both typically 10^{-2} or 10^{-3} times the size of the electric dipole term, unless that electric dipole interaction vanishes (as it does between states of the same n and L but different L_z in our paramagnetic resonance example). The second integral can be manipulated into more suggestive form as follows:

$$H_{kn}'\begin{pmatrix}\text{magnetic dipole}\\ \text{electric quadrupole}\end{pmatrix} = -\frac{kA}{2mc}\int \psi_n^*(\mathbf{r})ep_z y\psi_n(\mathbf{r})\, d\mathbf{r}$$

$$= -\frac{kAe}{2mc}\int \psi_k^*(\mathbf{r})\tfrac{1}{2}[(p_z y - zp_y)$$

$$+ (p_z y + zp_y)]\psi_n(\mathbf{r})\, d\mathbf{r}$$

$$= -\frac{e}{4mc}\left(\frac{\omega}{c}A\right)\int \psi_k^*(\mathbf{r})L_x\psi_n(\mathbf{r})\, d\mathbf{r}$$

$$- \frac{e}{4mc}\left(\frac{\omega}{c}A\right)\int \psi_k^*(\mathbf{r})(p_z y + zp_y)\psi_n(\mathbf{r})\, d\mathbf{r} \tag{11.61}$$

The first of these two integrals can clearly be identified with the interaction of the x component of the H field (of magnitude $A\omega/c$) with the x component of angular momentum. The multiplying constant e/mc is of appropriate dimensions to convert angular momentum to magnetic moment and is the constant β of the paramagnetic resonance example

$$H'_{nk}\text{ (magnetic dipole)} = -\frac{e}{4mc}H(L_x)_{kn} \qquad (11.62)$$

The second of the two integrals of Eq. (11.61) can be manipulated in a fashion similar to that followed in the electric dipole case, yielding eventually

$$H'_{kn}\text{ (electric quadrupole)} = -\frac{c}{4mc}\left(\frac{\omega}{e}A\right)\omega_{kn}m(zy)_{kn}$$

$$= -\left(\frac{\omega}{c}\right)Ee(zy)_{kn}/4 \qquad (11.63)$$

The quadrupole moment of a charge distribution is given by $\int \rho x_i x_j \, d\mathbf{r}$, and we can see that $e(zy)_{kn}$ is one component of this tensor quantity evaluated between two quantum states. The contribution to H'_{kn} and the resultant transition probability given by Eq. (11.63) is therefore called the *electric quadrupole contribution*. We may similarly process the higher-order terms in the series consequent upon the expansion of e^{iky} and find interactions corresponding to magnetic quadrupole, electric octopole, etc., interactions—each of less physical importance than the preceding. We shall not pursue this development further.

We have seen in this section that the effects of electromagnetic radiation incident upon an atomic system can be treated in a semiclassical fashion, leading to the prediction of transitions between various eigenstates of the atomic system if the incident frequency is properly chosen and if the dipole, quadrupole, etc., interaction of the system with the radiation is finite.

11.6 THE CONSTANT PERTURBATION: SCATTERING THEORY Surprisingly enough, one important branch of time-dependent perturbation theory, scattering theory, was developed to handle a set of problems where in fact the Hamiltonian contains no explicitly time-dependent terms.

The resolution of the apparent paradox is contained in the observation that the expansion of a state function of one Hamiltonian in the eigenfunctions of another Hamiltonian must have time-dependent expansion coefficients, even if all Hamiltonians involved are time independent.

Consider a time-independent Hamiltonian

$$H = H^0 + H' \qquad (11.64)$$

where H, H^0, and H' are all independent of time, just as in Sec. 10.1. We assume again that we know the eigenfunctions u_n and eigenvalues E_n^0 of H^0. In the preceding chapter we sought to build out of those u_n the proper eigenfunctions, ψ_k, of H. Once these ψ_k are known, any state function $\Psi(\mathbf{r},t)$ of the system can be expanded in these $\Psi_k(\mathbf{r},t)$, and the expansion coefficients will be constants determined by the initial conditions of the state, but thereafter independent of time.

Suppose that we chose instead to expand the state function $\Psi(\mathbf{r},t)$ in the "inappropriate" eigenfunctions of H^0 rather than in the "appropriate" eigenfunctions of the full Hamiltonian H.

$$\Psi(\mathbf{r},t) = \sum_n c_n(t)u_n(\mathbf{r})e^{-(i/\hbar)E_n^0 t} \qquad (11.65)$$

The evolution with time of $\Psi(\mathbf{r},t)$ is determined, of course, by H, and we obtain the equations for $c_n(t)$ by following identically the steps of Eqs. (11.3) through (11.8) of Sec. 11.1. The only difference will be that H' is now a function of spatial coordinates only, and we arrive at the result

$$-\frac{\hbar}{i}\,\dot{c}_k(t) = \sum_n H'_{kn}(\mathbf{r})c_n(t)e^{(i/\hbar)(E_k-E_n)t} \qquad (11.66)$$

where the matrix element $H'_{kn}(\mathbf{r})$ now contains no time dependence.

There are two major categories of problems for which we use this second approach, that of expanding the state function of the true time-independent Hamiltonian in the eigenfunctions of a similar but not quite identical time-independent Hamiltonian. One such case is that for which a perturbation $H'(\mathbf{r})$ is added to the system for some finite time and subsequently removed. Except for being "turned on" at one time and "turned off" at some later time, the perturbation does not explicitly contain time. Since the system before and after the perturbation has the same Hamiltonian H^0, it is reasonable to retain the eigenfunctions of this Hamiltonian as a basis system throughout the calculation and to regard the additional term H' as inducing transitions between states of the original Hamiltonian.

A second category for which the "constant" perturbation is treated usefully as a time-dependent case is in certain scattering problems. Imagine a particle incident from some remote region upon a scattering center of relatively restricted spatial extent. The particle interacts with the scattering center and, unless captured by the scattering center, departs from the interaction region in some direction not generally coincident with its incident direction. The particle in its initial state and in its final state, well removed from the scattering center in both cases, behaves like a free particle. It is convenient, then, to describe the initial and final states of the particle in terms of free-particle eigenfunctions. The particle certainly does not, however, obey a free-particle Hamiltonian throughout its course.

Let us write its Hamiltonian as a sum of two parts, a free-particle Hamiltonian plus a scattering potential, or

$$H = H^0 + H' \qquad (11.64)$$

where we now identify H' with the scattering potential.

The initial state of the particle is well represented by a wave packet of free-particle wave functions centered about $\mathbf{k}_0$, the propagation vector of the incident particle:

$$\Psi(\mathbf{r}, t = 0) = u_{k_0}(\mathbf{r})e^{-(i/\hbar)E_{k_0}t} \qquad (11.67)$$

Equation (11.67) may be regarded as an expansion of the initial wave function which has

$$c_{k_0}(t = 0) = 1 \qquad c_k(t = 0) = 0 \qquad \text{all } \mathbf{k} \neq \mathbf{k}_0 \qquad (11.68)$$

The final or emergent state may be any one of the continuum of states of free particles with $\mathbf{k}$ in any direction and of any magnitude. The situation is very much like that treated midway through Sec. 11.2, except that the perturbation is static, $\omega = 0$. For $\omega = 0$, the two terms of Eq. (11.19) merge and are simultaneously resonant, giving twice the $c_k(t)$ and four times the $|c_k(t)|^2$ of the harmonic perturbation. Making this simple correction, we can borrow wholesale the results developed in Eqs. (11.22) through (11.25), arriving at the transition probability per unit time

$$w_{k_0 k} = \frac{2\pi}{\hbar} |H'_{kk_0}|^2 \rho(E_k) \qquad (11.69)$$

The resonance condition $\omega_{kn} = (E_k - E_n)/\hbar = \omega$ now becomes

$$E_k - E_{k_0} = 0 \qquad (11.70)$$

since $\omega = 0$. Energy is conserved in the scattering inasmuch as we are assuming implicitly that the scattering potential does not change as a result of the scattering event. We are treating "elastic" scattering. The effective matrix element H'_{kk_0} is the integral

$$H'_{kk_0} = \frac{1}{(2\pi)} \int e^{-i\mathbf{k}\cdot\mathbf{r}} V(\mathbf{r}) e^{i\mathbf{k}_0 \cdot \mathbf{r}} \, d\mathbf{r} \qquad (11.71)$$

where $V(\mathbf{r})$ is the potential associated with the scattering center.

The transition probability occurring in scattering experiments is commonly expressed as "scattering cross section." The scattering cross section σ of a given scattering center is a measure of its efficiency in scattering particles out of an incident beam. The "differential cross section" of a scattering center is the rate at which it scatters particles from an incident beam of normalized (unity) particle flux density into a differential element of solid angle $d\Omega$. The "total cross section" of a scattering center is the integral of the differential cross section over the whole 4π steradians of solid angle, and is hence the total rate at which particles are scattered out of a beam of unity flux intensity. Both cross sections may be obtained from w_{kk_0} by inserting the appropriate $\rho(E_k)$ and multiplying by geometric and normalization factors.

Let us obtain first the differential cross section $d\sigma/d\Omega$. We first need to know $\rho(E_k)$ for the free-particle terminal states. This we know from Sec. 8.4.

$$\rho(E_k) = \frac{m^{3/2} E^{1/2}}{2^{1/2} \pi^2 \hbar^3} = \frac{mk}{2\pi^2 \hbar^2} \tag{11.72}$$

The $\rho(E_k)$ specified here, however, is that for all k of the same magnitude, independent of the orientation of k; so to find the density of states with k restricted to a differential solid angle $d\Omega$, we multiply $\rho(E_k)$ by $d\Omega/4\pi$, the differential solid angle element divided by the total solid angle 4π. We thereby obtain the scattering rate from an initial state of normalized probability density into the solid angle $d\Omega$.

$$R_{kk_0} = \frac{2\pi}{\hbar} |H'_{kk_0}|^2 \frac{mk}{2\pi^2 \hbar^2} \frac{d\Omega}{4\pi} = \frac{mk}{4\pi^2 \hbar^3} |H'_{kk_0}|^2 \, d\Omega \tag{11.73}$$

To convert this to a differential cross section, we must normalize the incident flux. Since the initial state has normalized probability density, the incident flux density will be proportional to the incident particle velocity, $v_0 = \hbar k_0/m$. We may convert the differential scattering rate R_{kk_0} into a differential cross section $d\sigma$ by dividing through by v_0.

$$d\sigma = \frac{mk}{4\pi^2 \hbar^3} |H'_{kk_0}|^2 \frac{m}{\hbar k_0} \, d\Omega \tag{11.74}$$

Finally, since the scattering probability is sharply peaked at $E_k = E_{k_0}$, and we are assuming elastic scattering, we insert $|k| = |k_0|$ into Eq. (11.74) and obtain

$$\frac{d\sigma}{d\Omega} = \left(\frac{m}{2\pi\hbar^2}\right)^2 |H'_{kk_0}|^2 \tag{11.75}$$

The total cross section is obtained, of course, by integrating $d\sigma/d\Omega$ over the whole solid angle.

The matrix element of the scattering center H'_{kk_0} has been evaluated for a number of different scattering potentials: coulombic repulsive, exponential, hard sphere, square well, etc. Some of these matrix elements are quite involved. The matrix element H'_{kk_0} cannot be too strong a function of k

or the scattering formalism developed above, called the *Born approximation*, will fail. The restriction upon the k dependence of H'_{kk_0} is required because the state function of the incoming particle is really a wave packet rather than a single plane wave, and if the packet is to preserve definition during the scattering, the various components cannot be affected too differently during the scattering or the wave packet is destroyed. The Born approximation usually works well if the spatial variation of the scattering potential is slow compared with the wavelength of the incident particle, i.e., for k_0 large, though there are also cases (the square well) where the scattering potential may have sharp gradients without destroying the usefulness of the Born scattering approximation.

A great deal of our knowledge of the structure of the nucleus and of fundamental particles has been obtained from scattering experiments and their interpretation. An extensive body of scattering theory has been developed to interpret these experiments in a manner more nearly complete and rigorous (especially in the high-energy limits) than the Born approximation allows. It is presumed that the main body of scattering theory is outside the primary professional interest of the reader; the Born approximation is just one corner of scattering theory, a corner perhaps of greater historical than practical interest. Extensive literature is available for those interested in a more complete and rigorous theory of scattering.

Summary

Time-dependent perturbation theory, developed in Chap. 11, provides the machinery for interpreting the interaction of atomic and molecular systems with the time-varying fields—electric, magnetic, acoustic, etc.—to which they are exposed in either their exploration or their use.

No "stationary" states exist for a system having a time-dependent Hamiltonian. Fortunately it is possible in most cases of physical or technological interest to divide the Hamiltonian into a time-independent portion H^0 and a time-dependent portion $H'(t)$ which may be treated as a perturbation upon H^0. The effect of $H'(t)$ may be meaningfully discussed in terms of the eigenstates $\Psi_n(\mathbf{r},t)$ of H^0, and in particular in terms of the manner in which it causes a time variation in the expansion coefficients of any general state $\Psi(\mathbf{r},t)$ in the basis states $\Psi_n(\mathbf{r},t)$. In general

$$-\frac{\hbar}{i}\dot{c}_k(t) = \sum_n H'_{kn}(\mathbf{r},t)c_n(t)$$

where $H'_{kn}(\mathbf{r},t)$ is the matrix element of H' between the states $\Psi_k(\mathbf{r},t)$ and $\Psi_n(\mathbf{r},t)$.

If the perturbing terms are harmonic in time and are small and if the system at $t = 0$ is in an eigenstate $\Psi_n(\mathbf{r},t)$ of H^0, the time-dependent expansion coefficient squared of any other state $\Psi_k(\mathbf{r},t)$ is given by

$$|c_k(t)|^2 = \frac{|H'_{kn}|^2}{4\hbar^2}\frac{\sin^2\left(\frac{\omega_{kn}\pm\omega}{2}\right)t}{\left(\frac{\omega_{kn}\pm\omega}{2}\right)^2}$$

where $\omega_{kn} = (E_k - E_n)/\hbar$ and ω is the frequency of the perturbation. Clearly this expression is resonant at $\omega = \pm\omega_{kn}$, indicating that the effect of the perturbation is large only when the perturbation is resonant with a difference in eigenenergies. When the perturbation is resonant, we can define a "transition rate" which is given by

$$w_{kn} = \frac{\pi|H'_{kn}|^2}{2\hbar}\rho(E_k)$$

where $\rho(E_k)$ is the density of terminal states at E_k, and is equal to unity for a single terminal state.

Since H' is Hermitian, the transition rate w_{kn} and its reverse w_{nk} are equal, so that rates of change of $|c_k(t)|^2$ and $|c_n(t)|^2$ depend upon their initial values, upon the "relative populations" of the two states.

The interaction of electromagnetic radiation with atomic systems can be treated in a semiclassical manner (quantized atom, classical electromagnetic field) if the $\mathbf{A}\cdot\mathbf{p}$ term in the Hamiltonian is regarded as the time-dependent perturbation upon the atomic system. The resulting transition rates can be classified as *electric dipole*, *magnetic dipole*, *etc.*, depending upon the form of the matrix element involved.

One form of time-dependent perturbation theory, that dealing with the "constant" perturbation, is useful for certain scattering problems. For the constant perturbation, $\omega = 0$, and the scattering is resonant only between initial and terminal states of the same energy (elastic scattering case) with the transition rate

$$w_{k_0k} = \frac{2\pi}{\hbar}|H'_{k_0k}|^2\rho(E_k)$$

which may be converted to a scattering cross section by the inclusion of the appropriate geometric and normalization constants.

Problems

11.1 A hydrogenic atom is subjected to a harmonically varying electric field, giving rise to a perturbation term in its Hamiltonian of the form

$$H' = Ez\cos\omega t$$

Determine the transition selection rules on l and m, that is, identify the rules governing when $\langle n'l'm'|\,H'\,|nlm\rangle$ will be nonzero. Note that the electric field acts only upon spatial coordinates, not spin coordinates, so the eigenfunctions of Chap. 9 may be used to answer the present question. Assume that the radial integral is always finite, i.e., that there are no simple selection rules involving n' and n.

What are the selection rules on l and m if

$$H' = Ex \cos \omega t$$

11.2 An important class of lasers and masers, the three-level masers, requires an atomic system whose energy-level scheme is shown in Fig. P11.2. The transition ① → ③ must be a "radiatively allowed" transition, as must be at least one of the transitions ③ → ② or ② → ①. By "radiatively allowed" we will mean in this case that an alternating electromagnetic field, producing a perturbation on the system of the form

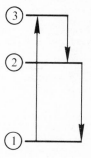

Fig. P11.2

$$H_e = E \cdot r \cos \omega t \qquad \text{or} \qquad H_m = H \cdot L \cos \omega t$$

will produce a transition between the states specified. Consider now the hydrogen atom of Chap. 9, which is a somewhat simplified model of hydrogen in which spin is ignored.

Do the three lowest levels of this hypothetical atom constitute a system that is satisfactory, according to the above criterion, for use as a three level laser?

You may assume that the difficult integral

$$\int_0^\infty R_{n'l'm'}rR_{nlm}r^2 \, dr \neq 0$$

for all the $R_{n'l'm'}$ and R_{nlm} involved. Do not attempt to evaluate the integral.

11.3 The pyramidal ammonia molecule NH_3 of Prob. 4.2 has an electric dipole moment **d** oriented along the symmetry axis of the pyramid. The molecule will therefore interact with an electromagnetic field and absorb energy at certain frequencies corresponding to differences in the rotational eigenenergies. Calculate the rotational microwave absorption spectrum of the NH_3 molecule (absorption position and relative intensities) at such a temperature that one-half the molecules are in the $L = 2$ rotational state.

11.4 A beam of atoms with $J = 1$ and magnetic moment $\boldsymbol{\mu} = g\beta\mathbf{J}$ is directed through an atomic-beam apparatus as depicted in Fig. P11.4. The atoms are moving in the $+y$ direction and pass first through a Stern-Gehrlach deflecting magnet which has both its field and the gradient of its field oriented in the z direction. The beam is split into its three components $J_z = 1$, 0, and -1, and those beams corresponding to $J_z = \pm 1$ are deflected off the beam axis, intercepted, and removed from further consideration in the experiment. The $J_z = 0$ molecules now pass between the poles of a magnet which generates a homogeneous magnetic field H_0 directed in the z direction. Between the poles of the magnet are also r-f coils which bathe the beam in a radio-frequency magnetic field $H_1 \cos \omega t$. After the atoms emerge from the homogeneous magnet, they pass once again through a Stern-Gehrlach deflecting magnet identical with the first magnet.

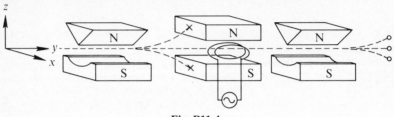

Fig. P11.4

Calculate the intensity of the three emergent beams **(a)** for H_1 directed along the z axis and **(b)** for H_1 directed along the x axis.

Assume that the time τ spent in the interaction region (homogeneous H_0 plus r-f H_1) is short enough and the H_1 field weak enough for perturbation theory to be applicable. Would we increase the intensity of the weak beams more by doubling the length of the interaction magnet (doubling τ) or by doubling the r-f field amplitude?

11.5 Obtain the differential cross section $d\sigma/d\Omega$ for a radially symmetric Gaussian scattering potential

$$V(r) = V_0 e^{-(r/R)^2}$$

where R is a parameter describing the effective radius of the potential. Use the Born-approximation approach.

Bibliography

The general formulation of time-dependent perturbation theory is included in most quantum mechanics books, for instance:

Schiff, L. I.: "Quantum Mechanics," 2d ed., chap. 8, McGraw-Hill Book Company, New York, 1955.

Dicke, R. H., and J. P. Wittke: "Introduction to Quantum Mechanics," chap. 14, Addison-Wesley Publishing Company, Inc., Reading, Mass., 1960.

Merzbacher, E.: "Quantum Mechanics," chap. 19, John Wiley & Sons, Inc., New York, 1961.

Messiah, A.: "Quantum Mechanics," vol. 2, chap. 17, Interscience Publishers, Inc., New York, 1962.

Bohm, D.: "Quantum Theory," part 4, Prentice-Hall, Inc., Englewood Cliffs, N.J., 1951.

The interaction of radiation with matter is treated especially in:

Heitler, W.: "Quantum Theory of Radiation," 3d ed., Oxford University Press, Fair Lawn, N.J., 1954.
Schiff, L. I.: "Quantum Mechanics," 2d ed., chap. 10, McGraw-Hill Book Company, New York, 1955.
Bohm, D.: "Quantum Theory," chap. 18, Prentice-Hall, Inc., Englewood Cliffs, N.J., 1951.
Louisell, W. H.: "Radiation and Noise in Quantum Electronics," chap. 5, McGraw-Hill Book Company, New York, 1964.

Scattering theory is treated more extensively in:

Schiff, L. I.: "Quantum Mechanics," 2d ed., chaps. 5 and 8, McGraw-Hill Book Company, New York, 1955.
Merzbacher, E.: "Quantum Mechanics," chap. 21, John Wiley & Sons, Inc., New York, 1961.
Messiah, A.: "Quantum Mechanics," vol. 2, chap. 19, Interscience Publishers, Inc., New York, 1962.

CHAPTER 12

Multiparticle Systems, Identical Particles, and the Pauli Exclusion Principle

12.1 ON THE DISTINGUISHABILITY OF PARTICLES The discussions and developments of the preceding chapters have invariably dealt with single-particle systems. Since most of the physical systems of practical interest—solids or atoms—are invariably multiparticle systems, we must examine how we extend our quantum-mechanical machineries to cover those multiparticle systems. It is also true that the multiparticle systems of real practical interest characteristically involve many *identical* particles, usually electrons. We are therefore interested in the quantum-mechanical description of systems containing many identical particles. It turns out that the quantum-mechanical description of a multiparticle system is drastically affected by whether or not the particles are "distinguishable."

What do we mean by "distinguishable particles?" We mean particles whose individual identity remains defined and measurable throughout the evolution of the system's dynamic behavior. There must exist experiments which will tell not only where the several particles are but also which particle is in which position. If the particles are not identical—if they have different masses, for example—they will always be distinguishable, and both classical mechanics and quantum mechanics must recognize this fact. If we place a "particle catcher" somewhere in space and "catch" a particle, we can, for distinguishable particles, always perform an additional experiment (e.g., weighing) to identify unambiguously the particle involved.

If, on the other hand, the several particles are dynamically identical, classical mechanics and quantum mechanics diverge on the question of distinguishability. In classical mechanics even identical particles may be distinguishable, because classical mechanics is completely deterministic. If we attach labels to our identical particles at the outset of their collective motion, we can thereafter trace without ambiguity the course of any one of them. Even after the collision of identical particles, it is, in principle at least, possible to identify the "incident" and the "struck" particle before and after the collision. Any trajectory can be traced with arbitrary precision back to the initial configuration and therefore to the initial labeling. For grosser classical cases, the dynamic entities can be literally labeled, as are dynamically equivalent billiard balls, and the labeling preserved through arbitrarily complicated interactions.

In quantum mechanics the situation is quite different. We have abandoned the concept of a precisely determined particle position for the concept of a probability density which may have considerable spatial extent. Suppose two particles occupy state functions whose probability densities overlap somewhat. Let us also assume for the present that the particles are spinless or are in identical spin states. If we place our "particle catcher" in this overlap region and "catch" a particle, we have no means of determining which of the two identical particles we have caught. There is no distinguishing experiment that we can perform on this particle, and, more importantly, there is no way to trace this particle unambiguously back to some initial configuration to obtain the initial labeling. All we know is that there is a finite probability that either particle might be at that point; this we know, and no more. Further, if we catch a particle in a region of space where only one of the probability densities is nonzero, we still cannot say with any certainty which particle we have caught, because the particles may have interchanged roles in the region of overlap. The two particles are then not only identical but indistinguishable as well. As we shall subsequently see, this property of indistinguishability has far-reaching and important consequences.

12.2 DISTINGUISHABLE PARTICLES Let us consider first the simpler case of distinguishable particles, and consider the simplest two-particle case here.

Suppose we have particle 1 of mass m_1 and particle 2 of mass m_2. We may write their Hamiltonian as

$$H = \frac{p_1^2}{2m_1} + \frac{p_2^2}{2m_2} + V(\mathbf{r}_1, \mathbf{r}_2) \qquad (12.1)$$

By $\mathbf{r}_1$ and $\mathbf{p}_1$ we mean the position and momentum coordinates of particle 1, and by $\mathbf{p}_2$ and $\mathbf{r}_2$ we mean the position and momentum coordinates of particle 2. We are assuming also a time-independent Hamiltonian for the present.

If the two particles are noninteracting, the potential term is separable in $\mathbf{r}_1$ and $\mathbf{r}_2$, and indeed the Hamiltonian itself becomes separable into the sum of two-single particle Hamiltonians.

$$H = \frac{p_1^2}{2m_1} + V_1(\mathbf{r}_1) + \frac{p_2^2}{2m_2} + V_2(\mathbf{r}_2)$$

$$= H_1 + H. \tag{12.2}$$

If the Hamiltonian is separable, then it follows that the eigenfunctions of H can be factored into a product wave function of the eigenfunctions of H_1 and H_2:

$$\Psi_{kl}(\mathbf{r}_1,\mathbf{r}_2 t) = \psi_k(\mathbf{r}_1)\psi_l(\mathbf{r}_2)e^{-(i/\hbar)(E_k{}^1 + E_l{}^2)t} \tag{12.3}$$

and the eigenenergies of H are the sums of the eigenenergies of H_1 and H_2.

$$E_{kl} = E_k^1 + E_l^2 \tag{12.4}$$

Note that $\psi_{kl}(\mathbf{r}_1,\mathbf{r}_2)$ is a function of *six* variables—the three components of $\mathbf{r}_1$ and three components of $\mathbf{r}_2$—and may be thought of as a function in this six-dimensional hyperspace. $\psi_{kl}(\mathbf{r}_1,\mathbf{r}_2)$ is the joint probability amplitude for finding particle 1 in the volume element between $\mathbf{r}_1$ and $\mathbf{r}_1 + d\mathbf{r}_1$ and for simultaneously finding particle 2 in the volume element between $\mathbf{r}_2$ and $\mathbf{r}_2 + d\mathbf{r}_2$. The probability distribution for particle 1 alone may be obtained by integrating out the probability distribution of particle 2.

$$\psi_{kl}^*(\mathbf{r}_1)\psi_{kl}(\mathbf{r}_1) = \int \psi_{kl}^*(\mathbf{r}_1,\mathbf{r}_2)\psi_{kl}(\mathbf{r}_1,\mathbf{r}_2)\, d\mathbf{r}_2$$

$$= \psi_k^*(\mathbf{r}_1)\psi_k(\mathbf{r}_1) \int \psi_l^*(\mathbf{r}_2)\psi_l(\mathbf{r}_2)\, d\mathbf{r}_2$$

$$= \psi_k^*(\mathbf{r}_1)\psi_k(\mathbf{r}_1) \tag{12.5}$$

Note also that

$$\iint \psi_{kl}^*(\mathbf{r}_1,\mathbf{r}_2)\psi_{kl}(\mathbf{r}_1,\mathbf{r}_2)\, d\mathbf{r}_1\, d\mathbf{r}_2 = 1 \tag{12.6}$$

not 2 for two particles, nor N for N particles.

For noninteracting distinguishable particles, the two-particle formulation above can readily be extended to N particles. The Hamiltonian will be separable into N single-particle Hamiltonians

$$H = H_1 + H_2 + \cdots + H_N \tag{12.7}$$

with eigenenergies

$$E_{\text{tot}} = E_k^1 + E_l^2 + \cdots + E_n^N \tag{12.8}$$

and product eigenfunctions

$$\Psi(\mathbf{r}_1, \mathbf{r}_2, \ldots, \mathbf{r}_N, t) = \psi_k(\mathbf{r}_1)\psi_l(\mathbf{r}_2) \cdots \psi_n(\mathbf{r}_N)e^{-(i/\hbar)E_{\text{tot}}t} \tag{12.9}$$

If the various particles are interacting, it becomes very difficult to make any generalizations about the nature of the appropriate eigenfunctions and eigenvalues. The correct eigenfunctions are no longer simple products of single-particle eigenfunctions. The correct eigenfunctions can always be constructed out of linear combinations of simple product wave functions, but this property follows from the completeness of the eigenfunction sets rather than from some simple relation between the eigenfunctions for the interacting and noninteracting situation. Consider, for instance, the hydrogen atom, which consists of two distinguishable interacting particles, a proton and an electron. If we remove the interaction, the two particles separately will obey free-particle Hamiltonians with plane-wave eigenfunctions. Couple the two particles together with a coulombic interaction and we obtain a center of mass which behaves like a free particle, plus the complicated hydrogenic wave functions describing the positions of the two particles relative to each other. The relation between the hydrogenic eigenfunctions and the plane-wave eigenfunctions of the two separate particles is not direct, nor is it obvious.

12.3 INDISTINGUISHABLE PARTICLES; SYMMETRIC AND ANTISYMMETRIC STATES We turn now to the important problem of multiparticle systems involving indistinguishable particles. We commence with the simplest such case: two noninteracting indistinguishable particles. In analogy with the distinguishable particle case, we may write our Hamiltonian

$$H = \frac{p_1^2}{2m} + \frac{p_2^2}{2m} + V_a(\mathbf{r}_1) + V_b(\mathbf{r}_2)$$
$$= H_a(1) + H_b(2) \tag{12.10}$$

We have changed notation slightly to reflect the indistinguishable nature of the particles. By $H_a(1)$ we mean the single-particle Hamiltonian determined by $p^2/2m$ and $V_a(\mathbf{r})$, and imagine that we have assigned to this single-particle Hamiltonian one of the two particles which we shall label No. 1. By $H_b(2)$ we mean, similarly, the other single-particle Hamiltonian determined by $p^2/2m$ and $V_b(\mathbf{r})$, and we assign to this Hamiltonian the other particle, which we shall label No. 2. Noting two representative eigenfunctions of H_a and H_b as $\psi_k^a(\mathbf{r})$ and $\psi_l^b(\mathbf{r})$, respectively, we can write a product wave function

$$\psi_{kl}(\mathbf{r}_1;\mathbf{r}_2) = \psi_k^a(\mathbf{r}_1)\psi_l^b(\mathbf{r}_2) \tag{12.11}$$

which is formally a solution of the separated Hamiltonian, Eq. (12.10), with the eigenvalue

$$E = E_k^{(a)} + E_l^{(b)} \tag{12.12}$$

The product wave function equation (12.11) specifies that particle 1 is in the kth eigenfunction of H_a and that particle 2 is in the lth wave function of H_b, and not vice versa. Does this wave function presume to say more than it is physically possible for the eigenfunction to specify?

Let us first dispose of the trivial case where the eigenfunction $\psi_k^a(\mathbf{r})$ of H_a and the eigenfunction $\psi_l^b(\mathbf{r})$ of H_b never overlap at all. That is, $\psi_k^a(\mathbf{r})$ is finite in one region of space, $\psi_l^b(\mathbf{r})$ is finite in an entirely different region of space, and there exists no common region where the two wave functions have nonzero values. Under such circumstances, the particles become, in fact, distinguishable, since the particle originally assigned to H_a will always remain in the domain of H_a and never escape to become confused with the particle of H_b. Though no test exists to distinguish particle 1 from particle 2, the particle found in the region where the $\psi_k^a(\mathbf{r})$ are nonzero is necessarily the particle originally assigned to H_a, and an identification is established. Under these circumstances, the product wave function of Eq. (12.11) is physically meaningful and acceptable. Under these circumstances, however, it is also foolish to bother with a two-particle formulation, since we have two totally distinct and physically separable systems which might as well be treated individually.

Suppose that $\psi_k^a(\mathbf{r})$ and $\psi_l^b(\mathbf{r})$ *do* overlap, as is the case with most systems of physical interest. Then, as discussed in Sec. 12.1, we cannot say which particle is in which wave function, and we cannot distinguish

$$\psi_{kl}(\mathbf{r}_1;\mathbf{r}_2) = \psi_k^a(\mathbf{r}_1)\psi_l^b(\mathbf{r}_2) \qquad (12.11)$$

from
$$\psi_{kl}(\mathbf{r}_2;\mathbf{r}_1) = \psi_k^a(\mathbf{r}_2)\psi_l^b(\mathbf{r}_1) \qquad (12.13)$$

The wave functions of Eq. (12.11) and Eq. (12.13) both presume to specify more about our system than it is possible to know: They specify that a particular assignment of particles to single-particle wave functions is made. Both wave functions are therefore unacceptable as true and meaningful eigenfunctions of the system. On the other hand, some combination of these wave functions, which would imply a mixture of the particle assignments, might well be a satisfactory eigenfunction. Let us explore this possibility.

The two wave functions of Eq. (12.11) and Eq. (12.13) are obtainable from each other by a permutation of the particle assignments. Let us define then the permutation operator P_{12} which interchanges particles 1 and 2 in their wave function assignments. Then

$$P_{12}\psi_{kl}(\mathbf{r}_1;\mathbf{r}_2) = \psi_{kl}(\mathbf{r}_2;\mathbf{r}_1)$$
$$P_{12}\psi_{kl}(\mathbf{r}_2;\mathbf{r}_1) = \psi_{kl}(\mathbf{r}_1;\mathbf{r}_2) \qquad (12.14)$$

P_{12}, also called the *exchange operator*, is another example (along with the parity operator) of a quantum-mechanical operator which has no meaningful classical equivalent.

Let us ask whether this exchange operator commutes with the Hamiltonian. The Hamiltonian is the operator associated with the total energy of the system, and this total energy will not depend upon how we label the dynamically identical particles involved. Therefore the Hamiltonian itself must be invariant under the permutation operator P_{12}.

$$P_{12}H(\mathbf{r}_1,\mathbf{p}_1;\mathbf{r}_2,\mathbf{p}_2) = H(\mathbf{r}_1,\mathbf{p}_1;\mathbf{r}_2,\mathbf{p}_2)$$
$$H(\mathbf{r}_2,\mathbf{p}_2;\mathbf{r}_1,\mathbf{p}_1) = H(\mathbf{r}_1,\mathbf{p}_1;\mathbf{r}_2,\mathbf{p}_2) \tag{12.15}$$

The Hamiltonian of Eq. (12.10) does not have this formal property. We can remedy this by introducing the symmetrized form

$$H_a(\mathbf{r}) + H_b(\mathbf{r}) = \tfrac{1}{2}[H_a(1) + H_b(2) + H_a(2) + H_b(1)] \tag{12.16}$$

We can now readily show that P_{12} commutes with the Hamiltonian, for

$$
\begin{aligned}
P_{12}[H(\mathbf{r}_1,\mathbf{p}_1;\mathbf{r}_2,\mathbf{p}_2)\psi_{kl}(\mathbf{r}_1;\mathbf{r}_2)] &= H(\mathbf{r}_2,\mathbf{p}_2;\mathbf{r}_1,\mathbf{p}_1)\psi_{kl}(\mathbf{r}_2;\mathbf{r}_1) \\
&= H(\mathbf{r}_1,\mathbf{p}_1;\mathbf{r}_2,\mathbf{p}_2)\psi_{kl}(\mathbf{r}_2;\mathbf{r}_1) \\
&= H(\mathbf{r}_1,\mathbf{p}_1;\mathbf{r}_2,\mathbf{p}_2)P_{12}\psi_{kl}(\mathbf{r}_1;\mathbf{r}_2) \quad (12.17)
\end{aligned}
$$

yielding

$$(P_{12}H - HP_{12}) = [P_{12},H] = 0 \tag{12.18}$$

Since P_{12} commutes with H, they must share a common set of eigenfunctions. If H were nondegenerate, P_{12} would share the unique set of eigenfunctions defined by H. However, H is not nondegenerate, for we know that $\psi_{kl}(\mathbf{r}_1;\mathbf{r}_2)$ and $\psi_{kl}(\mathbf{r}_2;\mathbf{r}_1)$ belong to the same eigenenergy. From the two eigenfunctions of H comprising the twofold degenerate manifold, we can certainly construct two new wave functions, linear combinations of the old, which are simultaneously eigenfunctions of P_{12} and of H. That $\psi_{kl}(\mathbf{r}_1;\mathbf{r}_2)$ and $\psi_{kl}(\mathbf{r}_2;\mathbf{r}_1)$ are not already eigenfunctions of P_{12} can be seen from Eq. (12.14). Let us call one of the simultaneous eigenfunctions (of H and P_{12}) $\psi_{kl}(\mathbf{r}_1,\mathbf{r}_2)$, where we have reduced the semicolon between $\mathbf{r}_1$ and $\mathbf{r}_2$ to the status of a comma, indicating that the order of writing $\mathbf{r}_1$ and $\mathbf{r}_2$ in the argument no longer implies an assignment of specific particles to specific single-particle wave functions. For such a wave function we require that

$$P_{12}\psi_{kl}(\mathbf{r}_1,\mathbf{r}_2) = \alpha\psi_{kl}(\mathbf{r}_1,\mathbf{r}_2) \tag{12.19}$$

where α is an eigenvalue of P_{12}. We do not yet know the value of α, but we do know that operating upon $\psi_{kl}(\mathbf{r}_1,\mathbf{r}_2)$ with P_{12}^2, interchanging particles twice, must yield again the original function.

$$
\begin{aligned}
P_{12}^2\psi_{kl}(\mathbf{r}_1,\mathbf{r}_2) &= \alpha^2\psi_{kl}(\mathbf{r}_1,\mathbf{r}_2) \\
&= \psi_{kl}(\mathbf{r}_1,\mathbf{r}_2) \tag{12.20}
\end{aligned}
$$

Hence we know that

$$\alpha^2 = 1 \qquad \alpha = \pm 1 \tag{12.21}$$

With this information we can construct by inspection the required eigenfunctions.

$$\psi_{kl}^+(\mathbf{r}_1,\mathbf{r}_2) = \frac{1}{\sqrt{2}}\,[\psi_k^a(\mathbf{r}_1)\psi_l^b(\mathbf{r}_2) + \psi_k^a(\mathbf{r}_2)\psi_l^b(\mathbf{r}_1)]$$

$$\psi_{kl}^-(\mathbf{r}_1,\mathbf{r}_2) = \frac{1}{\sqrt{2}}\,[\psi_k^a(\mathbf{r}_1)\psi_l^b(\mathbf{r}_2) - \psi_k^a(\mathbf{r}_2)\psi_l^b(\mathbf{r}_1)] \tag{12.22}$$

That these are the eigenfunctions of P_{12} can be readily demonstrated:

$$P_{12}\,\frac{1}{\sqrt{2}}\,[\psi_k^a(\mathbf{r}_1)\psi_l^b(\mathbf{r}_2) + \psi_k^a(\mathbf{r}_2)\psi_l^b(\mathbf{r}_1)]$$

$$= \frac{1}{\sqrt{2}}\,[\psi_k^a(\mathbf{r}_2)\psi_l^b(\mathbf{r}_1) + \psi_k^a(\mathbf{r}_1)\psi_l^b(\mathbf{r}_2)]$$

$$= (+\,1)\,\frac{1}{\sqrt{2}}\,[\psi_k^a(\mathbf{r}_1)\psi_l^b(\mathbf{r}_2) + \psi_k^a(\mathbf{r}_2)\psi_l^b(\mathbf{r}_1)]$$

$$P_{12}\,\frac{1}{\sqrt{2}}\,[\psi_k^a(\mathbf{r}_1)\psi_l^b(\mathbf{r}_2) - \psi_k^a(\mathbf{r}_2)\psi_l^b(\mathbf{r}_1)] \tag{12.23}$$

$$= \frac{1}{\sqrt{2}}\,[\psi_k^a(\mathbf{r}_2)\psi_l^b(\mathbf{r}_1) - \psi_k^a(\mathbf{r}_1)\psi_l^b(\mathbf{r}_2)]$$

$$= (-\,1)\,\frac{1}{\sqrt{2}}\,[\psi_k^a(\mathbf{r}_1)\psi_l^b(\mathbf{r}_2) - \psi_k^a(\mathbf{r}_2)\psi_l^b(\mathbf{r}_1)]$$

The eigenfunction of P_{12} belonging to $\alpha = +1$ is called a *symmetric wave function*. The eigenfunction belonging to $\alpha = -1$ is called an *antisymmetric wave function*.

The factor of $1/\sqrt{2}$ has been included for normalization, but we note now that this may not in fact be sufficient provision, since we have no guarantee that ψ_k and ψ_l, being eigenfunctions (in general) of different Hamiltonians, are orthogonal. In general,

$$|\psi_{kl}^\pm(\mathbf{r}_1,\mathbf{r}_2)|^2 = \frac{1}{\sqrt{2}}\,[\psi_k^a(\mathbf{r}_1)\psi_l^b(\mathbf{r}_2) \pm \psi_k^a(\mathbf{r}_2)\psi_l^b(\mathbf{r}_1)]^*$$

$$\times \frac{1}{\sqrt{2}}\,[\psi_k^a(\mathbf{r}_1)\psi_l^b(\mathbf{r}_2) \pm \psi_k^a(\mathbf{r}_2)\psi_l^b(\mathbf{r}_1)]$$

$$= \tfrac{1}{2}\{\psi_k^{a*}(\mathbf{r}_1)\psi_k^a(\mathbf{r}_1)\psi_l^{b*}(\mathbf{r}_2)\psi_l^b(\mathbf{r}_2) + \psi_k^{a*}(\mathbf{r}_2)\psi_k^a(\mathbf{r}_2)\psi_l^{b*}(\mathbf{r}_1)\psi_l^b(\mathbf{r}_1)$$

$$\pm\,[\psi_k^{a*}(\mathbf{r}_1)\psi_l^b(\mathbf{r}_1)\psi_l^{b*}(\mathbf{r}_2)\psi_k^a(\mathbf{r}_2) + \psi_k^{a*}(\mathbf{r}_2)\psi_l^b(\mathbf{r}_2)\psi_l^{b*}(\mathbf{r}_1)\psi_k^a(\mathbf{r}_1)]\} \tag{12.24}$$

Integrating over the relevant six-dimensional space, we obtain

$$\iint |\psi_{kl}^{\pm}(\mathbf{r}_1,\mathbf{r}_2)|^2 \, d\mathbf{r}_1 \, d\mathbf{r}_2 = \frac{1}{2}\left[1 + 1 \pm 2\int \psi_k^{a*}(\mathbf{r}_1)\psi_l^{b}(\mathbf{r}_1) \, d\mathbf{r}_1 \int \psi_l^{b*}(\mathbf{r}_2)\psi_k^{a}(\mathbf{r}_2) \, d\mathbf{r}_2\right]$$

(12.25)

An integral of the form

$$\int \psi_k^{a*}(\mathbf{r}_1)\psi_l^{b}(\mathbf{r}_1) \, d\mathbf{r}_1 = B$$

(12.26)

is known as an *overlap integral*, since it is a measure of the amount that the probability amplitude described by $\psi_k(\mathbf{r})$ overlaps that described by $\psi_l(\mathbf{r})$. Observing that

$$\int \psi_l^{b*}(\mathbf{r})\psi_k^{a}(\mathbf{r}) \, d\mathbf{r} = B^*$$

(12.27)

we arrive at

$$\iint |\psi_{kl}^{\pm}(\mathbf{r}_1,\mathbf{r}_2)|^2 \, d\mathbf{r}_1 \, d\mathbf{r}_2 = 1 \pm |B|^2$$

(12.28)

The appropriately normalized symmetric and antisymmetric wave functions are then

$$\psi_{kl}^{\pm}(\mathbf{r}_1,\mathbf{r}_2) = [2(1 \pm |B|^2)]^{-\frac{1}{2}}[\psi_k^{a}(\mathbf{r}_1)\psi_l^{b}(\mathbf{r}_2) \pm \psi_k^{a}(\mathbf{r}_2)\psi_l^{b}(\mathbf{r}_1)] \quad (12.29)$$

For an appreciable number of cases of real physical interest, the overlap integral B will be zero. For the two-electron atom, for instance, ψ_k and ψ_l are different eigenfunctions of the same central-force Hamiltonian, and are therefore orthogonal. On the other hand, there are many instances when $H_a(\mathbf{r})$ and $H_b(\mathbf{r})$ are different, and the overlap integral is substantial. Such situations arise, for instance, in molecules and solids, where electrons may be assigned to wave functions centered on different nuclei.

Examining the probability densities associated with the symmetric and antisymmetric wave functions $\psi_{kl}^{\pm}(\mathbf{r}_1,\mathbf{r}_2)$, we see that the wave functions represent truly different spatial distributions of probability density. Let us ask, for instance, for the probability of finding *both* particles at the same point in space, $\mathbf{r}_1 = \mathbf{r}_2 = \mathbf{r}$. For the antisymmetric wave function,

$$\psi_{kl}^{-}(\mathbf{r},\mathbf{r}) = [2(1 - |B|^2)]^{-\frac{1}{2}}[\psi_k^{a}(\mathbf{r})\psi_l^{b}(\mathbf{r}) - \psi_k^{a}(\mathbf{r})\psi_l^{b}(\mathbf{r})] \equiv 0 \quad (12.30)$$

and the two particles are *never* found simultaneously at the same point in space. For the symmetric functions, on the other hand,

$$\psi_{kl}^{+}(\mathbf{r},\mathbf{r}) = [2(1 + |B|^2)]^{-\frac{1}{2}}[\psi_k^{a}(\mathbf{r})\psi_l^{b}(\mathbf{r}) + \psi_k^{a}(\mathbf{r})\psi_l^{b}(\mathbf{r})]$$
$$= 2[2(1 + |B|)]^{-\frac{1}{2}}\psi_k^{a}(\mathbf{r})\psi_l^{b}(\mathbf{r})$$

(12.31)

and the probability of finding *both* particles simultaneously at the same point in space is increased by a factor of as much as 2 (depending on the exact value of $|B|^2$) over what it would be for the unsymmetrized two-particle state function $\psi_{kl}(\mathbf{r}_1;\mathbf{r}_2)$. Two particles in an antisymmetric state behave as if they repelled each other; two particles in a symmetric state behave as if they attracted each other, even though we have introduced no interaction between the two particles.

The difference in the spatial distribution of probability between $\psi_{lk}^+(\mathbf{r}_1,\mathbf{r}_2)$ and $\psi_{kl}^-(\mathbf{r}_1,\mathbf{r}_2)$ can be further illustrated by asking for the probability distribution of just one particle, regardless of the position of the other particle. By Eq. (12.4) we know this to be

$$
\psi_{kl}^{\pm*}(\mathbf{r}_1)\psi_{kl}^{\pm}(\mathbf{r}_1) = \int \psi_{kl}^{\pm*}(\mathbf{r}_1,\mathbf{r}_2)\psi_{kl}^{\pm}(\mathbf{r}_1,\mathbf{r}_2)\, d\mathbf{r}_2
$$

$$
= \frac{1}{2(1 \pm |B|^2)} \int [\psi_k^a(\mathbf{r}_1)\psi_l^b(\mathbf{r}_2) \pm \psi_k^a(\mathbf{r}_2)\psi_l^b(\mathbf{r}_1)]^*
$$

$$
\times [\psi_k^a(\mathbf{r}_1)\psi_l^b(\mathbf{r}_2) \pm \psi_k^a(\mathbf{r}_2)\,\psi_l^b(\mathbf{r}_1)]\, d\mathbf{r}_2
$$

$$
= \frac{1}{2(1 \pm |B|^2)} [\psi_k^{a*}(\mathbf{r}_1)\psi_k^a(\mathbf{r}_1) + \psi_l^{b*}(\mathbf{r}_1)\psi_l^b(\mathbf{r}_1)
$$

$$
\pm B^*\psi_k^{a*}(\mathbf{r}_1)\psi_l^b(\mathbf{r}_1) \pm B\psi_l^{b*}(\mathbf{r}_1)\psi_k^a(\mathbf{r}_1)] \qquad (12.32)
$$

Schematically, we may describe this probability density as

$$
\psi_{kl}^{\pm*}(\mathbf{r}_1)\psi_{kl}(\mathbf{r}_1) = \frac{1}{2(1 \pm |B|)^2}\left[\left(\begin{array}{l}\text{the probability density} \\ \text{associated with } \psi_k^a\end{array}\right)\right.
$$

$$
+ \left(\begin{array}{l}\text{the probability density} \\ \text{associated with } \psi_l^b\end{array}\right)
$$

$$
\pm B\left(\begin{array}{l}\text{a convolution of} \\ \psi_k^a \text{ and } \psi_l^b\end{array}\right)
$$

$$
\left.\pm B^*\left(\begin{array}{l}\text{the same convolution} \\ \text{of } \psi_k^a \text{ and } \psi_l^b\end{array}\right)^*\right] \qquad (12.33)
$$

If ψ_k^a and ψ_l^b are orthogonal (for instance, different eigenstates of the same central-force Hamiltonian, as they would be for a two-electron atom), the overlap B is zero, and the probability density is the same as if the particle spent half its time in one single-particle state and half its time in the other. The probability density of the second particle is identical with that of the first, regardless of whether the particle is in a symmetric or an antisymmetric two-particle state. The individual particle positions are nonetheless correlated, with a high probability of finding the two particles close together for the symmetric state and a low probability of finding the particles close together for the antisymmetric state.

If ψ_k^a and ψ_l^b are not orthogonal (for instance, are single-particle states centered on different points, as is the case for a diatomic molecule), the overlap B is not zero and the symmetric and antisymmetric states represent truly different spatial probability distributions. Consider the two-electron diatomic molecule H_2. Figure 12.1 shows schematically the symmetric and antisymmetric probability distribution. The symmetric state increases the probability density in the overlap region, while the antisymmetric state reduces the total probability density in the overlap region.

We have seen that the two particles seem to "attract" each other in the symmetric state and to "repel" each other in the antisymmetric state. So long as we do not introduce any real (e.g., electrostatic) interaction

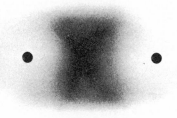

Symmetric state

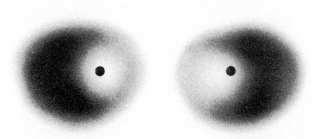

Antisymmetric state

Fig. 12.1 *Schematic of the symmetric and antisymmetric probability densities for the diatomic molecule.*

between the particles, the symmetric and antisymmetric states remain degenerate, as we can confirm by a direct calculation:

$$\langle \psi_{kl}^{\pm}(\mathbf{r}_1,\mathbf{r}_2) \,|H_a(\mathbf{r}) + H_b(\mathbf{r})|\, \psi_{kl}^{\pm}(\mathbf{r}_1,\mathbf{r}_2) \rangle$$

$$= \frac{1}{2(1 \pm |B|^2)} \iint [\psi_k^a(\mathbf{r}_1)\psi_l^b(\mathbf{r}_2) \pm \psi_k^a(\mathbf{r}_2)\psi_l^b(\mathbf{r}_1)]^*[H_a(\mathbf{r}) + H_b(\mathbf{r})]$$

$$\times [\psi_k^a(\mathbf{r}_1)\psi_l^b(\mathbf{r}_2) \pm \psi_k^a(\mathbf{r}_2)\psi_l^b(\mathbf{r}_1)] \, d\mathbf{r}_1 \, d\mathbf{r}_2$$

$$= \frac{1}{2(1 \pm |B|^2)} [E_k^a + E_l^b \pm 2 |B|^2 (E_k^a + E_l^b) + E_k^a + E_l^b]$$

$$= E_k^a + E_l^b \qquad\qquad\qquad\qquad\qquad\qquad (12.34)$$

The correlation of particle position is not a result of gain in energy through correlation; it is purely a result of symmetrizing the state functions.

Consider now what happens to the eigenenergies of the system if the particles *do* interact. Suppose the particles are charged (for instance, are electrons). Their charge must be of the same sign (or they wouldn't be identical particles), so the particles will repel one another. The antisymmetric state will be of lower energy because the correlation already present keeps the particles apart and lowers their energy as compared with the symmetric state where the particles correlate in such a fashion as to remain close together. The correlation exists regardless of whether or not the interaction exists and does not result from the interaction.

Let us introduce an interaction $V_{ab}(\mathbf{r}_1,\mathbf{r}_2)$ between the two identical particles. The interaction $V_{ab}(\mathbf{r}_1,\mathbf{r}_2)$ must be symmetric under particle interchange

$$P_{12}V_{ab}(\mathbf{r}_1,\mathbf{r}_2) = V_{ab}(\mathbf{r}_1,\mathbf{r}_2) \qquad\qquad (12.35)$$

or the two particles could be distinguished on the basis of their roles in this interaction. The energy of the system including the interaction V_{ab} is

$$\langle \psi_{kl}^{\pm}(\mathbf{r}_1,\mathbf{r}_2) \,|H_a(\mathbf{r}) + H_b(\mathbf{r}) + V_{ab}(\mathbf{r}_1,\mathbf{r}_2)|\, \psi_{kl}^{\pm}(\mathbf{r}_1,\mathbf{r}_2) \rangle$$

$$= E_k^a + E_l^b + \frac{1}{(1 \pm |B|^2)}(J \pm K) \quad (12.36)$$

where

$$J = \iint \psi_k^{a*}(\mathbf{r}_1)\psi_l^{b*}(\mathbf{r}_2)V_{ab}(\mathbf{r}_1,\mathbf{r}_2)\psi_k^a(\mathbf{r}_1)\psi_l^b(\mathbf{r}_2) \, d\mathbf{r}_1 \, d\mathbf{r}_2$$

$$\qquad\qquad\qquad\qquad\qquad\qquad\qquad\qquad (12.37)$$

$$K = \iint \psi_k^{a*}(\mathbf{r}_1)\psi_l^{b*}(\mathbf{r}_2)V_{ab}(\mathbf{r}_1,\mathbf{r}_2)\psi_k^a(\mathbf{r}_2)\psi_l^b(\mathbf{r}_1) \, d\mathbf{r}_1 \, d\mathbf{r}_2$$

The first integral J, which is called the *direct interaction*, can be seen to be the expectation value of V_{ab} when one particle is in state ψ_k^a and the other is in state ψ_l^b. Such an interaction term would occur also in the classical two-body problem or for two distinguishable particles. The other integral

K, called the *exchange-energy* term, is peculiar to the quantum mechanics of identical particles. The two particles have "exchanged roles" when the two-particle state was conjugated. Note that the exchange-energy term enters the eigenvalue of the symmetric state with a positive sign and the eigenvalue of the antisymmetric state with a negative sign, and is therefore primarily responsible for the difference in energy between the symmetric and antisymmetric states. The exchange energy—a purely quantum-mechanical effect—underlies many important physical effects—covalent bonding and ferromagnetism, to name two.

12.4 SPIN, FERMIONS, BOSONS, AND THE PAULI EXCLUSION PRINCIPLE

The Hamiltonian for any two-particle system involving indistinguishable particles must be invariant under exchange of the particles; otherwise the particles could be distinguished on the basis of their unique dynamical roles. It therefore follows that if the two particles involved are at some time in a purely symmetric or purely antisymmetric state, they will always remain in the purely symmetric or antisymmetric state. No interaction or perturbation, static or time-dependent or of whatever degree of complexity, will mix states of opposite symmetry. A system starting life in an antisymmetric state will remain forever in an antisymmetric state; likewise for a system starting life in a symmetric state.

How does a particle choose the type of state in which it is destined to spend all eternity? Its fate is determined entirely by its intrinsic spin. It is an experimental fact—not deducible on any theoretical grounds—that particles whose total spin quantum number s is 0 or an integer (1, 2, 3, ..., n) are always found in symmetric state functions, and particles whose total spin quantum number is half integral ($s = \frac{1}{2}, \frac{3}{2}, \frac{5}{2} \cdots$) are always found in antisymmetric state functions. The particles fundamental to the structure of atoms, molecules, and solids (as distinct from sub-nuclear particles) are primarily antisymmetric spin $\frac{1}{2}$ particles; the electron, proton, and neutron all have $s = \frac{1}{2}$. The deuteron, a compound particle, has $s = 1$ and is always found in symmetric states. Several of the "quasi-particles," such as the photon and phonon, have an effective spin of 1 and are symmetric particles.

We must now face up to the existence of intrinsic spin, which we have side-stepped for so long. The state function for a particle must specify its spin state as well as its spatial state. The complete state function for a two-particle system should then be written

$$\psi_{kl}^{\pm}(\mathbf{r}_1\boldsymbol{\sigma}_1, \mathbf{r}_2\boldsymbol{\sigma}_2) = [2(1 + |B|^2)]^{-\frac{1}{2}} [\psi_k^a(\mathbf{r}_1\boldsymbol{\sigma}_1)\psi_l^b(\mathbf{r}_2\boldsymbol{\sigma}_2) \pm \psi_k^a(\mathbf{r}_2\boldsymbol{\sigma}_2)\psi_l^b(\mathbf{r}_1\boldsymbol{\sigma}_1)]$$

$$(12.38)$$

where the spin coordinates are indicated by σ_1, σ_2. The state function must be symmetrized under particle interchange, and the particle takes with it both space and spin coordinates, as is indicated in Eq. (12.38). The total state function, including spin coordinates, must be symmetrized because of the indistinguishability of the particles involved.

As remarked earlier, the particles of most interest to us in atomic, gaseous, and solid-state problems are the antisymmetric particles of spin $\frac{1}{2}$, the electron in particular. Because of the antisymmetric nature of the state function such particles must occupy, they obey an important rule known as the *Pauli exclusion principle: Two identical antisymmetrical particles can never occupy the same single-particle state.*

The Pauli exclusion principle follows directly from the definition of the antisymmetric state given in Eq. (12.38). Suppose we let the two particles occupy the same state, that is, $\psi_k^a \equiv \psi_l^b$. Then

$$\psi_k^-(\mathbf{r}_1\sigma_1, \mathbf{r}_2\sigma_2) = N[\psi_k^a(\mathbf{r}_1\sigma_1)\psi_k^a(\mathbf{r}_2\sigma_2) - \psi_k^a(\mathbf{r}_2\sigma_2)\psi_k^a(\mathbf{r}_1\sigma_1)] \equiv 0 \quad (12.39)$$

where N is the normalizing constant. The probability density of the anti-symmetric state becomes everywhere identically zero if we put both particles into the same state. The Pauli exclusion principle states no more and no less than this.

It is obvious that the statistics which antisymmetric particles will obey will be different from those which symmetric particles will obey. Suppose we have a multielectron system (for instance, a piece of solid conductor) and we cool it down to some very low temperature. All the electrons will wish to drop to the lowest possible energy state, to slow down and get rid of their kinetic energy. But as soon as one electron has entered the lowest energy state, that state is "full," and the next electron must occupy a different state. The state must differ in at least one quantum number, typically s_z, to constitute a "different" state. The third electron must find a still different state, since it is identical under interchange with either of the first two. As the low-energy states fill up, additional electrons must occupy states of higher and higher energy, even at 0° Kelvin. Therefore we have in metals electrons of very high kinetic energy, much greater than kT, and the average energy of the electrons is much greater than the energy of the lowest states. The statistical mechanics of such antisymmetric one-to-a state particles are called *Fermi-Dirac statistics*, after its inventors, and the particles which obey these statistics are called *fermions*. All particles with $s = (2n + 1)/2$ are fermions.

Symmetric particles obey no such exclusion principle, because $\psi_{kl}^\pm(\mathbf{r}_1\sigma_1, \mathbf{r}_2\sigma_2)$ does not vanish when $\psi_k^a = \psi_l^b$. We may place as many particles as we wish into the same state. At low temperatures a collection of symmetric particles will all "condense" into the lowest energy single-particle state; the average energy of the ensemble will be very much like the expectation energy of the lowest single-particle state. The statistics appropriate to such an ensemble are called the *Einstein-Bose statistics*, and the particles which obey these statistics are called *bosons*. All particles with $s = 0, 1, 2, \ldots, n$ are bosons.

The Pauli exclusion principle is most important for understanding atomic structure. As we build up the periodic table by adding protons and neutrons to the nucleus and electrons to its charge cloud, each additional electron must occupy a different, usually higher-energy state function. The variety of chemical and physical properties of the elements results from just this fact. If the electron were a boson, all atoms would be chemically similar to hydrogen, and life as we know it could not exist.

12.5 SEPARABLE STATE FUNCTIONS; SYMMETRIZED SPIN FUNCTIONS

The total state function of the two-electron system, including both space and spin coordinates, must be symmetrized under particle interchange. If there is no interaction between the intrinsic spin of the particles and their spatial configuration, the Hamiltonian is separable in spatial and spin coordinates and the wave function may be factored into the product of a space state function and a spin state function:

$$\psi_{kl}(\mathbf{r}_1\boldsymbol{\sigma}_2, \mathbf{r}_2\boldsymbol{\sigma}_2) = \psi_{kl}(\mathbf{r}_1,\mathbf{r}_2)\chi_{kl}(\boldsymbol{\sigma}_1,\boldsymbol{\sigma}_2) \qquad (12.40)$$

The interaction between the particle spin and the spatial configuration is never truly zero, but in many cases it is quite small and may be usefully treated as a perturbation on the noninteracting case. A good first-order approximation to the true state functions is then the separated space- and spin-product state function of Eq. (12.40). Many problems in atomic, gaseous, and solid-state physics can be usefully treated in this approximation. Let us consider therefore the properties of the product wave function.

It is useful for the manipulation of the product wave functions to invent two operators P_{12}^r and P_{12}^σ which operate on the space wave function $\psi_{kl}(\mathbf{r}_1,\mathbf{r}_2)$ and the spin wave function $\chi_{kl}(\boldsymbol{\sigma}_1,\boldsymbol{\sigma}_2)$ only. These are nonphysical operators in the sense that we cannot interchange only particle spin or only particle positions; we interchange whole particles. They are nevertheless useful operators, as we shall see. The exchange operator P_{12} is the product of these two partial-interchange operators:

$$P_{12} = P_{12}^r P_{12}^\sigma \qquad (12.41)$$

By arguments entirely parallel to those used to establish the eigenvalues of P_{12}, we may show that the eigenvalues of both P_{12}^r and P_{12}^σ are also ± 1.

We already know how to produce space wave functions symmetrized under P_{12}^r; they are precisely the wave functions of Eq. (12.29). Let us see if we can construct symmetrized spin wave functions $\chi^{\pm}(\sigma_1, \sigma_2)$.

The particle of greatest interest to most problems concerned with the physical properties of real materials is the electron. We will consider therefore the special case of the particle with spin $\frac{1}{2}$, and construct symmetrized two-particle spin wave functions for this case. The $s = \frac{1}{2}$ particle has two possible states, corresponding to $s_z = +\frac{1}{2}$ and $s_z = -\frac{1}{2}$. We will use a common shorthand notation for these two states, the α and β notation, which have the following correspondence:

$$|s = \tfrac{1}{2}, s_z = +\tfrac{1}{2}\rangle = \alpha$$
$$|s = \tfrac{1}{2}, s_z = -\tfrac{1}{2}\rangle = \beta \tag{12.42}$$

The α and β spin functions are known as the *spin up* and *spin down* states, respectively, for obvious reasons.

From the single-particle spin functions α and β, we can construct four two-particle spin functions:

$$\alpha(1)\alpha(2)$$
$$\alpha(1)\beta(2)$$
$$\beta(1)\alpha(2)$$
$$\beta(1)\beta(2) \tag{12.43}$$

where $\alpha(1)$ means particle 1 assigned to the α state, etc. The first and fourth of these spin functions are symmetric as they stand; the second and third must be combined to give symmetrized states. When this is done, we end up with three symmetric and one antisymmetric state.

Symmetric	*Antisymmetric*
$\alpha(1)\alpha(2)$	
$\dfrac{1}{\sqrt{2}} [\alpha(1)\beta(2) + \alpha(2)\beta(1)]$	$\dfrac{1}{\sqrt{2}} [\alpha(1)\beta(2) - \alpha(2)\beta(1)]$
$\beta(1)\beta(2)$	

(12.44)

The three symmetric states are forms of $\chi^{+}(\sigma_1, \sigma_2)$ and belong to the eigenvalue $+1$ of P_{12}^{σ}; the antisymmetric state is one form of $\chi^{-}(\sigma_1, \sigma_2)$ and belongs to the eigenvalue -1 of P_{12}^{σ}.

The eigenvalues of the product operator P_{12} are the products of the eigenvalues of the factor operators P_{12}^r and P_{12}^{σ}. A state belonging to the $+1$ eigenvalue of P_{12} may be composed of the product of two symmetric *or* two antisymmetric separated wave functions. A state belonging to the

-1 eigenvalue of P_{12} may be composed of the product of one symmetric and one antisymmetric separated wave function.

$$\psi^+(\mathbf{r}_1\boldsymbol{\sigma}_1, \mathbf{r}_2\boldsymbol{\sigma}_2) = \begin{cases} \psi^+(\mathbf{r}_1,\mathbf{r}_2)\chi^+(\boldsymbol{\sigma}_1,\boldsymbol{\sigma}_2) \\ \psi^-(\mathbf{r}_1,\mathbf{r}_2)\chi^-(\boldsymbol{\sigma}_1,\boldsymbol{\sigma}_2) \end{cases}$$

$$\psi^-(\mathbf{r}_1\boldsymbol{\sigma}_1, \mathbf{r}_2\boldsymbol{\sigma}_2) = \begin{cases} \psi^+(\mathbf{r}_1,\mathbf{r}_2)\chi^-(\boldsymbol{\sigma}_1,\boldsymbol{\sigma}_2) \\ \psi^-(\mathbf{r}_1,\mathbf{r}_2)\chi^+(\boldsymbol{\sigma}_1,\boldsymbol{\sigma}_2) \end{cases} \tag{12.45}$$

An antisymmetric particle like the electron may therefore be found in either symmetric or antisymmetric space wave functions, *provided* the spin wave function associated is of the opposite symmetry. The *total* state function must be antisymmetric for the electron. If the space state is partly symmetric and partly antisymmetric, the spin state must be such that the total state function remains antisymmetric.

Before proceeding to an example of two-electron wave functions, we will digress briefly to point out that in symmetrizing the spin wave functions for the two $s = \frac{1}{2}$ particles, we have more or less inadvertently illustrated some of the features typical of the addition of angular momenta. Let us consider the total spin angular momentum of a two-particle system.

$$\mathbf{S} = \mathbf{s}_1 + \mathbf{s}_2 \tag{12.46}$$

Let us now form the operators S^2 and S_z.

$$\begin{aligned} S^2 &= (\mathbf{s}_1 + \mathbf{s}_2)^2 \\ &= s_1^2 + s_2^2 + 2\mathbf{s}_1 \cdot \mathbf{s}_2 \\ &= s_1^2 + s_2^2 + s_1^+ s_2^- + s_1^- s_2^+ + 2s_{1z}s_{2z} \end{aligned} \tag{12.47}$$

and
$$S_z = s_{1z} + s_{2z} \tag{12.48}$$

In Eq. (12.47), $\mathbf{s}_1 \cdot \mathbf{s}_2$ has been expanded into a form useful for many calculations; the reader may verify that the expansion in single-particle promotion and demotion operators is correct.

Let us operate now with S^2 and S_z upon the symmetrized spin wave functions of Eq. (12.44). We find that the three symmetric spin functions are all eigenfunctions of S^2 belonging to the eigenvalue $2\hbar^2$, and are eigenfunctions of S_z belonging to the eigenvalues $+\hbar$, 0, and $-\hbar$, respectively. The single antisymmetric spin function is an eigenfunction of S^2 and of S_z belonging to the eigenvalues $0\hbar^2$ and $0\hbar$, respectively.

The symmetric spin function therefore corresponds to the two separate spins adding vectorially to give an angular momentum with quantum number $S = 1$. The eigenvalue of S^2 for such a state is $S(S + 1)\hbar^2 = 2\hbar^2$, and the eigenvalues of S_z are 0, $\pm\hbar$. The two single-particle spins are "parallel" in the symmetric two-particle spin state. This state is called a *triplet* state for reasons rooted in historical spectroscopy, but bearing obvious connection to the threefold degeneracy of S^2.

The antisymmetric spin function corresponds to the two separate spins adding vectorially to give an angular momentum with quantum number $S = 0$. The two spins are "antiparallel." This state is known as a *singlet* state, since S^2 is nondegenerate.

12.6 THE HELIUM ATOM Perhaps the simplest example of a system involving two identical particles and displaying the effects of exchange degeneracy is the helium atom. The helium atom has two electrons bound to a relatively massive nucleus of charge $+2e$, where e is the magnitude of the charge on the electron. We shall ignore the motion of the massive nucleus and write the Hamiltonian for the helium atom as

$$H = \frac{p_1^2}{2m} - \frac{2e^2}{r_1} + \frac{p_2^2}{2m} - \frac{2e^2}{r_2} + \frac{e^2}{|\mathbf{r}_1 - \mathbf{r}_2|} \tag{12.49}$$

We have also neglected in this approximation the interaction of the electron spins with each other and with the spatial coordinates. These interactions are perhaps two orders of magnitude smaller than the coulombic electrostatic interactions we are retaining as the dominant terms. The above Hamiltonian can be represented as

$$H = H_a(\mathbf{r}) + H_b(\mathbf{r}) + V_{ab}(\mathbf{r}_1,\mathbf{r}_2) \tag{12.50}$$

where $H_a(\mathbf{r})$ and $H_b(\mathbf{r})$ are the two (identical) single-particle Hamiltonians and $V_{ab}(\mathbf{r}_1,\mathbf{r}_2)$ is an interaction term we shall treat as a perturbation.

The eigenfunctions of the single-particle Hamiltonian are the hydrogenic wave functions with the eigenenergies

$$E_{nlm} = -\frac{mZ^2e^4}{2\hbar^2}\frac{1}{n^2} = -\frac{Z^2E_0}{n^2} \tag{12.51}$$

where $E_0 = me^4/2\hbar^2$ and is the energy of the lowest state of the hydrogen atom. Let us discuss first the lowest energy, or "ground," state of the helium atom. The lowest energy configuration for the two electrons obviously comes when both electrons are in the lowest energy spatial state, $\psi_{100}(\mathbf{r})$. The corresponding symmetrized two-particle spatial wave functions are then

$$\psi_{100,100}^+(\mathbf{r}_1,\mathbf{r}_2) = \tfrac{1}{2}[\psi_{100}(\mathbf{r}_1)\psi_{100}(\mathbf{r}_2) + \psi_{100}(\mathbf{r}_2)\psi_{100}(\mathbf{r}_1)]$$

$$\psi_{100,100}^-(\mathbf{r}_1,\mathbf{r}_2) = \frac{1}{N}[\psi_{100}(\mathbf{r}_1)\psi_{100}(\mathbf{r}_2) - \psi_{100}(\mathbf{r}_2)\psi_{100}(\mathbf{r}_1)] \equiv 0 \tag{12.52}$$

The antisymmetric space state for both particles in the same state vanishes identically. The lowest energy eigenstate of the helium atom will therefore have the symmetric space state of Eq. (12.52). To obtain a total state function which is antisymmetric, as it must be for two electrons, we must associate with the symmetric space state the antisymmetric spin state $\chi^-(\sigma_1,\sigma_2)$ of Eq. (12.44). The ground state of the helium atom is then a singlet state whose wave function is

$$\psi_0(\mathbf{r}_1\sigma_1,\mathbf{r}_2\sigma_2) = \frac{1}{\sqrt{2}}\,\psi_{100,100}^+(\mathbf{r}_1,\mathbf{r}_2)[\alpha(1)\beta(2) - \alpha(2)\beta(1)] \qquad (12.53)$$

The energy of the lowest state will be

$$E_{100,100} = -Z^2 E_0 - Z^2 E_0 + \langle \psi_{100,100}^+(\mathbf{r}_1,\mathbf{r}_2)\,|V_{ab}|\,\psi_{100,100}^+(\mathbf{r}_1,\mathbf{r}_2)\rangle \qquad (12.54)$$

The coulombic interaction of two electrons in ψ_{100} states has been computed, so we know the value of $\langle |V_{ab}| \rangle$ above. In fact,

$$\langle \psi_{100,100}^+(\mathbf{r}_1,\mathbf{r}_2)\,\Big|\,\frac{e^2}{|\mathbf{r}_1 - \mathbf{r}_2|}\,\Big|\,\psi_{100,100}^+(\mathbf{r}_1,\mathbf{r}_2)\rangle = \frac{5}{4}ZE_0 \qquad (12.55)$$

so the helium ground-state energy is

$$E_{100,100} = -2Z^2 E_0 + \tfrac{5}{4}ZE_0 \qquad (12.56)$$

The energy calculated here can be compared to experiment for several values of Z, since neutral helium, singly ionized lithium, triply ionized beryllium, etc., all are two-electron atoms. The experimental quantity to be measured is the energy required to remove both electrons from bound states; the "second ionization potential." In Table 12.1 we compare the experimental values of $E_{100,100}$ for several atoms or ions with the theoretical values given by Eq. (12.56). Our approximate theory gives strikingly good results.

The energy of the "excited" states of the helium atom can also be calculated from our approximate Hamiltonian, Eq. (12.49). Let us calculate the energy for an excited state such that one electron is in a ground hydrogenic state ψ_{100} and the second electron is in some general excited hydrogenic state ψ_{nlm}. We note parenthetically that the excited states of the neutral helium atom which we actually find are mostly of this character, since it requires less excitation energy to ionize the helium atom (take one electron to infinity) than it does to raise both electrons present to their first excited states ψ_{2lm}. The antisymmetric wave functions which can be constructed from the single-particle assignments assumed above are

$$\begin{aligned} \psi_{100,nlm}^+(\mathbf{r}_1,\mathbf{r}_2)\chi^-(\sigma_1,\sigma_2) \qquad \text{(singlet)} \\[4pt] \psi_{100,nlm}^-(\mathbf{r}_1,\mathbf{r}_2)\chi^+(\sigma_1,\sigma_2) \qquad \text{(triplet)} \end{aligned} \qquad (12.57)$$

The eigenenergies may be calculated, again using perturbation theory, from Eqs. (12.49) and (12.50). The eigenenergies, to first order in V_{ab}, are

$$E_{100,nlm} = -Z^2 E_0 - \frac{Z^2 E_0}{n^2} + J_{100,nlm} \pm K_{100,nlm} \qquad (12.58)$$

where J is a "coulomb integral" of the form

$$J_{100,nlm} = \iint \psi_{100}^*(\mathbf{r}_1)\psi_{nlm}^*(\mathbf{r}_2) \frac{e^2}{|\mathbf{r}_1 - \mathbf{r}_2|} \psi_{100}(\mathbf{r}_1)\psi_{nlm}(\mathbf{r}_2)\, d\mathbf{r}_1\, d\mathbf{r}_2 \qquad (12.59)$$

TABLE 12.1

Comparison of Theoretical and Experimental Values of Ground-state Energies of Heliumlike Atoms*

Atom or Ion	Z	Values of $E_{100,100}$ (ev)	
		Theory	Experiment
He	2	74.42	78.62
Li$^+$	3	192.80	197.14
Be^{2+}	4	365.31	369.96
B^{3+}	5	591.94	596.4
C^{4+}	6	872.69	876.2

*After L. Pauling and E. B. Wilson, "Introduction to Quantum Mechanics", p. 165, McGraw-Hill Book Company, New York, 1935.

and K is an exchange integral of the form

$$K_{100,nlm} = \iint \psi_{100}^*(\mathbf{r}_1)\psi_{nlm}^*(\mathbf{r}_2) \frac{e^2}{|\mathbf{r}_1 - \mathbf{r}_2|} \psi_{100}(\mathbf{r}_2)\psi_{nlm}(\mathbf{r}_1)\, d\mathbf{r}_1\, d\mathbf{r}_2 \qquad (12.60)$$

The exchange integral K appears with a positive coefficient in the eigenenergy of the singlet state (which has a symmetric space state function) and with a negative coefficient in the eigenenergy of the triplet state (which has an antisymmetric space state function). The integrals J and K are both positive, since they represent a measure of the repulsive energy of like charges. The triplet state therefore always lies lower than the singlet arising from the same single-particle configuration. The energy levels of such a set of two-particle helium states are sketched in Fig. 12.2.

Figure 12.3 is the energy-level diagram for neutral helium, as determined from spectroscopic measurements. Note that it may be divided into a set of triplet states and a set of singlet states, with corresponding triplet

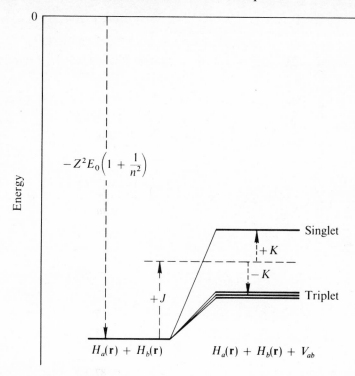

Fig. 12.2 *Eigenenergies of two-particle states of helium atom derived from ψ_{100} and ψ_{nlm} single-particle states.*

states always lying somewhat lower. The experimental spectrum shows that the S^2 degeneracy predicted by our approximate Hamiltonian is removed when more subtle interactions, in particular the $\mathbf{L} \cdot \mathbf{S}$ interaction, are included. We do not propose to discuss the helium energy-level diagram in detail; it should be pointed out to the reader, however, that there are no features of this energy-level diagram, including the classification of the "allowed" and "forbidden" optical transitions, that he is not now in a position to understand and calculate for himself.

12.7 MULTIPARTICLE STATE FUNCTIONS Though we have in this chapter addressed ourselves to the multiparticle problem, we have in fact restricted our attention to the two-particle case. Let us lift that restriction and contemplate briefly the multiparticle system, the N-particle system. We can in a textbook of this scope make only a few observations on the eigenfunctions and eigenvalues of such complex systems, but it is worth noting that much of what we have learned about simpler cases applies

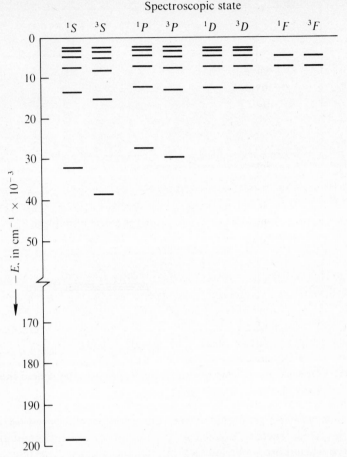

Fig. 12.3 *Energy-level diagram for the helium atom. (The splitting of the triplet states is too small to be resolved on this scale.)*

also to the more complex situations.

Consider the state function for an *N*-particle system. This state function specifies the space and spin coordinates of all the particles as a function of time, and obeys a Schrödinger equation, just as did our single-particle state function. Suppose the state function is for *N* identical particles; this is really the case of physical interest. Then the state function must be either symmetric, if the *N* particles are bosons, or antisymmetric, if the *N* particles are fermions. The symmetric state function must remain unchanged under the permutation P_{ij} of *any two* particles; the antisymmetric state function must change sign upon the interchange of *any two* particles.

How do we go about constructing eigenfunctions with such properties?

Our starting point for the N-particle system is the same as that for the two-particle system: the N single-particle wave functions. We divide the Hamiltonian into N single-particle Hamiltonians and a collection of inter-action terms. If the interactions are relatively weak, the first trial wave functions, product wave functions of the N single-particle eigenfunctions, will give us the eigenvalues of the system with fair accuracy. If the inter-actions are substantial, the wave functions will have to be improved by the techniques of perturbation theory. Suppose then that we have a set of N single-particle wave functions $u_1(\mathbf{r}\boldsymbol{\sigma})$, $u_2(\mathbf{r}\boldsymbol{\sigma})$, ..., $u_N(\mathbf{r}\boldsymbol{\sigma})$. From them, making a particular assignment of particles to state functions, we can construct an N-particle product state function:

$$\psi_1 = u_1(\mathbf{r}_1\boldsymbol{\sigma}_1)u_2(\mathbf{r}_2\boldsymbol{\sigma}_2)u_3(\mathbf{r}_3\boldsymbol{\sigma}_3)\cdots u_N(\mathbf{r}_N\boldsymbol{\sigma}_N) \tag{12.61}$$

This state function is, of course, not symmetrized under particle inter-change. If we interchange two particles (particles 1 and 2, for instance), we have a second product state:

$$\psi_2 = u_1(\mathbf{r}_2\boldsymbol{\sigma}_2)u_2(\mathbf{r}_1\boldsymbol{\sigma}_1)u_3(\mathbf{r}_3\boldsymbol{\sigma}_3)\cdots u_N(\mathbf{r}_N\boldsymbol{\sigma}_N) \tag{12.62}$$

There are, in fact, $N!$ distinct two-particle permutations P_{ij} of N particles, and therefore $N!$ state functions similar to ψ_1 and ψ_2 above. There is exactly one function which is a sum of all the ψ_i which is totally symmetric and exactly one state function which is a sum of all the ψ_i which is totally antisymmetric.

The totally symmetric state function, that which is invariant under any P_{ij}, is relatively easy to construct. It is composed simply of the linear sum of all the $N!$ ψ_i, each taken with a positive sign.

$$\psi^+ = (N!)^{-\frac{1}{2}} \sum_{i=1}^{N!} \psi_i \tag{12.63}$$

The task of computing eigenvalues with this function, a sum of $N!$ terms each of which is a product of N single-particle state functions, is enormous, but is, in principle at least, fully defined and straightforward.

The totally antisymmetric state, that which changes sign under any particle permutation P_{ij}, is of greater physical interest, but it is more difficult to construct. Fortunately, J. C. Slater invented many years ago a remarkably straightforward way to generate this complex function. Consider the state function specified by the determinant

$$\psi^- = (N!)^{-1} \begin{vmatrix} u_1(\mathbf{r}_1\boldsymbol{\sigma}_1) & u_1(\mathbf{r}_2\boldsymbol{\sigma}_2) & \cdots & u_1(\mathbf{r}_N\boldsymbol{\sigma}_N) \\ u_2(\mathbf{r}_1\boldsymbol{\sigma}_1) & u_2(\mathbf{r}_2\boldsymbol{\sigma}_2) & \cdots & u_2(\mathbf{r}_N\boldsymbol{\sigma}_N) \\ u_3(\mathbf{r}_1\boldsymbol{\sigma}_1) & u_3(\mathbf{r}_2\boldsymbol{\sigma}_2) & \cdots & u_3(\mathbf{r}_N\boldsymbol{\sigma}_N) \\ \cdots & \cdots & \cdots & \cdots \\ u_N(\mathbf{r}_1\boldsymbol{\sigma}_1) & u_N(\mathbf{r}_2\boldsymbol{\sigma}_2) & \cdots & u_N(\mathbf{r}_N\boldsymbol{\sigma}_N) \end{vmatrix} \tag{12.64}$$

This determinant is a compact notation for a sum of $N!$ terms, each of which is a product of N single-particle state functions, with the coefficient of each term being either $+1$ or -1. Interchanging any two particles in the state function is equivalent to interchanging two columns of the determinant. Interchanging two columns of a determinant changes the sign of the determinant, so ψ^- is antisymmetric under any permutation P_{ij}.

Observe further that the Pauli exclusion principle is built in for the determinental wave function. If any two single-particle state functions u_i and u_j are the same, the determinant will have two identical rows; interchanging these rows changes the sign of the determinant but does not change the determinant itself. It must therefore be true that the determinantal wave function is identically zero. No two of the N particles may occupy the same state function, or the antisymmetric wave function vanishes.

The manipulation of these determinantal wave functions and their application to real problems are subjects that are too long and too complex to develop here. In principle no conceptual input not already familiar to the reader is required; in practice, however, great ingenuity is required to obtain results with a finite amount of labor. For a thorough development of this subject, the reader is referred to "Quantum Theory of Atomic Structure," Vols. 1 and 2, by J. C. Slater, the originator of the determinantal wave function.

Summary

Most real systems are multiparticle, usually multielectron systems. Quantum mechanics makes some specific predictions about the properties of systems composed of more than one indistinguishable particle.

The state function for two identical particles must be fully symmetric or fully antisymmetric in the two particles. If P_{12} is the particle interchange operator, then

$$P_{12}\Psi(\mathbf{r}_1\sigma_1, \mathbf{r}_2\sigma_2, t) = \pm\Psi(\mathbf{r}_1\sigma_1, \mathbf{r}_2\sigma_2, t)$$

The symmetric and antisymmetric space states represent physically different probability distributions. Two particles in a symmetric space state are correlated in such a fashion that they appear to "attract" each other; two particles in an antisymmetric state tend to "repel" each other, even if there is in fact no interaction between the particles and no difference in energy between the symmetric and antisymmetric states.

Particles with half-integral angular momentum (electrons, protons, neutrons) always appear in totally antisymmetric states, obey Fermi-Dirac statistics, and are called *fermions*. Particles with integral angular momentum (including $j = 0$) always appear in totally symmetric states, obey Einstein-Bose statistics, and are called *bosons*.

If two identical particles interact, the symmetric and antisymmetric states will have different energies:

$$E = E_0 + (J \pm K)$$

where E_0 is the system energy in the absence of the interaction, J is an interaction term which has a simple classical equivalent, and K is an "exchange" energy which has no classical equivalent.

The antisymmetric multiparticle state function vanishes identically if more than one particle occupies the same single-particle state function. The Pauli exclusion principle describes this fact in the language "No two fermions can ever occupy the same state."

For the two-particle system, it is frequently useful to factor the state function into spatial state functions and spin state functions which can be symmetrized (under particle exchange) separately.

The Slater determinantal wave function is a convenient and useful way to construct the fully antisymmetric N-particle state function.

Problems

12.1 Consider the symmetric and antisymmetric two-electron spin functions of Eq. (12.44). Verify the statements in the text that the symmetric states are eigenfunctions of S^2 belonging to $S = 1$ and that the antisymmetric state is an eigenfunction of S^2 belonging to $S = 0$. Verify also that these states are eigenfunctions of the operator S_z with the eigenvalues 0, $\pm\hbar$.

12.2 Show that the symmetric and antisymmetric states of Eq. (12.44) are eigenfunctions of the spin permutation operator

$$P^\sigma_{12} = \tfrac{1}{2}(1 + 4\mathbf{s}_1 \cdot \mathbf{s}_2)$$

belonging to the eigenvalues $+1$ and -1, respectively.

12.3 A commonly occurring form of the interaction between two spins is

$$W = \mathbf{S}_1 \cdot \mathbf{S}_2$$

Write the matrix for W for two-spin $\tfrac{1}{2}$ particles, using the four properly symmetrized two-particle spin functions as a basis for the representation.

12.4 Two antisymmetric particles, spin $\tfrac{1}{2}$ fermions, are harmonically bound to the same point and constrained to oscillate in one dimension (x) only.

    a Regarding the particles as noninteracting, write the total wave functions, space and spin, associated with the three lowest eigenenergies of the total system. Denote the single-particle space wave functions by $\psi_0(x)$, $\psi_1(x)$, etc., and do not bother writing out the explicit form with all its normalizing constants and Hermite polynomials.

b Using the two-electron wave functions generated in part **a** above, write the matrix for the perturbation

$$H' = A\mathbf{S}_1 \cdot \mathbf{S}_2 \delta(x_1 - x_2)$$

Does H' commute with the Hamiltonian of the two-particle harmonic oscillator?

c Sketch the behavior of the energy levels of part **a** above when the perturbation H' is introduced and the interaction amplitude A is increased from zero to some value $|A| > 5\hbar\omega$. Consider both A positive and A negative cases.

d Will applying a magnetic field to the system (including H'), giving a further energy

$$H'' = B\mathbf{H} \cdot (\mathbf{S}_1 + \mathbf{S}_2)$$

lift any degeneracies not already lifted by H'?

12.5 The lowest energy state of the helium atom is, as discussed in the text, the state $\psi_{100,100}^{+}(\mathbf{r}_1,\mathbf{r}_2)\chi^{-}(\sigma_1,\sigma_2)$ which has an energy $-W_{11}^0 + J_{1s,1s}$.

a Show, using first-order perturbation theory and zeroth-order (separable) wave functions, that the first excited group of states and their energies is as follows:

	State	Energy
First excited group	$\psi_{100,21m}^{+}(\mathbf{r}_1,\mathbf{r}_2)\chi^{-}(\sigma_1,\sigma_2)$	$-W_{12}^0 + J_{1s,2p} + K_{1s,2p}$
	$\psi_{100,21m}^{-}(\mathbf{r}_1,\mathbf{r}_2)\chi^{+}(\sigma_1,\sigma_2)$	$-W_{12}^0 + J_{1s,2p} - K_{1s,2p}$
	$\psi_{100,200}^{+}(\mathbf{r}_1,\mathbf{r}_2)\chi^{-}(\sigma_1,\sigma_2)$	$-W_{12}^0 + J_{1s,2s} + K_{1s,2s}$
	$\psi_{100,200}^{-}(\mathbf{r}_1,\mathbf{r}_2)\chi^{+}(\sigma_1,\sigma_2)$	$-W_{12}^0 + J_{1s,2s} - K_{1s,2s}$
Lowest state	$\psi_{100,100}^{+}(\mathbf{r}_1,\mathbf{r}_2)\chi^{-}(\sigma_1,\sigma_2)$	$-W_{11}^0 + J_{1s,1s}$

The symmetrized two-particle space states above are eigenfunctions of the total orbital angular-momentum operator L^2, where $\mathbf{L} = l_1 + l_2$.

b Show that $\psi_{100,21m}^{\pm}(\mathbf{r}_1,\mathbf{r}_2)$ belongs to the eigenvalue $2\hbar^2$, corresponding to $L = 1$ in units of $\hbar$.

c Show that $\psi_{100,200}^{\pm}(\mathbf{r}_1,\mathbf{r}_2)$ belongs to the eigenvalue $L = 0$ in units of $\hbar$.

d Show that the space states $\psi_{100,21m}^{\pm}(\mathbf{r}_1,\mathbf{r}_2)$ are eigenfunctions of L_z belonging to the eigenvalues $m\hbar$.

The total spin angular momentum $(\mathbf{S} = s_1 + s_2)$ and the total orbital angular momentum of an atomic state interact to give an energy of the form

$$H' = \lambda \mathbf{L} \cdot \mathbf{S}$$

e Show that the $\mathbf{L} \cdot \mathbf{S}$ interaction given by H' will produce off-diagonal elements in the total Hamiltonian (LL_z, SS_z representation) only between states having the same value of $J_z = L_z + S_z$.

The ninefold degeneracy of the states of eigenenergy $-W_{12}^0 + J_{1s,2p} - K_{1s,2p}$ will be partially removed by the $\lambda \mathbf{L} \cdot \mathbf{S}$ interaction.

f Calculate the matrix elements (a few within this manifold)

	L	L_z	S	S_z
$\langle 1m_l 1m_s \lvert H' \rvert$	1	0	1	1 $\rangle$
$\langle 1m_l 1m_s \lvert H' \rvert$	1	0	1	0 $\rangle$
$\langle 1m_l 1m_s \lvert H' \rvert$	1	1	1	$-1 \rangle$

g Will degenerate or nondegenerate perturbation theory be required to solve for the perturbed eigenenergies correct to second order in H'? Why?

Bibliography

Additional treatment of the helium atom and of multiparticle systems may be found in:

Pauling, L., and E. B. Wilson: "Introduction to Quantum Mechanics," chap. 12, McGraw-Hill Book Company, New York, 1935.

Messiah, A.: "Quantum Mechanics," vol. 2, chap. 14, Interscience Publishers, Inc., New York, 1962.

Bohm, D.: "Quantum Theory," chap. 19, Prentice-Hall, Inc., Englewood Cliffs, N.J., 1951.

Merzbacher, E.: "Quantum Mechanics," chap. 18, John Wiley & Sons, Inc., 1961.

Dicke, R. H., and J. P. Wittke: "Introduction to Quantum Mechanics," chap. 17, Addison-Wesley Publishing Company, Inc., Reading, Mass., 1960.

Formation of the Hamiltonian Operator in Curvilinear Coordinates

The Hamiltonian operator for a dynamical system can be constructed, in the Schrödinger formulation of quantum mechanics, by a literal substitution of operators for their corresponding observables in the classical Hamiltonian function of the system. This is called the *correspondence method* of forming the Hamiltonian operator. We may, for instance, form for a single particle the classical Hamiltonian, in cartesian coordinates,

$$H = \frac{1}{2m}(p_x^2 + p_y^2 + p_z^2) + V(\mathbf{r}) \qquad (A.1)$$

and make the substitutions

Observable		Operator
x	$\rightarrow$	x
p_x	$\rightarrow$	$\frac{\hbar}{i}\frac{\partial}{\partial x}$
y	$\rightarrow$	y

$$(A.2)$$

etc. We obtain then a valid Hamiltonian operator, which may also be written

$$H_{\text{op}} = -\frac{\hbar^2}{2m}\nabla^2 + V(\mathbf{r}) \qquad (A.3)$$

To obtain the Hamiltonian operator in curvilinear coordinates, we may simply express ∇^2 in its appropriate invariant form in the desired coordinate scheme.

289

It is also possible to obtain the Hamiltonian operator in curvilinear coordinates directly from the classical Hamiltonian in curvilinear coordinates, using the generally valid operator associations

$$\begin{array}{ccc}
\textit{Observable} & & \textit{Operator} \\[4pt]
q_j & \leftrightarrow & q_j \\[6pt]
p_j & \leftrightarrow & \dfrac{\hbar}{i}\dfrac{\partial}{\partial q_j}
\end{array} \qquad\qquad \text{(A.4)}$$

Unless considerable care is exercised, however, the resulting operator may not be correct. The root of the difficulty is that there exist several ways of writing the Hamiltonian, ways which are classically equivalent but quantum-mechanically nonequivalent. For instance, since q_j and p_j commute in the classical case,

$$\frac{1}{r^2}p_r r^2 = \frac{1}{r}p_r r = p_r = r p_r \frac{1}{r} \qquad\qquad \text{(A.5)}$$

etc., which is certainly not true for the associated noncommuting operators

$$\frac{1}{r^2}\frac{\partial}{\partial r}r^2 \neq \frac{1}{r}\frac{\partial}{\partial r}r \neq \frac{\partial}{\partial r} \neq r\frac{\partial}{\partial r}\frac{1}{r} \qquad\qquad \text{(A.6)}$$

etc.

There is one unique way of writing the classical Hamiltonian such that the operator associations of Eq. (A.4) lead to a valid Hamiltonian operator.[1] The specification of the "correct" Hamiltonian requires first the definition of several metric parameters.

In a general curvilinear coordinate system, the square of the element of length may be written as

$$ds^2 = \sum_{i=1}^{3}\sum_{j=1}^{3} g_{ij}u_i u_j \qquad\qquad \text{(A.7)}$$

where the curvilinear coordinates are u_1, u_2, and u_3 and g_{ij} may be written as a 3×3 matrix with the determinant

$$g = \begin{vmatrix} g_{11} & g_{12} & g_{13} \\ g_{21} & g_{22} & g_{23} \\ g_{31} & g_{32} & g_{33} \end{vmatrix} \qquad\qquad \text{(A.8)}$$

For orthogonal curvilinear systems,

$$g_{ij} = 0 \qquad \text{if } i \neq j \qquad\qquad \text{(A.9)}$$

[1] Podolski, B. *Phys. Rev.* 32: 812, 1928.

and we have a diagonal matrix

$$
g = \begin{vmatrix} g_{11} & 0 & 0 \\ 0 & g_{22} & 0 \\ 0 & 0 & g_{33} \end{vmatrix} = \begin{vmatrix} g_1 & 0 & 0 \\ 0 & g_2 & 0 \\ 0 & 0 & g_3 \end{vmatrix} \tag{A.10}
$$

where we drop the double index, since it is no longer necessary.

We define one further quantity:

$$
[g_i] = \frac{\text{cofactor of } g_i}{g} \tag{A.11}
$$

With these metrical coefficients now established, we can write the Hamiltonian in a form which will, upon direct operator substitution, yield a valid Hamiltonian operator. This "correct" Hamiltonian is

$$
H = \frac{1}{2m} \sum_{i=1}^{3} g^{-\frac{1}{2}} p_i g^{\frac{1}{2}} [g_i] p_i + V(\mathbf{r}) \tag{A.12}
$$

That this classical Hamiltonian leads to the correct Hamiltonian operator may be verified by direct substitution, using common curvilinear coordinate systems, such as spherical or cylindrical coordinates.

Index